AN INTRODUCTION TO
POLITICAL PHILOSOPHY

AN INTRODUCTION TO
POLITICAL PHILOSOPHY

A. R. M. MURRAY

LONDON
COHEN & WEST LTD

First published in 1953
by Cohen & West Ltd
Broadway House, 68–74 Carter Lane
London, E.C.4

Reprinted 1959 and 1966

Printed in Great Britain by
Cox & Wyman Ltd., London, Fakenham and Reading

PREFACE

THERE are, no doubt, a variety of ways in which political philosophy can be introduced to those who are assumed to have made no study of philosophy at all, and there may well be differences of opinion as to which of these methods is the best. In the present volume I have attempted to define what seem to me the fundamental issues of the subject by giving some account of the historical theories which discuss them, but the list of those selected is far from exhaustive, and other authors might well have made a different selection. It is, of course, impossible to embody a comprehensive survey of the history of political thought in a book of modest compass, and there are already larger works, such as Professor G. H. Sabine's *History of Political Theory*, which have already done this with conspicuous success.

Moreover, the present volume is intended to be, not primarily a history of political thought, but a critical examination of it with a view to defining the basic assumptions which have been made by the great political thinkers of the past, and the fundamental issues about which controversy still continues. My selection of the theories for discussion has therefore been determined by the conclusions which I have reached about the nature of those issues and the theories which define them most effectively.

The first chapter, in which I attempt to define the nature and scope of philosophy generally, and its application in the field of politics, is inevitably somewhat abstract, and any reader who finds it difficult should omit it on a first reading, and proceed straight to Chapter II, where some of the main issues of moral and political philosophy are defined in the simple terms employed by the early thinkers of Ancient Greece. But the study of the first chapter is essential at some stage if the logical foundations of political philosophy are to be appreciated, and only so can political philosophy in the proper sense be understood. For unless an examination of these logical foundations is undertaken, political philosophy reduces, in effect, to political science, and never raises the essentially philosophical question of the extent to which the moral assumptions made by political theories can be rationally justified. The final chapter on 'The Justification of Government' attempts to define the basic issues which have emerged in the historical chapters, and to relate them to the logical alternatives set forth in Chapter I.

As the book is based on the lectures which I have been delivering during the past seven years to London University Extension Classes in Social Philosophy, it will, I hope, prove of special assistance to future classes in this subject. But I hope that it will also be of value to University students elsewhere, and that it may help to enlighten the general reader who wishes to acquire some knowledge of what philosophy has to say about the main issues of contemporary politics.

I wish to take this opportunity of acknowledging the great help which I have received in the preparation of the book from my friends, Professor H. B. Acton, D.Phil., of the Chair of Philosophy in Bedford College, London, and Mr. E. W. Jones, M.A., Barrister-at-Law and one of my colleagues on the Panel of Extension Lecturers in Social Philosophy. Both were good enough to read the entire typescript and to make many valuable suggestions. While they must not, of course, be held in any way responsible for what I have written, I am deeply conscious of the way in which their criticisms have helped me to work out my own position. I must also acknowledge the debt which I owe to the excellent classes which I have had the good fortune to teach, for the searching questions which I have been asked during the discussion hour which follows every lecture have helped me, in no small measure, to develop and clarify my views. Finally, I must thank the Clarendon Press for kindly allowing me to quote a number of passages from the late Professor F. M. Cornford's translation of Plato's *Republic*.

A. R. M. M.

CONTENTS

CHAPTER I

The Nature and Scope of Political Philosophy

UNTIL the beginning of the present century philosophy was generally regarded as a source of knowledge which transcended, both in scope and certainty, the discoveries of natural science. Science, it was agreed, marked an advance on the uncritical and often unrelated beliefs of ordinary life, yet it was itself based on the observations of the senses and consisted of the uncertain generalizations based upon them; whereas philosophy was assumed to answer questions about such subjects as the existence of God, the nature of knowledge, and the authority of the moral law upon which sense-experience, from its very nature, could throw no light. On such subjects, it was believed, reason was alone competent to pronounce and, when it did so, its conclusions were characterized by a logical and universal certainty which the generalizations of natural science could never claim.

That philosophical knowledge is certain and indubitable is a claim which, in a broad sense, all philosophers have made, or at least implied; and if a short and simple definition of philosophy were sought the title of the late Professor Dewey's Gifford Lectures—'The Quest for Certainty'—might serve as a starting point at least. For all philosophers have claimed, or at least implied, that philosophical knowledge not only is, but must be, true. But this general agreement has not prevented fundamental differences of opinion regarding the nature and scope of such knowledge; and since these differences are reflected in the application of philosophy to the problems of political theory it is important to be aware, however generally, of their nature.

The different conceptions of philosophy ultimately depend upon different conceptions of the nature of indubitable knowledge. The propositions of mathematics are usually cited as typical illustrations of such knowledge. For example, the proposition 'Two plus two equals four' is said to be necessarily and universally true on the ground that, once we have grasped its meaning, we

I

recognize that it must be necessarily and universally true, and because further instances of its truth do not increase our certainty that it must always be true. Its falsity, in other words, is inconceivable. On the other hand, there are numerous propositions of which the falsity is perfectly conceivable. It may be true that 'The cat is black' or that 'Poliomyelitis is caused by a virus', but these propositions are not necessarily true. On the contrary, their falsity is perfectly conceivable, even if observation appears to confirm their truth.

Analytic and Synthetic Propositions

The distinction just illustrated is variously referred to as the distinction between *rational* and *empirical* knowledge, or between *a priori* and *a posteriori* knowledge, or between *truths of reason* and *truths of fact*. And it is generally true to say that all philosophers have claimed, or at least implied, that their theories are rational and *a priori*. Where they have differed is in their view of the scope of such knowledge. And the main difference has been that some have held that rational knowledge is always *analytic*, while others have held that it is sometimes *synthetic*.

The difference between analytic and synthetic propositions was defined by the German philosopher Immanuel Kant (1724–1804) as follows: Analytic propositions, he said, 'add nothing through the predicate to the concept of the subject, but merely break it up into those constituent concepts that have all along been thought in it, although confusedly', while synthetic judgments 'add to the concept of the subject a predicate which has not been in any wise thought in it, and which no analysis could possibly extract from it'.[1] The difference is, in short, that the predicate in an analytic proposition is contained within the meaning of the subject, while in a synthetic proposition the predicate is not contained within the meaning of the subject but adds something related to it. Kant illustrated the difference by the two propositions 'All bodies are extended' and 'All bodies are heavy'. The former, he thought, is analytic, because the concept of 'extension' is part of the meaning of 'body', while the latter is synthetic because the concept of 'heaviness' is not part of the meaning of 'body', but only a quality which it acquires when it is placed in a gravitational field.

[1] *Critique of Pure Reason*, Second Edition, Introduction.

Kant's definition drew attention to an important difference between analytic and synthetic propositions, although not all analytic propositions naturally fall into the simple subject-predicate form which his examples illustrate. The essential characteristic of an analytic proposition is that it defines the meaning, or part of the meaning, of its subject and does not describe unessential features which may, or may not, belong to it. A cube of iron has a certain weight at sea level, a smaller weight at the top of a high mountain, and no weight at all at a certain point between the earth and the moon; but these differences are not essential elements in the meaning of the description 'cube of iron'. It is clear, on the other hand, that if the cube of iron had no extension it would not be a cube of iron, since extension is an essential part of the meaning of the phrase 'cube of iron'. In other words, to deny an analytic proposition is self-contradictory since that is simultaneously asserting and denying the same thing. It is, to borrow Bertrand Russell's example, like saying 'A bald man is not bald'.[1]

Modern philosophers have devoted much attention to the study of analytic propositions, and many would agree with Professor Ayer that 'a proposition is analytic when its validity depends solely on the definitions of the symbols it contains',[2] and that this is so because analytic propositions 'do not make any assertion about the empirical world. They simply record our determination to use words in a certain fashion.'[3] They are, in other words, tautologies; and the reason why we think it worth while to assert them and sometimes, as in mathematics, to draw elaborate deductions from them, is that our reason is too limited to recognize their full significance without going through these complex verbal processes.

These considerations may appear to be extremely abstract and their connection with what is commonly understood as 'political philosophy' far from obvious; but in fact this connection is both simple and fundamental. For philosophy is the 'quest for certainty', and if certainty is a characteristic of propositions, then an inquiry into the nature and scope of certain, i.e. *a priori*, propositions must be the essential task of all philosophy. If, in

[1] *The Problems of Philosophy*, p. 129.
[2] *Language, Truth, and Logic*, Second Edition, p. 78.
[3] op. cit., p. 84.

other words, the general object of philosophy is to discover the nature and implications of rational thinking, then an enquiry into the nature of the propositions by which rational thinking is expressed is necessarily one of the most important tasks of philosophy so understood.

All philosophers who have recognized the distinction between analytic and synthetic propositions have agreed that analytic propositions are necessary and *a priori*. Controversy has centred on the question whether synthetic propositions may also sometimes be *a priori*. And the different answers given to this question have determined very different conceptions of the scope and purpose of philosophy. For if the propositions of philosophy must always be *a priori*, and *a priori* propositions must always be analytic, it follows that the propositions of philosophy must always be analytic.

Now one important class of proposition which is never analytic is the class of *existential propositions*, i.e. propositions asserting something of the real world. While it is necessarily true that 2 plus 2 equals 4, it is not necessarily true that there are four distinguishable objects in the real world. For example, if I have £2 in one pocket and £2 in another, it necessarily follows that I have £4 in both pockets, but it is for empirical observation to ascertain whether in fact I have £2 in one pocket and £2 in another pocket. This simple example illustrates the important principle that analytic propositions apply only in a hypothetical sense to the real world. No analytic proposition of the form 'A is B' can be asserted categorically of the real world. It can only be asserted in the hypothetical form 'If X (some existing thing) is A then it must be B.' But the proposition asserting that X is in fact A is synthetic and cannot be necessarily true unless synthetic propositions can be *a priori*.

Thus if *a priori* propositions are always analytic, philosophy will be unable to demonstrate the truth of any proposition about the existing world except in so far as it is logically implied by an existential proposition whose truth has been established (if it can be established) by empirical observation. The function of philosophy, in other words, will be to examine the implications of propositions and not to demonstrate their truth.

As already mentioned, however, it was widely believed until some fifty years ago that philosophy could establish facts about the existing world quite independently of experience. Philosophy was, indeed, often looked to for a rational justification of beliefs, such as religious or moral beliefs, already held on non-rational grounds, and it was assumed that this justification could be given independently of experience. But during the present century there has been a strong reaction from these methods and a growing acceptance of the alternative view that the function of philosophy is to clarify rather than to extend the content of human knowledge.

The theory that *a priori* thinking can never by itself establish a truth about the existing world is known as Empiricism, since it always asserts that such propositions can be established only by empirical observation. The alternative theory that *a priori* thinking can by itself establish truths about the existing world is known as Rationalism. And it is clear from the preceding discussion that Rationalism can be defended only if synthetic *a priori* propositions are possible. For if such propositions are not possible no proposition about the existing world can be established *a priori*, and some form of Empiricism must therefore be accepted.

Hume's Empiricism

Before the present century, when the doctrine has received wide support, the most celebrated exponent of Empiricism was the Scottish philosopher David Hume (1711–1776), now generally recognized to have been one of the greatest philosophers of all time. Hume held that the only propositions which are certainly true are those which describe 'relations of ideas', by which he meant analytic relationships in the sense defined above. Those which describe 'matters of fact', i.e. synthetic propositions, cannot be rationally justified, although they can be accepted as true in so far as they are justified by direct observation. But of course the great majority of synthetic propositions—in particular, the so-called 'laws' of science—go far beyond this and make assertions which cannot be justified by experience.

Thus Hume argued that the belief in the universal truth of scientific laws follows repeated observations of the sequences which they describe; but he denied that there is any necessity in these sequences, or even in the occurrence of the belief that they are universal and necessary. If I infer that, because all observed samples of arsenic have proved to be poisonous, therefore all samples whatsoever are poisonous, no logical justification of this inference can, according to Hume, be given. It is just a fact that, following on the observation of numerous samples of arsenic which prove to be poisonous, everybody believes that all samples whatsoever will prove to be poisonous. But there is, according to Hume, no rational justification for this belief; it just happens to occur following on experience of the effects of arsenic in a limited number of instances, and just happens to have proved a reliable guide in practice. There is no guarantee that it will prove to be true of all instances whatsoever. Thus there is nothing 'reasonable' in the belief in the *a priori* sense.

Hume reached the same sceptical conclusions about the general propositions of morality. He thought it obvious that these propositions are synthetic, and argued that they cannot therefore be *a priori*. Such propositions as 'Jealousy is evil' or 'Lying is wrong' are, he thought, obviously synthetic in that their predicates are not part of the meaning of the subjects. And such propositions cannot be *a priori*, for no necessary connection can, in his view, be discerned between the subject and the predicate. Hence the basis for these moral generalizations must be the same as the basis for the generalizations of natural science—the observation of a limited number of instances. And this is not a rational ground for asserting them.

Having denied that moral generalizations have any logical necessity, Hume set himself to analyse the empirical evidence on which they are based. He reached the conclusion that the basis of such generalizations is a peculiar type of sentiment or feeling. When I say 'Honesty is good' I am, according to Hume, saying, in a rather specific sense of the word 'like', 'I like honesty'. I am, in fact, describing not an inherent quality of honesty but a feeling excited in me by the contemplation of honesty. This feeling Hume called the 'pleasing sentiment of approbation'. He thought that moral disapproval in the same way expresses a *sentiment* of disapprobation. Thus Hume concluded that there is nothing 'rational' or 'logical' in morality and that it is impossible to show, on *a priori* grounds, that moral propositions are true or false. Their truth or falsity depends on the purely empirical question whether they are or are not accurate descriptions of the feelings to which they relate.

Hume's scepticism is therefore of a revolutionary character, for it implies that neither the principles of natural science nor the laws of morality have any universal necessity, and that practical thinking is of an essentially irrational character. Our belief in such generalizations as 'Arsenic is poisonous' or 'Lying is wrong' is not, according to Hume, arrived at by any logical argument, but is simply a natural belief which occurs in certain situations, and whose occurrence cannot be explained on *a priori* grounds. All attempts to show that such beliefs are necessarily true must, in his view, completely fail.

The consequences of Hume's scepticism are most striking in the sphere of morality, for they imply that there cannot be what Kant was later to call a 'categorical imperative'. This is the principle of unconditional obligation to do what is right. All historical codes embody this principle, for they are composed of 'laws' of the type set forth in the Decalogue, which imply an unconditional obligation to do or to refrain from doing certain acts. But on Hume's theory a moral judgment is the assertion that something excites a certain feeling, and there is no reason why this feeling should be universally experienced, nor any sense in saying that it *ought* to be universally experienced, for the word 'ought' is, on Hume's theory, itself an expression of a feeling.

Hume carried his attack on conventional assumptions about morality even further, for he argued that, even if moral judgments of some form are made, there is no rational relationship between such a judgment and the act to which it relates. The cause of an act is always a 'passion' or desire, and reason has the subordinate function of specifying the probable conditions or consequences of attaining the object of the desire which causes the act. Reason, he said, is 'the slave of the passions, and can never pretend to any other office than to serve and obey them'.[1] There is, he therefore holds, no justification for the distinction commonly drawn between acting 'from reason' and acting 'from emotion'; *all* action is, in the end, caused by emotion, and reason, from its very nature, can affect action only by exhibiting its probable conditions and consequences. Once this has been done, it is a purely empirical question whether the anticipated end, with all its conditions and consequences, will or will not be desired, and will, or will not, be desired with sufficient intensity to result in action.

[1] *Treatise of Human Nature*, II, iii, 3.

Thus if Hume's analysis is right the assumptions made in ordinary moral thinking are vitiated by two fundamental errors. In the first place, moral judgments are not assertions that certain acts or ends possess certain qualities; they are assertions that some person or group of persons experiences a certain kind of feeling when contemplating these acts or ends. And, secondly, there cannot be any *reason* why one does, or why one ought to, act in a certain way. The causes of action are desires or 'passions' and reason can affect acts only by showing what the probable conditions or consequences of specified acts are likely to be, and thus changing the nature of the anticipated results of acts. Thus, according to Hume, moral approval and condemnation are expressions of feelings—perhaps feelings of a peculiar and specific kind—which may well influence the conduct of those to whom such approval or condemnation is addressed, but which do so in a purely casual manner. They cannot, from their very nature, ever constitute a *reason* why certain acts ought or ought not to be done.

The subordinate function which Hume attributed to reason may be briefly described as that of applying scientific generalizations. Of course these generalizations are not 'rational' in the *a priori* sense for they are synthetic propositions, and only analytic propositions are, in Hume's view, *a priori*. But on the assumption —which experience seems to justify[1]—that both physical and mental events occur in accordance with certain general laws, it is rational to look for these laws and to apply them with a view to predicting the future course of events. The process is rational in the strict sense in so far as it consists in drawing the logical implications of a hypothesis. If all arsenic is poisonous, it follows *a priori* that *this* piece of arsenic is poisonous, but neither the proposition that all arsenic is poisonous nor the proposition that this is a piece of arsenic is *a priori*. Both of these propositions are empirical and cannot be rationally justified.

The Rationalism of Kant and Hegel

Hume's revolutionary account of the function of reason naturally evoked a reaction, and the philosophies of the great

---

[1] This does not, of course, mean that experience can in practice ever provide a logically valid proof of the 'uniformity of Nature', but only that experience never reveals anything which is inconsistent with the assumption of that principle.

German thinkers Immanuel Kant (1724–1804) and Georg Wilhelm Friedrich Hegel (1770–1831) were attempts to restore to reason the positive functions which Hume had denied to it. Kant and Hegel sought to do this by stressing the active function of the mind in knowledge and, in particular, by arguing that, while synthetic propositions may by themselves be devoid of logical necessity, they are characterized by another kind of necessity (which Kant called 'transcendental necessity') derived from the mind in which they originate. They are necessary, not in the logical sense that their falsity is inconceivable, but in the transcendental sense that experience could not take the form which it does take unless they were assumed to be universally true. Such, in brief, is Kant's theory of the nature of causal and moral laws. He admits that they are synthetic but claims that they are none the less *a priori* in the transcendental sense. His theory is 'idealist' in the sense that he holds the stuff of experience to be not independent objects but our *ideas of* or *judgments about* objects. And while he believes that there are independent objects —which he calls 'things-in-themselves'—he holds that these are necessarily unknowable except in the form of appearances conditioned by the way in which the mind, in view of its structure, is bound to apprehend them.

Many philosophers would question whether a theory of this sort constitutes any real answer to Hume's empiricism. They would question whether 'transcendental' necessity is more than the empirical regularity admitted by Hume—whether, for example, the fact that we always interpret our experience in terms of causal regularities justifies the conclusion that we necessarily interpret it in this way. It must at least be admitted that Hume and other philosophers who think like him have not interpreted their experience in this way. And it is difficult to see why the almost universal belief in causal determination cannot be adequately described, as Hume described it, in terms of habit.

Apart from this general objection to Kant's theory, Hegel thought that it was vitiated by the fundamental contradiction of asserting, on the one hand, that all knowing takes the form of judging, and yet claiming that experience cannot be explained except on the assumption that there are things-in-themselves. As Hegel was quick to observe, these propositions are essentially contradictory; if it is impossible for us to have cognitive experience which does not take the form of judging it is impossible for us to know or conceive of or make any consistent assertion about things-in-themselves, for in so doing we are interpreting them in accordance with the way in which our minds are bound to think. Things-in-themselves which are thought about and talked about cannot be things-in-themselves; they must be things as they appear to the thinker.

Hegel therefore arrived at the conclusion that Kant did not carry his argument far enough, and that its logical implication is that cognitive experience consists exclusively of judgments.[1] We cannot, Hegel thought, get 'behind' judgments to 'things', for a 'thing' can be apprehended only through a judgment which asserts something about it. In the same way, there is no justification for supposing that we are aware of 'facts' of which the truth cannot be questioned. 'Facts' are what people believe to be facts, and are thus judgments just as much as any other part of experience. They are, in practice, those judgments which, at a given time, are consistent with all other judgments; but this does not imply that they will not at a later date be questioned and rejected as false. For long it was accepted as a fact that the earth was flat, but this assumption was later found to be inconsistent with other judgments which appeared to be more generally consistent with experience as a whole, and it was therefore rejected as false. Thus, according to Hegel, the truth of a judgment does not consist, as is commonly supposed, in its *correspondence* to a 'fact' but in its *coherence* with other judgments; and it is thus liable to be rejected as false in the light of further experience. It follows that truth is not an absolute but a relative conception, since a judgment which is true in relation to the other judgments of one person's experience may be false in relation to the other judgments of another person's experience. In ancient times it was perfectly consistent with everybody's experience to believe that the earth was flat; but it would no longer be consistent to believe this in view of the judgments generally accepted as evidence that the earth is a spheroid.

Philosophers differ widely regarding the importance and

[1] By a 'judgment' is here meant the 'assertion of a proposition'. The word thus serves to emphasize the active function of the mind upon which Kant and Hegel laid so much stress.

validity of Hegel's philosophy. By some it is regarded as the final consummation of human thought, which both solves and explains the difficulties which are inherent in other systems. To others it appears to deny the validity of thought altogether in its rejection of the concept of absolute truth at the finite level. But the majority of philosophers would probably agree that it is worthy of serious consideration. For, even if the doctrine of the Absolute Idea[1] cannot be defended, Hegel may have been justified in denying the existence of undubitable 'facts', and in arguing that the most 'factual-looking' assertions involve a subjective element of interpretation, so that their truth or falsity can be described only in the light of their coherence with other synthetic judgments which are similarly open to question. On the other hand, even if Hegel's Coherence Theory of Truth is accepted, it does not follow that all possible judgments constitute a logically related system of which the necessity could be apprehended by anyone with a sufficiently comprehensive experience. The only logical relationship which appears to relate many judgments is that of *consistency*, and if that is so it cannot be inferred that experience necessarily takes the form which it does take, or that the experience of different individuals must ultimately be harmonized in the Absolute. For other judgments might have been equally consistent with the rest of experience. It is only if the universe is first *defined* as that which has certain specified characteristics that it follows *a priori* that it must have these characteristics and could not conceivably have other characteristics. But this definition is an analytic proposition and does not imply that the universe *must* have the characteristics which it actually does have.

For the above reasons it is very doubtful whether either Kant or Hegel was successful in refuting the essential principles of Hume's Empiricism; and many modern philosophers would agree with Hume that reason has only a hypothetical application to the real world. On this view it can never establish the truth of a belief, but can only demonstrate its logical implications; while in the sphere of conduct it can never justify the ends of action but can only devise the most effective means for attaining the ends determined by the irrational 'passions'.

[1] The doctrine that only the whole truth about everything is completely coherent, and therefore absolutely true. See Chapter XI below.

The Implications of Empiricism

If the foregoing conception of the nature and scope of reason is accepted, it follows that philosophy has a more limited scope than has been widely assumed in the past. Its function will be to discover the logical implications of beliefs, not to provide a rational justification of their truth. Their truth, whether defined in terms of coherence or correspondence, will never be rationally justified, and their logical implications will have neither more nor less truth than the beliefs themselves. Philosophy, in other words, will be concerned with meaning and not with truth. Truth will be the objective of science, and will be reached by generalization from experience, i.e. by discovering the general laws describing regularities of coexistence and sequence. Science will differ fundamentally from philosophy in that the formulation of these generalizations is not a rational process, and their application to experience has only a hypothetical validity. There is, for example, no rational justification for inferring that, because all examined samples of arsenic have proved to be poisonous, therefore all samples whatsoever must be poisonous; but *if* it is assumed that all samples whatsoever are poisonous, then it follows, as a logical implication, that any given sample must be poisonous.

In short, if the Empiricist Theory is accepted, reason will apply only hypothetically to experience, and it will be impossible to provide a categorical demonstration of the truth of any proposition about what exists or what occurs. It will only be possible for reason to show what are the logical implications of such a proposition, i.e. to show what must exist or must occur on the *assumption* that X exists or occurs. But this latter assumption cannot itself be rationally justified—except, of course, in the hypothetical sense that it may, in turn, be logically implied by yet another proposition assumed to be true. In short, every synthetic proposition either is, or is based upon, an assumption which cannot be rationally justified.

Before the present century, most philosophers believed that at least some synthetic propositions could be rationally justified, and that some empirical propositions could therefore be established by philosophy. Hegel sought to remove the doubts which gradually assailed this position by arguing that, although the rationality of synthetic propositions may not be evident at the level of finite experience, it would be obvious at the level of an infinite experience. In one form or another the rationalist theory is still accepted by many philosophers, but during the past fifty years it has been widely questioned, and many philosophers have felt bound to accept the basic principles of Hume's Empiricism.

There are, therefore, two different and incompatible conceptions of the nature and scope of philosophy between which a choice has to be made. They derive from different conceptions of the nature and function of human reason. And it is clear that, if the Empiricist Theory is accepted, the function of philosophy will be radically different from that commonly assigned to it in the past. For its function will be not to discover truth but to elucidate meaning. In its application to reality it will have to start from beliefs which cannot be verified and from ideals which cannot be justified. And these limitations to the power of reason are inevitable unless some way can be found of justifying the Kantian thesis that 'synthetic *a priori* judgments are possible'.

The significance of Empiricism may be otherwise expressed by saying that it implies that the only possible application of reason to the real world is in science, and that this application takes a hypothetical form. All attempts to establish truths about the real world by *a priori* reasoning alone are bound to fail, since they necessarily involve at least one proposition asserting that something exists or occurs, and such a proposition is necessarily synthetic, and therefore not *a priori*. The logical implications of such a synthetic proposition can, of course, be deduced *a priori*; but these logical deductions do not, in the strict sense, establish new facts of existence but only reveal the fuller meaning of that which has been assumed, without rational justification, to exist.

The most important type of deduction from synthetic existential propositions is found in applied science, where the logical implications of the special kind of synthetic propositions known as 'scientific laws' are deduced. These propositions have no *a priori* foundation, nor, as Hume showed, are they logically implied by the synthetic propositions known as 'observed facts'. They simply provide what frequently proves to be useful practical guidance in anticipating events, and they are said to be 'justified' in so far as they do this. In other words, they are hypotheses which have logical implications and which are justified in so far as these implications are consistent with observation.

But such justification will necessarily fall short of logical certainty unless all the infinite possible implications of the hypothesis are verified by observation; and such comprehensive verification is certain to be impracticable.

The Empiricist Theory of Morality

Similarly, the Empiricist Theory implies that moral reasoning is truly rational only in so far as it takes a scientific form. There is no *a priori* way of establishing that X is good or bad, or right or wrong. For moral propositions are synthetic propositions, and are therefore without *a priori* certainty. All that can be asserted with *a priori* certainty is that *if* 'X is good' is true, then the propositions which are logically implied by 'X is good' are also true. If, for example, it is true that 'All pleasures are good', then it follows logically that a pleasure is good whatever its source and nature. And if this implication is held to be false, then the general principle by which it is implied must be rejected, just as the Law of Gravity would have to be rejected if some material bodies were found not to obey it. Thus the Empiricist Theory implies that there can be no ultimate demonstration of the truth or falsity of a moral proposition; all that reason can show is whether it is consistent with other moral propositions, and what its logical implications are.

The other logical possibility open to the empiricist is the view that moral propositions are analytic, and therefore *a priori* certain. But this would imply that moral characteristics must be part of the meaning of that to which they are attributed, and this does not seem to be the case. For it does not appear to be self-contradictory to deny a proposition which asserts that X is good or bad or right or wrong, as it would be if such a proposition were analytic. On the contrary, there is widespread disagreement about such propositions, most obviously if we compare the moral beliefs which prevail in different communities, or in the same community at different epochs of its history, but also to some extent within the same community at a given time. For example, there are in Britain today sharp differences of opinion about the morality of gambling, divorce, and blood sports. Some people believe that these things are, within limits, blameless, while others hold that they are unconditionally wrong; but, while both opinions cannot be true, it does not seem that either is self-contradictory. It would, of course, be self-contradictory to say that gambling is legitimate if evil were an inherent part of the meaning of gambling, but the argument that evil is an inherent part of the meaning of gambling would usually be rejected as 'begging the question' on the ground that the question whether gambling is good or bad is a question of substance and not of definition. Of course there is no logical way of refuting anyone who obstinately maintains that the moral propositions which he asserts are analytic, and that anyone who denies these propositions is talking nonsense, any more than there is any logical way of refuting the person who asserts that 2 plus 2 equals 5; but this point of view can only be justified by disregarding the beliefs which are inconsistent with it instead of accounting for them.

The general assumptions made about the nature and scope of *a priori* knowledge have therefore important implications for the analysis of moral experience, since it is only on the assumptions of Rationalism that it is possible to avoid the conclusion that moral propositions are empirical descriptions, whether or not these descriptions can be reduced without remainder to non-moral propositions.[1] And both of these alternatives represent a radical departure from the assumptions commonly made about the nature of moral experience. For the first alternative implies that moral propositions are purely empirical descriptions devoid of any rational necessity; while the second implies that moral propositions can be expressed without loss of meaning as non-moral propositions, and that it is therefore misleading to speak of them as 'moral' propositions and thus imply that they describe a special and distinctive type of experience.

Some modern philosophers have raised the further question whether sentences which appear to express moral propositions are not, in part, expressions of a non-cognitive type of experience. They contend that a moral sentence is only in part the expression of a proposition, and is in part the direct expression of a feeling or a volition. This analysis has sometimes been described in picturesque terms as the 'Boo-Hurrah' Theory of Morality—meaning that moral sentences are, in part at least, not expressions of propositions at all but of feelings, just as booing and cheering are admitted to be expressions of feelings. Again, it may be

[1] The second alternative has been called the 'Naturalistic' Theory of Morality by Professor G. E. Moore. See his *Principia Ethica*, Chapter II.

argued that sentences in which the word 'ought' appears are, in part at least, the direct expression of *conative* attitudes or commands. Whether or not these suggestions are justified, it is important to remember that the philosopher is not directly concerned with feelings or conations but only with *propositions about* feelings or conations—such as the proposition asserting that moral sentences are in part a direct expression of feelings or conations, and only partly an expression of propositions about such feelings and conations. And it is not clear that the theories just referred to are doing more than drawing attention to the fact that the subject of a proposition is one thing and the proposition another, and forgetting that it is with propositions alone that the philosopher is directly concerned.

If—as language certainly suggests—moral experience is a specific and distinctive kind of experience, the Naturalistic Theory of Morality must be rejected; and if the Rationalist Theory of synthetic *a priori* propositions is also rejected, it will be necessary to accept the Empiricist Theory of Morality. According to this theory moral propositions will be without any rational necessity, and rational arguments based upon them will therefore be of a hypothetical character. Given that 'A is good' it will be possible to deduce by a strictly rational process that 'B is good' and that 'C is good' if these propositions are logically implied by 'A is good';[1] but the original premise 'A is good' will be a belief or assumption without rational necessity. In other words, it may be possible to show that B and C must be good if A is good; but it will not be possible to show that A must be good—except, of course, in a hypothetical sense if the proposition 'A is good' is in turn implied by yet another proposition whose truth is assumed.

In general, the major implication of Empiricism is that rational argument about the real world necessarily takes a hypothetical form. This is a direct consequence of the denial that synthetic propositions can be *a priori*, for all assertions of existence are synthetic, and therefore without *a priori* necessity. Moral arguments must, for the same reason, be hypothetical in character and thus incapable of justifying the ultimate premises upon which they are based.

[1] As will be the case if, for example, B and C are members of the more general Class A, or universal conditions of A.

Political Philosophy

These conclusions have important consequences for political philosophy, for the latter has usually taken the form of an attempt to justify certain assumptions about the methods and aims of government. In most political philosophies this justification has been a moral justification, and has taken the form of an argument that certain forms of government, e.g. a democratic constitution, and they alone, are morally justifiable. This type of political philosophy is therefore essentially an application of moral philosophy to the political field. And it is in this sense that the phrase 'political philosophy' appears to be generally understood; for when it is said, as it is often said in political journalism, that certain differences of policy can be traced, in the end, to different 'political philosophies', it is obvious that by different political philosophies is meant different assumptions about what it is right or wrong to do in politics.

On the other hand, in the case of a few political philosophies—most notably those of Machiavelli, Hobbes, and Bentham—a naturalistic conception of morality has been held, and no attempt has therefore been made to justify government on moral grounds. The justification offered has been conditional on the truth of an empirical assumption about the object of government, which has usually been identified with the desire of the majority of people. Thus Machiavelli believed that everyone desires strong and efficient government; Hobbes believed that everyone desires peace and security; and Bentham believed that everyone desires happiness. None of these philosophers held that there is any objective sense in which people *ought* to desire these ends; it is, they held, simply a fact that the large majority of people or all people do desire them, and it is the function of the political philosopher to ascertain what type of political organization is most likely to achieve them. In doing so he is, of course, acting as a political scientist rather than as a political philosopher, for he is simply attempting to define the sort of political principles which must be observed in order to achieve the end which most people are believed to desire, without pronouncing in any way upon the moral worth of this end. His function is therefore strictly analogous to that of a medical officer of health applying scientific knowledge to promote the health of those whom he serves. The strictly philosophical task of such a political philosopher ends with his *a priori* demonstration that there is no moral reason why one end should be chosen rather than another, and that the function of the politician is to devise the most effective means for attaining the end which is generally desired.

It is, however, unusual for political philosophers to avoid making some assumption of a moral character. For without such an assumption it is difficult to define the end of government in a sense that is not wholly arbitrary. If there is no reason why one end should be chosen rather than another there is no reason why the desire of the majority should be preferred to the desire of the minority or to the politician's own personal ambitions. Even if Hobbes is justified in his assumption that everyone desires peace and personal security above all things, there is no reason why a statesman should seek to realize these ends rather than, for example, his own personal ambitions unless the former is morally better than the latter. It is, indeed, possible to define the ends of government without moral assumptions and in a way that is not wholly arbitrary if, and only if, everyone—both rulers and ruled —desire the same ends. For in that case there can be no dispute about what ends are desired. And this does, indeed, seem to be an implicit assumption of the theories of Machiavelli and Hobbes and Bentham. According to these theories the politician's only problem is to devise the most effective means to the ends which everyone is assumed to desire.

Classification of Political Theories

Political philosophies may, therefore, be provisionally divided into Moral and Naturalistic Theories of the State. Moral Theories are those which claim to justify government on moral grounds, while Naturalistic Theories are those which claim to justify it on scientific grounds. The justification provided by Moral Theories claims to be categorical and unconditional, whereas that provided by Naturalistic Theories is necessarily hypothetical, since it is necessarily conditional upon the desire for a certain end. In Moral Theories the ends of government are defined as the ends which ought to be pursued. In Naturalistic Theories these ends are defined as the ends which are desired. Moral Theories tell us what we ought to do, while Naturalistic Theories tell us what we must do if we wish to achieve certain ends. But if different people desire different ends there is no way by which a Naturalistic Theory can determine which end ought to be preferred, since such discrimination would involve a moral judgment.

Moral Theories have fallen under two main heads according as the good of the state or the good of the individual has been regarded as primary. On the one hand it has been held that the good of the state defines the standard to which the individual ought to conform, and, on the other hand, it has been held that the good of the individual defines the purpose which the state ought to serve. The first type of theory has been variously known as the *Organic* or *Collectivist Theory* and the second as the *Machine* or *Individualist Theory*, and the division corresponds roughly to the popular distinction between 'totalitarian' and 'democratic' theories of government. When the Individualist Theory defines the moral ideal as *pleasure* it is commonly known as *Utilitarianism*, since the methods and aims of government are then judged to be good in so far as they are *useful* in promoting people's pleasure, or, as it is often said, 'the greatest happiness of the greatest number'.

But although political theories can be readily divided into Moral and Naturalistic Theories, there is another, and equally fundamental, division. Whether or not moral concepts are, as the Moral Theory asserts, specific and indefinable in terms of non-moral concepts, there remains the question whether the propositions in which these terms appear are *a priori* or empirical.[1] If, for the reasons set forth above,[2] it is agreed that moral propositions are in any case synthetic, it will follow that they must be empirical unless, as Rationalism asserts, synthetic propositions can be *a priori*. Thus, whether or not moral terms can be defined in naturalistic terms, moral propositions must be empirical unless the fundamental premise of Rationalism is true.

The historical examples of the Moral Theory have in nearly every case been based on the premises of Rationalism, for almost all have assumed that the propositions of morality are *a priori* and possess a categorical necessity. Hume's moral theory is a notable exception to this generalization, for he maintained both

---

[1] For example, whether or not 'the good' can be defined as 'the desired', it is quite a distinct question whether a proposition such as 'Benevolence is good' is *a priori* or empirical.

[2] p. 14.

that moral experience is a specific and irreducible type of experience and that moral propositions are none the less wholly empirical. But most historical examples of Empiricist Theories have also been Naturalistic Theories, like the theories of Machiavelli, Hobbes, and Bentham.

On the other hand, so long as the issue between Rationalism and Empiricism is left open, there is no reason why Rationalism should not be combined with a Naturalistic Theory of Morality. For then, even if moral conceptions can be defined in terms of non-moral conceptions, they may be necessarily related to the subject of the propositions in which they occur if it is possible for a proposition to be at once synthetic and *a priori*. It is, indeed, quite consistent to combine either a Moral or a Naturalistic Theory of Morality with either a Rationalist or Empiricist Theory since the latter represent the alternative views which may be held about the logical status of moral propositions, while the former represent alternative views which may be held about the meaning of moral concepts. On the other hand, if Empiricists are right in holding that the basic premise of Rationalism—that synthetic propositions may be *a priori*—is self-contradictory, the rationalist form of both Moral and Naturalistic Theories is automatically ruled out, and the issue narrowed to a choice between the empiricist forms of the Moral and Naturalistic Theories.

Political theories may therefore be broadly classified as follows:

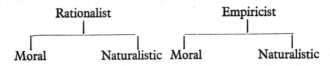

Rationalist   Empiricist

Moral   Naturalistic Moral   Naturalistic

While the historical examples of the Moral Theory have in nearly all cases assumed a rationalist form, the validity of this type of theory is, as already explained, conditional on the possibility of synthetic *a priori* propositions. If the possibility of such propositions is denied, then the validity of the rationalist form of Moral Theory must also be denied, and one or other form of the Empiricist Theory must be accepted. And in that case politics must be a science—either a moral or a natural science, but in either case a science—in which the only rational activity will be the verification and application of scientific generalizations. For even if these generalizations be of a moral character, they will lack *a priori* necessity, and the process of discovering them will be a purely empirical enquiry directed to the discovery of the moral beliefs which are actually held about the rights and duties of states and citizens. Such an enquiry cannot, on the assumptions of the Empiricist Theory, lead to the discovery of *a priori* moral propositions expressed in categorical imperatives.

It is, therefore, only on the assumptions of Rationalism that there can, strictly speaking, be 'political philosophy' in the usual sense. For by a 'political philosophy' is usually meant a fundamental moral proposition or propositions providing a categorical justification for certain political ideals; and it is only on the assumptions of Rationalism that such propositions are possible. On the assumptions of Empiricism, which imply that moral propositions are synthetic and empirical, political philosophy begins and ends with the *a priori* proposition that politics is a science, and that science alone can offer the politician rational guidance in his activities.

Thanks to the work of Hume's modern successors, the Logical Positivists, it can, I think, be fairly said that there is only one important alternative to thoroughgoing Empiricism, namely the special type of Rationalism known as Hegelian Idealism. The dogmatic claims of Plato and other pre-Hegelian Rationalists to have discovered moral principles of *a priori* certainty cannot withstand scrutiny, but the Hegelian theory that certainty can be attained at the level of infinite mind is less easy to refute. Indeed, Hegel's theory is plausible just because, although it does not offer finite man the complete certainty of absolute truth, it does claim to show the way by which absolute truth may be progressively approached, and synthetic propositions thus placed in an order of logical priority. To the empiricist, on the other hand, a synthetic proposition is justified not by logic but by 'observation'—although in the case of the large majority of these propositions the justification is not conclusive.

The merits of Hegel's theory will be examined in a later chapter. It is sufficient for the present to note how the contrast between Rationalism and Empiricism is reflected in both moral and political philosophy. Indeed, as already observed, the very possibility of moral and political philosophy as commonly understood depends upon the possibility of propositions that are at once synthetic and *a priori*. If, as the empiricist contends, such propositions are not possible, the application of reason in both morals and politics must necessarily assume a scientific form, and cannot hope to find a directive for action which is more than hypothetical. If, on the other hand, the rationalist is right in holding that moral propositions can be at once synthetic and necessary, the basis for a categorical justification of political ideals exists. In short, the nature of the justification which can be given for political ideals depends, in the end, on the nature of *a priori* propositions. And if these propositions cannot be synthetic it follows that the assumptions commonly made about the nature of that justification must be rejected.

The naïve conception of a political philosophy as a set of dogmatic axioms defining the rights and duties of the state and the individual conceals the basic purpose of philosophy. For philosophy consists essentially in directing the process of thinking upon itself with a view to ascertaining what thought consists in, and what it can establish. To lay down moral dogmas about the rights and duties of governments and citizens without first considering how far this is a rational process is the very antithesis of philosophy properly conceived.

Definition of Philosophy

In the light of the foregoing considerations, philosophy may be briefly defined as *the study of the nature and implications of rational thought*. From this general study conclusions may be drawn about the implications of rational thought in specific fields, such as the moral and political, and these implications constitute moral and political philosophy. And if, as the empiricist believes, philosophy leads to the conclusion that the rational part of experience is much smaller than is commonly supposed, this is itself a rational proposition of the first importance.

The purpose of the present chapter has been to indicate, in the most general and summary fashion, the logical and metaphysical background of political philosophy. Large issues have been touched on which could not be adequately discussed in less than a volume devoted to their special consideration. But enough will have been said for the purpose of the present book if it has been made clear that political philosophy is not an independent subject but is intimately bound up with the great issues of logic and metaphysics. In the following chapters an attempt will be made to show more precisely what form this connection takes. It will be argued that the broad division in political philosophy is between the Rationalist and Empiricist Theories, and that this division reflects, and depends upon, the division between rationalist and empiricist theories of logic and knowledge. If this is so, no final answer can be given to the questions of political philosophy without a decision on these broader issues, but a necessary and important task will have been accomplished if the problems of political philosophy are reduced to their ultimate and logical form.

CHAPTER II

The Political Theories of the Sophists

Philosophy in Ancient Greece

IF philosophy is understood in the sense defined in the previous chapter, the first philosophical thinking of any consequence took place in Ancient Greece in the sixth century B.C. There had, it is true, been considerable speculation before this time about many of the questions with which philosophy is concerned, but the basis of belief was generally found in religion or mythology or tradition, and little or no attempt was made to subject this basis to rational scrutiny. It was the Greeks of the sixth century B.C. who first sought, in a determined and systematic fashion, to arrive at a conception of reality based on genuinely rational foundations.

During the sixth century B.C. these early philosophers generally concentrated their efforts on reaching some simple and comprehensive conception of reality as a whole and took little interest in the problems of political philosophy. But it is necessary to understand the nature of their achievement in this broader field if the origin and purpose of their political theories are to be properly appreciated. It may be said that, in general, their early enquiries were directed to answering the question 'What is reality?'[1] The first philosophers were impressed, above all, by the apparent complexity and irrationality of the universe, and they sought to find behind this appearance some relatively simple reality which would be intelligible and orderly to the human mind. One of the earliest of these theories was that of Thales, who lived from about 600–550 B.C., and about whose views we learn in the writings of Herodotus, Aristotle, and others. Thales put forward the theory that the underlying reality is water, and that the various solid, liquid, and gaseous substances which are experienced are different forms which this reality may take. The theory appears to have been based on the consideration that water can assume either a solid form (as ice) or a gaseous form

[1] Cf. Burnet's *Greek Philosophy*, Part I.

(as steam), from which it was deduced that all material substances whatsoever are different forms of water. With the advance of scientific knowledge the inadequacy of this theory became apparent, but it is an early illustration of an ideal which has influenced both scientific and philosophical theory ever since— the ideal of explaining the variety and complexity of the apparent world as the appearance of some relatively simple and homogeneous reality. Thus the atomic theory of matter is a modern example of the sort of explanation which Thales was trying to work out, and many philosophical theories have sought to reduce the apparent variety of the physical world to the appearances or effects of some simple reality such as matter or mind.

However inadequate the theories of Thales and some of his successors may appear in the light of modern knowledge, they were sufficiently plausible to convince the early philosophers that the physical world was not a formless complex of chance happenings, but was subject to laws which methodical investigation could reveal. Until about 500 B.C. this also seemed to be true of the smaller universe of the state, except that there was no need to look for the laws, since they were expressed by the unchanging customs and conventions which were handed down from generation to generation and never questioned. But in the fifth century B.C. this unquestioning acceptance of tradition began to crumble because in that century the Greeks began to travel and establish colonies, and these adventures brought them into contact with communities who observed customs and laws very different from their own. For the first time they had to recognize that their own customs and laws were not universal and to consider whether there was any reason for believing them to be better than others. And their first reaction was to conclude that one set of laws was as good as another for the purpose of the community which accepted them. Hence they drew a distinction between the unchanging rules of physical Nature and the variable forms of man-made Law. The former they regarded as essentially objective, and the latter as essentially subjective.

The Sophists

These early social philosophers are commonly known as the 'Sophists' or 'wise men' 'Wise man' was the original meaning of the word 'sophist', although it now usually indicates someone

3

who is clever and plausible rather than wise and honest. Indeed, the modern meaning of the word is substantially the meaning which the Sophists, by their practices, gave to it. For many of them concentrated on the teaching of rhetoric, and by this was meant the art of arguing persuasively irrespective of the real merits of the case. The importance of this art arose from the fact that during the greater part of the fifth century B.C. Athens had a democratic constitution, and it was important for those who administered policy to be able to justify their actions before the popular assembly.

The Sophists were the first professional teachers of Ancient Greece. In most cases they either demanded, or received, fees for teaching, and their pupils were generally those who hoped to succeed in public life. But they did not belong to any central establishment, and they did not share any common outlook which automatically made them members of a 'school'. Many were engaged in the day-to-day business of teaching, but a few tried to work out a consistent social philosophy, and a short account of the principal doctrines which they advocated will now be given.

Protagoras

Protagoras of Abdera (500–430 B.C.), whose doctrines are described in Plato's dialogue *Protagoras*, put forward an interesting theory which attempted to combine recognition of the essential subjectivity of moral laws with a practical method of achieving that acceptance of a common code of law and convention upon which the cohesion and survival of a society depend. His view of the subjectivity of law was expressed in the dictum that 'Man is the measure of all things, of things that are that they are, and of things that are not that they are not.' Plato explains this doctrine as meaning that 'things are to me as they appear to me and to you as they appear to you'.[1] Whether or not Protagoras believed this to be true of all judgments whatsoever, he undoubtedly believed it to be true of moral judgments in the sense that the judgment 'X is right' is true to the person making it while the judgment 'X is not right' may be equally true to another person.

Protagoras recognized that general acceptance of this doctrine might have serious practical consequences. If people became generally aware that one moral belief was as true as another they

[1] *Theaetetus*, 152 b.

might well come to discard all moral beliefs whatsoever, and gratify their individual desires in complete disregard of their social duties. Protagoras therefore argued that, although all beliefs are equally true, some are *better* than others, namely the beliefs of the average and representative man, and that it is the function of the Sophist to persuade everyone to accept those 'better' beliefs. The different beliefs which are likely to be held by a minority of persons are, in Protagoras's view, just as true, but they are not so good in the sense that they differ from the beliefs held by the majority, and thus tend to cause dissension and controversy. But if those who hold these unconventional beliefs can be persuaded to adopt the more usual beliefs of the majority, the cause of social cohesion and stability will be promoted. Thus while Protagoras believed that all moral beliefs are subjective, he was prepared to defend the traditional morality of a community on utilitarian grounds if that morality were generally accepted. For it was, he thought, useful in promoting the social cohesion and stability which everyone desired. If, on the other hand, conventional morality were challenged or opposed by any appreciable section of the community, there was a serious danger that law and order might give way to anarchy. Thus Protagoras claimed that the Sophists performed a useful function in persuading people to accept the 'better' moral beliefs, even if they were not in any objective sense 'truer' than other moral beliefs, for he thought that civilized society depended upon the general acceptance of such beliefs. Without them, Protagoras thought, men would live in what Hobbes was later to call a 'state of nature', and their condition would then be no better than that of animals.

Expressed in modern terms, the theory of Protagoras is that moral beliefs are purely subjective, but that they discharge a useful function in upholding the law and order which are the basis of a civilized society. These will be assured if a coherent set of beliefs is generally accepted throughout a given society, and if that acceptance is maintained and strengthened by effective 'propaganda'. There is, of course, no strictly *moral* reason why that acceptance 'ought' to be promoted, but there is a *logical* reason if (*a*) such acceptance of a coherent set of beliefs is a necessary condition of social stability, and (*b*) the members of the society in question desire social stability.

Thus Protagoras accepted the general view of the Sophists

that Law, in contrast to Nature, was subjective and man-made, but he claimed that it was justified—in a utilitarian sense—by the function which it performed in maintaining a condition which the great majority of men desired.

Antiphon

A more critical theory of Law was advanced by the Sophist Antiphon, who lived in the latter part of the fifth century B.C., and of whose writings an interesting fragment has survived.[1] Antiphon held that men are subject to Laws of Nature in the same sense as inanimate objects. Just as all material bodies must conform to the law of gravity, so all human beings must feel and will and think in accordance with certain psychological laws. Of these psychological laws Antiphon thought that the most fundamental is the desire to live and be happy and to avoid death and unhappiness. But the laws of society often interfere with the operation of this Law of Nature since they restrain people from performing acts, e.g. stealing, which might bring them happiness. Antiphon admitted that there is a sound reason for observing the laws of society if to break them would involve the shame of conviction and the pain of punishment, for these consequences are painful to the individual, and to court them is therefore to violate the fundamental Law of Nature. But whenever an individual can increase his happiness by breaking the Law of Society and avoiding detection and punishment, it is, Antiphon thought, in accordance with the Law of Nature for him to do so.

The weakness of this theory is that it ignores the inevitable social relationships in which a man must live. The laws forbidding theft and murder may at times stand in the way of what a given individual would like to do; but they also prevent other people from doing to him what would undoubtedly be to his disadvantage. Indeed, the majority of civil laws are of potential advantage, as well as disadvantage, to an individual. As Hobbes subsequently recognized, a theory based upon the assumption that self-interest is the primary motive of human conduct is tenable only if it recognizes that self-interest may be quite different from the gratification of an immediate impulse, and that the achievement of personal happiness depends in no small measure upon

[1] A translation of this fragment has been incorporated as an Appendix to Chapter III of Sir Ernest Barker's *Greek Political Theory*.

controlling these immediate impulses and obeying civil laws made in the interest of all. Antiphon's principle might, indeed, have a useful application in a society ruled by a dictator ready to sacrifice his subjects' interests in pursuing his own, but apart from such circumstances the principle is fraught with grave dangers to the interests of both the individual and society.

Callicles

A theory which closely resembles that of Antiphon is attributed by Plato to Callicles in the dialogue *Gorgias*. According to Plato, Callicles held that Nature is governed by the law of force, while civil and moral laws are normally the result of contracts made by the weak to defraud the strong of what their strength would otherwise secure for them. In a state of nature the survival of the fit would be the effective rule of life, whereas the laws of society frequently reverse this principle and compel the strong to assist the weak. Callicles thought that his theory was supported by the considerations that in both the animal kingdom and the sphere of international relations,[1] in neither of which there are restrictive laws, the rule of force is the operative principle. Hence, Callicles concludes, the rule of force is natural, and should not be opposed by the laws of society.

It is not clear from what Plato tells us about Callicles' theory whether (to put the point in modern terms) he was defending a naturalistic theory of morality by defining 'right' in terms of 'might', or whether he was merely arguing that, as a matter of fact, it is morally desirable that the strong should get their way. The fact that he tried to deduce what ought to happen in human society from what does happen in the animal kingdom suggests that the second interpretation is probably correct, and that his theory is therefore not a naturalistic one; but in either case the inference from what does happen to what ought to happen is necessarily fallacious.

Thrasymachus

Whether or not Callicles' theory was naturalistic, there can be no doubt that the views attributed to Thrasymachus by Plato in the *Republic* are completely naturalistic. Thrasymachus was

---

[1] In more recent times various attempts have, of course, been made to introduce the 'rule of law' into international relations.

another Sophist of the late fifth century B.C., and he is introduced in Book I of the *Republic* as a supporter of the theory that 'just or right means nothing but what is to the interest of the stronger party.'[1] The subsequent discussion makes it clear that by this he meant that whatever the strongest individual or group in a community does in pursuit of his or their interest defines what is meant by 'right action'. There neither is nor can be any conflict between what the 'sovereign' power in a community does and what that community recognizes to be right since the actions of the sovereign power, or the actions which it approves, are what is *meant* by right actions. Minority groups may, indeed, challenge this conception of right actions, but their alternative conception cannot be effective unless and until they can compel the majority to accept it.

Plato examines this theory in some detail in the *Republic*, and advances, through the mouth of Socrates, a number of arguments which he obviously regards as a conclusive refutation. Thus Socrates argues (*a*) that strong men are not in fact motivated simply by a desire to exploit their strength. By a form of argument which Plato frequently employed, Socrates contends that the strong man or ruler is a sort of craftsman, skilled in the art of government, and that this art, like the art of the physician or the ship's captain, must, to achieve its ends, care for the welfare of those who constitute its raw material. Just as the physician tries to treat his patients successfully and the ship's captain tries to sail his ship with skill, so, Socrates argues, the ruler inevitably cares for the good of his subjects and will not therefore be interested solely in dominating them. As Socrates puts it, 'No form of skill or authority provides for its own benefit, it always studies and prescribes what is good for its subject—the interest of the weaker party.'[2]

(*b*) Socrates also compares the art of governing to the tuning of a musical instrument, and argues that, just as the musician will fail to tune his instrument properly if he goes beyond a certain pitch, so the ruler can pass beyond the limit which will give him the maximum power which he is capable of achieving.[3]

---

[1] *Republic*, I, 337 (translation by F. M. Cornford).   [2] ibid., I, 346.
[3] A modern illustration of this principle is the fate of Hitler after his refusal to accept the settlement reached at the Munich Conference in October, 1938, and in ultimately losing all his power by placing no limit to his ambitions.

(c) Finally, Socrates argues that everything has a proper and characteristic function, that function being the work 'for which that thing is the only instrument or the best'.[1] Thus the function of a man's soul is not the uncontrolled gratification of desire, which is characteristic of the lower animals, but the exercise of those functions which man *alone* can perform, such as deliberating and subordinating his instinctive desires to rational principles of conduct. If a man does behave as if he were a mere physical force or an unreasoning animal he is not discharging his intended function and will miss that happiness and contentment which is the natural result of the performance of that function.

The apparent object of these arguments is to show that power for its own sake is not, in practice, what strong men actually desire. It is argued that they desire to promote what they believe to be the good of those in their power and that they exercise their power in accordance with rational principles of conduct. This may well be so, but the arguments seem to miss the real point of Thrasymachus's theory. The latter does not imply, as Socrates seems to think, that strong men are exclusively interested in exploiting and increasing their strength. What Thrasymachus said was that 'right means nothing but what is to the *interest* of the stronger party'. The fact that Thrasymachus spoke of the *interest* of the stronger party shows that he recognized that the strong might desire other things than strength, for 'interest' means 'that which promotes the satisfaction of desire', and there is no reason why the desire of a strong man should necessarily be for more power. The point which Thrasymachus was trying to make is that whatever the strong man desires he can—if his strength is sufficient—achieve; and if he happens to be the sovereign power of the state (and is therefore, by definition, inferior to no other power within the state) *his* conception of what is right or wrong will have to be accepted, in practice if not in theory, by his subjects.

If the foregoing interpretation of Thrasymachus's theory is correct he was not, as some of his interpreters have supposed, attempting to defend absolute dictatorship. He was simply arguing that the moral code of a community is identical with the moral code of its dominant political force, whether that be a monarchy or an oligarchy or a majority of the whole people. He was saying

[1] *Republic*, I, 352.

in a slightly different way what Marx said many centuries later in his dictum that 'the ruling ideas of each age have ever been the ideas of its ruling class'.[1] In short, he was subscribing to the Sophistic theory that Law (as distinct from Nature) is man-made, and adding that in practice it is made by the dominating power in a state.

It is true that law, in the purely legalistic sense of statute law, is made by the sovereign power of the state. But the theory of Thrasymachus further implies that *moral* law—the law of justice and right—also has this origin. His theory also implies that all laws made by the soverign power of a state are made by that power for the furtherance of its own interests. Many philosophers would reject these implications and argue that a theory which reduces morality to law, and law to an expression of self-interest, is quite inadequate as an analysis of the relevant facts. They would argue that many laws[2] are based not on the self-interest of the sovereign but on objective moral principles, and that these principles cannot be accounted for in terms of self-interest.

Subjective and Objective Theories of Morality

In theory the distinction between interest and duty is of great importance, but in practice it is difficult to draw. For in practice it is difficult to say whether the sovereign power desires something because it is, say, pleasant or popular, or because it is good; what it desires determines what it is *interested* in obtaining and this in turn determines the laws which it makes for the community. On the other hand, it is of great theoretical importance whether or not 'the good' is identified with 'the desired', for if the two conceptions are synonymous 'the good' must have a subjective and 'man-made' origin—as Thrasymachus and the other Sophists believed. If, on the other hand, the two conceptions are not synonymous, the question whether, in a given instance, that which is desired *is* good is a question of significance and importance.

Thus the Sophists drew attention to a question which has remained fundamental throughout the history of philosophy and still gives rise to much debate and controversy. It is the question

[1] *Manifesto of the Communist Party*, p. 150 (Allen and Unwin, 1948).
[2] E.g. laws forbidding cruelty to animals.

whether moral laws are created by man or are, like the laws of the physical universe, objective principles independent of man's feelings and desires. If they are objective principles they constitute a valid basis for inferring what, in a categorical sense, a man ought to do. If, on the other hand, moral laws are, as the Sophists believed, expressions of desire or interest, there can be no valid ground for inferring that they 'ought' to be obeyed except in the hypothetical sense that if certain consequences are desired these laws *must* be obeyed. Thus if moral laws are objective there is a valid sense in which (assuming that theft is wrong) it can be said that I ought not to steal; but if these laws are subjective a statement of this sort must be interpreted as meaning that I must not steal *if* I wish to avoid the risk of punishment or the risk of endangering the structure of the society whose benefits I enjoy or some other consequence.

Most of the Sophists accepted the subjective interpretation of morality, and the four theories which have been described above are representative examples of the way in which they defended this common principle. In each case the 'right' was regarded as synonymous with some other conception of an empirical character which could be observed and sometimes measured in the situations in which it was found. Their theories differed only in the empirical conception with which the 'right' was identified. On the whole, the definitions suggested by Antiphon and Callicles appear inadequate to account for many of the moral judgments of actual experience, but the definitions proposed by Protagoras and Thrasymachus are sufficiently comprehensive to merit serious consideration as an analysis of moral judgments.

As already observed, an important implication of the subjective theory is that all apparently categorical arguments about obligation are really hypothetical arguments about the necessary means to certain ends. The inference that something ought to be done becomes the inference that something must be done if a certain result is desired. It was for this reason that Protagoras thought that the Sophists discharged a valuable function by influencing people to accept the laws which promote and strengthen the law and order which, he believed, the large majority of people desired.

Both Socrates and Plato thought that this reduction of obligation to interest destroyed the essential foundation of morality and was fraught with the gravest dangers to personal and social life. They conceived one of their main tasks to be the demonstration of the objective nature of moral distinctions, and in the next chapter an attempt will be made to estimate the success or otherwise of their attempt.

CHAPTER III

Plato's Theory of the Ideal State

Socrates and Plato

IT IS generally agreed that Plato (427–347 B.C.) was one of the greatest and most influential thinkers of antiquity. His thoughts have come down to us for the most part in a series of twenty-six dialogues, in the majority of which his teacher Socrates (469–399 B.C.) is the principal speaker. It is true that some scholars—notably the late Professors John Burnet and A. E. Taylor—held that the dialogues in which Socrates is the principal speaker are substantially accurate records of the theories and arguments of Socrates himself, and that only the last dialogues, such as the *Statesman*, *Timæus*, and *Laws*, in which Socrates does not appear, describe the theories of Plato. On the whole, however, this interpretation has not been generally accepted, and in this chapter the theories expounded by Socrates in the *Republic* will, in accordance with the usual practice, be referred to as Plato's theories. Even if some of these theories were originally advanced by Socrates, it seems reasonable to assume that Plato would not have expounded them in such detail unless he had accepted them as being, in the main, both true and important; and it is hardly likely that, when expounding these theories, Plato would not modify them in the light of his own critical reflections.

Unlike Plato, Socrates left no writings of his own, but Plato's dialogues provide us with a vivid impression of his personality and outlook. There is no exact parallel in modern times to the position which he occupied in Athenian society. A man of similar interests and aptitudes would today probably be a university teacher of philosophy, but when Socrates lived there was nothing corresponding to a university. Higher education, as we should call it, was carried on by the professional teachers known as the Sophists, who offered instruction to anyone who was willing to pay for it. Socrates thought the receipt of such payment degrading, but his method of teaching was in many ways similar to that of the Sophists, although the doctrines which he taught were different.

Socrates taught by the method of question and answer, which was known as 'dialectic'. He was ruthless in exposing uncritical assumptions and pretentious dogmas of all sorts, and his criticism of the democratic constitution of Athens appears to have been the real reason for his trial and condemnation to death, although the alleged offence was that of not worshipping the recognized gods of the state and corrupting the young by teaching them to follow his example. Yet, combined with this tendency to question and challenge existing beliefs, he had a firm faith in certain fundamental principles—the immortality of the soul, the objectivity of moral standards, and the reality of an unchanging world behind the world of sense and time. Nor did he ever question the guidance he received from an inner 'voice' which, he claimed, spoke to him from time to time, and which he regarded as a 'divine sign' that should always be respected.

Plato was a pupil of Socrates and, apart from two short interludes when he participated in active politics, he devoted his life to the teaching of philosophy. His teaching was of a more formal character than Socrates', and it was conducted in an institution called the *Academy*, which Plato founded, probably about the year 387 B.C., when he was forty years of age. The Academy was set up by Plato primarily for the disinterested pursuit of knowledge and this distinguished it from other contemporary teaching institutions, which aimed at preparing their students for the practical business of life. The Academy was, in fact, one of the earliest universities in the modern sense of the word, and its activity continued without interruption for nearly a thousand years.

The 'Republic'

The theory which will be discussed in the present chapter is the Theory of the Ideal State expounded in Plato's dialogue the *Republic*. While, as in all the earlier dialogues, the exposition of the theory is made by Socrates, it will be referred to, for the reasons previously mentioned, as Plato's theory, although Socrates may well have inspired some of its basic ideas. The theory is presented as a constructive alternative to what Plato regarded as the false and dangerous teaching of the Sophists, and it is inspired throughout by acceptance of the Socratic axiom that 'virtue is knowledge'.

As already observed, Socrates lived from 469 to 399 B.C. and Plato from 427 to 347 B.C. A. E. Taylor has shown that the available evidence indicates that the action of the *Republic* must be supposed to have taken place about the time of the Peace of Nicias in the spring of 421 B.C. This makes it probable that, in so far as the dialogue is historically accurate, it records what Socrates was saying about the age of forty-eight.

It is difficult to place the *Republic* in any one category of philosophical discussion. It examines problems of ethics and political philosophy as well as those of logic, metaphysics and psychology. This is indeed one of the great merits of the work, for it draws attention to the important fact that the different branches of philosophy are intimately connected and that ethical and political doctrines cannot be finally assessed without consideration of their logical and metaphysical assumptions.

The main object of the dialogue was to refute the Sophists' theory that moral principles have a subjective foundation and to show that they have, on the contrary, a rational and objective basis. Plato thinks that the essence of morality is *justice*, but it is important to recognize that he is using the word in a much wider sense than would now be customary. The English word 'justice' is derived from the Latin word *ius*, which means 'what is enforced by human authority'. That is an essentially legal conception, but for Plato the word had a *moral* significance, and is probably best translated simply as 'goodness'.

The object of the *Republic* is, then, to enquire into the nature of goodness and the way in which it may be known. As already observed, this enquiry is conducted through the medium of a dialogue. The speakers are: Socrates; Cephalus, a retired merchant living at the Piræus; Polemarchus, Lysias, and Euthydemus —sons of Cephalus; Thrasymachus, the Sophist; and Plato's elder brothers, Glaucon and Adeimantus.

Definition of Justice

The first object of the discussion is to arrive at a satisfactory definition of justice. Cephalus, who is a retired merchant with considerable means, suggests that justice consists in rendering to

God and man whatever is their due. Socrates has little difficulty in showing that this definition is circular, since the definition of the word 'due' would raise the same problems as the definition of justice itself. Various other suggested definitions of justice are then examined, including that of Thrasymachus, the Sophist. Thrasymachus's theory that justice is simply 'whatever is to the interest of the stronger party' was discussed in the preceding chapter, and Plato's reasons for rejecting this definition briefly examined. It was suggested that both Plato and other critics of Thrasymachus's theory missed the essential point of his definition, which identifies justice not with mere strength but with whatever is sought by those who are strong. Understood in the latter sense, Thrasymachus's definition is much more plausible, and by no means obviously inadequate. But Plato rejects it for the reasons noted in the preceding chapter, and goes on to examine what he regards as a much more plausible and dangerous theory.

The Theory of Glaucon and Adeimantus

The new theory is expounded by Glaucon and Adeimantus, although they make it clear that they do not accept it and are advancing it mainly in order to be satisfied by Socrates that it is false. It is the theory that virtue is based on expediency, that men are really self-interested but that they appreciate that they will advance their interests more effectively by respecting moral principles than by ignoring them. On the other hand, the theory implies that if, in any circumstances, it is possible to ignore one of these principles with impunity and thereby advance one's interest, there is no wrong in doing so; and it is this implication which Glaucon and Adeimantus find so disturbing.

The theory put forward by Glaucon and Adeimantus is the earliest expression of a doctrine which has been defended by several political philosophers and which was, in particular, the basis of Hobbes's theory of the state. It traces the origin of political morality to a contract made by a group of people with one another to obey certain rules which they believe will promote their several interests. Thus the theory attempts to explain political obligation, like moral obligation generally, wholly in terms of self-interest. In so doing it explains morality away, perhaps less obviously than the theory of Thrasymachus, but not less completely.

Plato's Theory of the Three Classes

The theory described by Glaucon and Adeimantus provides the starting point for the development of Socrates' own positive views about the nature of justice. He sees no way of refuting the doctrine directly, but is confident that its inadequacy will become apparent when it is contrasted with the positive views which he is about to develop. This he does by transferring the argument from the level of the individual to that of the community. He thinks that the nature of virtue will be more readily apparent if it is studied on a larger and more conspicuous scale than that of individual conduct. So he proceeds to investigate the nature of virtue in the state. His argument starts with an historical account of the origin of social life. This arises, he thinks, because no individual is self-sufficient and every individual must therefore co-operate with those who can supply his needs in return for his contributing to theirs. After the basic necessities have been supplied a demand arises for luxuries and amusements, and these generally require additional sources of supply abroad and thus create the need for a standing army to defend trade routes and communications. Finally, he thinks that it is obviously necessary to have a controlling body which determines the policy of the state and the proper relationship of its different classes. Thus the conclusion is reached that a civilized community requires three basic classes of citizens, namely (i) the producers, i.e. those (both employers and employed) engaged in providing the material needs and creating the material wealth of the community; (ii) the auxiliaries, i.e. the army and police, who maintain law and order and defend the state from enemies both within and without; and (iii) the guardians, i.e. those who are responsible for formulating and applying the policy of the state. They constitute what we should now simply call 'the government'.

Socrates thinks that in an Ideal State these three classes are each distinguished by a dominant characteristic. The producers are characterized by *temperance*, by which he means readiness to recognize the authority of the guardians. The auxiliaries are characterized by *courage*, by which he means readiness to face danger and fight bravely in overcoming it. And the guardians are characterized by *wisdom*, by which he means a capacity for true judgment, particularly about the moral value of things. Finally there is, in the Ideal State, a fourth element which pervades all classes and maintains them in their proper relationship to each other. This, Socrates suggests, is what is meant by *justice*, or the fundamental virtue of a good state. It maintains the natural harmony which ensures the proper functioning of all the parts. Just as the health of the physical body depends on a pervading harmony between its different organs, so the virtue of a state depends upon a harmony between its different parts. It is because Socrates regards the state as thus resembling a physical organism, and its parts as deriving their value from the function they perform in maintaining the well-being of the whole, that he is sometimes said to hold an Organic Theory of the State.

Having reached this conclusion about the essential nature of justice in the state, Socrates applies it to the analysis of the individual personality. He does this by pointing out that the three fundamental classes in the state correspond exactly to the three primary motives of action in the individual, namely appetite, spirit, and reason. This threefold division corresponds in some respects to the distinction drawn by certain modern psychologists between willing, feeling, and thinking, although 'spirit' is only one special type of feeling. Socrates calls the three basic motives respectively the *appetitive*, *spirited*, and *rational* elements in human nature, and suggests that the desire of the producers to create material wealth arises out of the basic physical desires of human nature; that the readiness of the auxiliaries to face and surmount danger is due to the emotions (particularly pride and courage) which dominate them; and that the wisdom of the guardians consists in the power of rational judgment. Socrates then concludes that, just as justice in the state consists in the maintenance of the right relationship between the three classes, so virtue in the individual consists in the maintenance of the correct relationship between the acquisitive appetites, the military spirit, and the rational powers of human nature. To quote his own words:

> Justice is produced in the soul, like health in the body, by establishing the elements concerned in their natural relations of control and subordination, whereas injustice is like disease and means that this natural order is inverted.[1]

Republic, IV, 444.

This conception of virtue may seem strange, but, in its application to the community, it is characteristic of all Organic Theories of the State. According to such theories, morality depends upon the relationship of the individual to the state, and is measured by the individual's success in making his proper contribution to the needs of the community. Moreover, the Organic Theory implies that the whole is more important and more valuable than the part, and that the part derives its value and, to some extent, its character, from its embodiment in the whole. This is obviously true of a part of a living body, since this cannot survive, as a living element, in separation from the body. Another important implication of an Organic Theory is that different parts have different degrees of importance. Just as the stomach is a more important part of the human body than the tonsils, so an Organic Theory discriminates between the different levels of importance of different classes or individuals in the community. In short, an Organic Theory asserts (*a*) that the state is an organism, and (*b*) that its citizens are good in so far as they discharge their proper function within it.

Plato's Criticism of Democracy

An important feature of the theory attributed to Socrates is the proposal that the control of policy should be placed wholly in the hands of the guardians. The justification for this proposal is given in Book V. It is there argued that the guardians ought to have supreme power because reason is their dominating faculty and because they can therefore be relied on to distinguish truly between what is right and what is wrong. For the morality of the state's policy can be ensured only if its direction is placed in the hands of those whose actions are determined by reason. Hence the auxiliaries and producers, who are dominated by other characteristics, should not be allowed to share in the control of policy. In modern terms, the theory is that a minority of men are capable of sound judgment about what is right and what is wrong and should therefore be given complete control over policy. Plato is entirely opposed to the democratic principle that every citizen should be allowed to express his view, and exercise his influence, in determining policy, since he thinks it obvious that those primarily suited for the life of business or soldiering, or not otherwise trained for the functions of government, are not

4

dominated by reason and cannot therefore be relied on to make the right decisions. He elaborates this point by referring to the Sophists who teach 'nothing else than the opinions and beliefs of the public itself when it meets on any occasion'[1] and call this wisdom. Of this practice he says:

> It is as if the keeper of some huge and powerful creature should make a study of its moods and desires, how it may best be approached and handled, when it is most savage or gentle and what makes it so, the meaning of its various cries and the tones of voice that will soothe or provoke its anger; and, having mastered all this by long familiarity, should call it wisdom, reduce it to a system, and set up a school. Not in the least knowing which of these humours and desires is good or bad, right or wrong, he [the Sophist] will fit all these terms to the fancies of the great beast and call what it enjoys good and what vexes it bad. He has no other account to give of their meaning; for him any action will be 'just' and 'right' that is done under necessity, since he is too blind to tell how great is the real difference between what must be and what ought to be.[2]

Such is Plato's attitude to the 'will of the people' and the democratic theory that it should be carried out by the executive government. To Plato such a system is one of pure force, in which government is 'done under necessity', without any attempt to ascertain whether it is morally right to gratify the demands of the populace.

Opinion and Knowledge about Goodness

Plato thinks that if a system of government is to be moral it must be conducted in accordance with moral *knowledge* and not merely moral *opinion*. The average citizen may well hold the opinion that the objects of his desire are good but he cannot, Plato says, know whether or not they are really good unless he is aware of the distinction between the essence of goodness and its many apparent manifestations; for if he does not appreciate this distinction he will not know whether a thing which appears to him to be good really is good.

To explain the nature of this distinction Plato interrupts his

[1] ibid., VI, 493.   [2] ibid., VI. 493.

discussion of political problems and considers the nature of the distinction between opinion and knowledge in general terms. He explains this distinction in terms of another distinction—that between what he calls *Forms* and their particular manifestations. This is illustrated by the distinction between 'beauty itself and the multiplicity of beautiful things' or, in general terms, between the 'real essence' and the 'many manifestations'.[1]

The distinction closely resembles that drawn by modern philosophers between 'particulars' and 'universals'. Every individual orange, for example, is a distinct particular but is characterized by certain qualities of colour, taste, smell, etc., which can characterize any number of oranges. Such qualities are called *universals* because they appear to be present in an indefinite number of particular oranges, and it is because of this that we can say of each of these oranges that it is yellow or sweet, etc.[2] In the same way, Plato is suggesting that, if a thing is beautiful, it is because it partakes of the Form of beauty. From this he concludes that, if we wish to know, and not merely believe, that a certain thing is beautiful, we must be acquainted with the Form of beauty, since all beautiful things are made beautiful by the presence of that Form. In modern terms knowledge—as distinct from mere belief or opinion—depends upon acquaintance with universals.

Plato is, of course, particularly concerned to define the conditions under which knowledge of the Form of goodness can be attained, since 'without having had a vision of this Form no one can act with wisdom, either in his own life or in matters of state'.[3] In the light of his earlier discussion he might have been expected to maintain that knowledge of goodness depends upon acquaintance with the Form of goodness. Sometimes he seems to imply a view of this sort, but elsewhere he makes it quite clear that he regards the Form of goodness as much more than a simple universal. It is, he says, not only that which makes good things good but also that which enables us to apprehend their goodness. And he compares it to the sun which is responsible both 'for

[1] ibid., VI, 493-494.
[2] I ignore, as irrelevant to the purpose of this illustration, the fact that different oranges may be characterized by different shades of yellow or different degrees of sweetness.
[3] *Republic*, VII, 517.

making our eyes see perfectly and making objects perfectly visible'.[1] Thus Socrates is made to say:

> This, then, which gives to the objects of knowledge their truth and to him who knows them his power of knowing, is the Form or essential nature of Goodness. It is the cause of knowledge and truth; and so, while you may think of it as an object of knowledge, you will do well to regard it as something beyond truth and knowledge, and, precious as these both are, of still higher worth. And, just as in our analogy light and vision were to be thought of as like the Sun, but not identical with it, so here both knowledge and truth are to be regarded as like the Good, but to identify either with the Good is wrong. The Good must hold a yet higher place of honour.[2]

The exact meaning of this passage is far from clear, but at least it implies that the Form of the Good is far more complex and fundamental than a simple universal like 'beautiful' or 'blue'. If Socrates had said that goodness is the Form in which good things participate, just as beauty is the Form in which beautiful things participate, the theory would have been comparatively easy to understand, however inadequate it might have appeared. But Socrates says quite specifically that, while goodness may be thought of as an object of knowledge, it is really 'beyond truth and knowledge'. Thus he regards the Form of the Good as something very different from a universal characteristic. At this point, indeed, he seems to be anticipating the Hegelian theory of reality as a complex logical whole of which human experiences of all kinds are partial and imperfect manifestations.

Whatever view is taken of Socrates' meaning at this obscure point in his argument,[3] it is clear that he believes (*a*) that there is a real and objective distinction between good and bad acts or ends, and (*b*) that it is possible for at least some human beings to acquire the knowledge necessary to recognize this distinction. But he believes that very few are capable of doing so. The few who have this capacity are the philosophers.

---

[1] ibid., VI, 507.   [2] ibid., VI, 508.
[3] At VI, 504, he speaks as though the Form of the Good were a simple universal, for he says that 'the highest object of knowledge is the essential nature of the Good, from which everything that is good and right derives its value for us'

Socrates defines a philosopher as one 'whose passion it is to see the truth'.[1] And by 'seeing the truth' he means discerning 'the essence as well as the things that partake of its character, without ever confusing the one with the other'.[2] And this, he thinks, justifies the paradoxical conclusion that philosophers should be kings:

> Unless either philosophers become kings in their countries or those who are now called kings and rulers come to be sufficiently inspired with a genuine desire for wisdom; unless, that is to say, political power and philosophy meet together . . . there can be no rest from troubles, my dear Glaucon, for states, nor yet, as I believe, for all mankind.[3]

Plato, in short, is advocating a form of government by experts. Democratic systems, in which the people themselves determine the general objectives of policy, he condemns because under them 'any action will be "just" or "right" that is done under necessity',[4] i.e. the necessity of satisfying public demand; and it is inconceivable 'that the multitude should ever believe in the existence of any real essence, as distinct from its many manifestations, or listen to anyone who asserts such a reality'.[5] But while there is much force in this argument if an objective distinction between right and wrong is accepted, it is by no means clear how the experts are to be selected in practice.

Plato thinks that two important conditions must be observed in the selection and training of these experts. In the first place, those who seem most likely to achieve knowledge of the Good must have their minds suitably trained for this purpose. And, secondly, they must live in such circumstances as will minimize all temptations to deviate from the path of duty which their philosophic insight reveals to them.

Education of the Guardians

Plato proposes that a provisional selection of guardians should be made at the age of twenty after completion of the normal course of education which they are to share with other citizens. This preliminary education covers (i) *grammatic* (i.e. reading and writing); (ii) *music* (i.e. learning and reciting poetry, lyre-playing

[1] ibid., V, 475. [2] ibid., V, 476. [3] ibid., V, 473.
[4] ibid., VI, 493. [5] ibid., VI, 494.

and singing lyric poetry, and the rudiments of arithmetic and geometry); and (iii) *gymnastic* (i.e. gymnastic exercises and athletics). Education in these subjects is to be normally followed, at the age of eighteen, by two years' military training after which, for the majority of citizens, the process of education is complete. The provisional selection of guardians is made by a sort of trial by ordeal.[1] They are to be subjected to 'ordeals of toil and pain', and exposed successively to terrors and temptations, and only those who pass through these ordeals without departing from the standards of conduct prescribed in their earlier education will be accepted as probationers for the office of guardian. In short, these tests are for the purpose of selecting those with the right sort of character for the responsibilities of guardianship.

But it is also necessary to train the minds of prospective guardians so that they may recognize the nature of the Good, and act in accordance with it when governing the community. Socrates thinks that a prolonged course of study in mathematics and philosophy is the most effective sort of training for this purpose because it will 'draw the soul from the world of change to reality'.[2] As he says of arithmetic, 'it forces the mind to arrive at pure truth by the exercise of pure thought'.[3] He therefore prescribes a course of study extending over ten years, and covering arithmetic, geometry, solid geometry, astronomy and harmonics (the mathematics of musical rhythms). The study of history, which in modern times has usually been regarded as of great importance for a statesman, Plato never mentions. As its subject matter belongs to the world of change, he would have regarded it as incapable of revealing the eternal truths upon the application of which good government depends. On the other hand, mathematics consists wholly of universal propositions whose truth is independent of time and change, and he believes that prolonged study of such a subject will familiarize the mind with the distinction between the world of change and the world of timeless reality, and assist it to discover the timeless principles of goodness which he believes are just as independent of the changing world as the propositions of mathematics.

The programme of mathematical study is to occupy the prospective guardians from the age of twenty to the age of thirty, after which five years are to be devoted to the study of dialectic.

[1] ibid., III, 413–4.   [2] ibid., VII, 521.   [3] ibid., VII, 525.

Dialectic is described by Socrates as the 'journey' made 'by one who aspires, through the discourse of reason unaided by any of the senses, to make his way in every case to the essential reality and perseveres until he has grasped by pure intelligence the very nature of Goodness itself'.[1] To do this it is necessary to 'take a comprehensive view of the mutual relations and affinities which bind all these sciences together'.[2] In short, dialectic is what we should call philosophy, in that it examines and correlates the assumptions made in the different branches of science and goes beyond them to examine the ultimate principle of Goodness from which, Plato believes, mathematics and all other sciences derive their truth.

Whatever Plato may have meant by the Form of the Good, he seems to believe that there are universal and necessary principles of goodness which the mind is assisted to discover by previous study of the universal and necessary principles of mathematics. When the probationary guardians have attained to a clear knowledge of these principles they will be ready to assume the full responsibilities of guardianship by taking the principle of the Good 'as a pattern for the right ordering of the state and of the individual, themselves included'.[3]

The probationary guardians are not, however, expected to be fully prepared for this responsibility when they complete their study of dialectic at the age of thirty-five. Plato thinks that they must first take 'military commands and other offices suitable to the young, so that they may not be behind their fellow citizens in experience'.[4] This practical work is to continue for fifteen years, and only those who discharge these subordinate responsibilities satisfactorily, and who pass a further series of character tests,[5] will ultimately be selected, at the age of fifty, for the supreme responsibilities of statesmanship. Even then, most of their time will be spent in study, though 'they will all take their turn at the troublesome duties of public life and act as Rulers for their country's sake, not regarding it as a distinction, but as an unavoidable task'.[6]

But it is not, Plato thinks, sufficient to ensure that appropriate education brings the rulers to achieve a vision of the Good. Steps must also be taken to minimize the temptations which might

[1] ibid., VII, 532. [2] ibid., VII, 531, C. [3] ibid., VII, 540.
[4] ibid., VII, 539. [5] ibid., VII, 540. [6] ibid., VII, 540.

deflect them from the path of duty thus revealed. Of such temptations Plato regards those which arise from personal interests or
possessions as the most dangerous. Hence the rulers of the Ideal
State must live without private property or money and receive
the essentials of life as an allowance from the state. They must
likewise be deprived of normal family life and live together like
soldiers in a camp, since otherwise they might be tempted to put
the interests of their wives and families before the good of the
community. Their children must be the issue of temporary unions
based on eugenic principles, and neither these children nor their
mothers must be regarded as in any way the property of the
fathers. They must be 'held in common'.[1] By such a mode of life
the rulers will be protected against the temptations of private
interests:

> This manner of life will be their salvation, and make them
> the saviours of the commonwealth. If ever they should come
> to possess land of their own and houses and money, they will
> give up their guardianship for the management of their
> farms and households and become tyrants at enmity with
> their fellow citizens instead of allies.[2]

These proposals have led some people to suppose that Plato
was at heart a 'communist'. But it is clear that this is not true in
the modern sense of the word. Plato's object in depriving the
rulers of private property was not economic but moral. He did
not, like a modern communist, advocate the 'nationalization' of
the means of production and distribution in the economic interest
of the whole community. What he advocated was the prohibition
of private possessions to the rulers of the state so that no conflict
should arise between their private interests and their public duty.
There is no evidence that Plato favoured the abolition of private
property among the producers, who would, in any case, constitute the larger part of the community and be mainly responsible
for carrying on its economic life.

The importance of eliminating all personal interests and
ambitions from the lives of the rulers is emphasized in a further

---

[1] This does not mean that the relationship of men and women should
be promiscuous, but that a woman should be available for mating with
whichever man is eugenically best suited to her.

[2] *Republic*, III, 416.

passage where Plato argues that 'access to power must be confined to men who are not in love with it'.[1] This, he thinks, is a
further reason why rulers ought always to be philosophers: 'The
life of true philosophy is the only one that looks down upon
offices of state.'[2] Only so can there be any assurance that the good
of the community will not be sacrificed to personal ambition.
Those with 'vested interests' to care for are, in Plato's view,
automatically unfitted for statesmanship.

Plato finally emphasizes that his account of the Ideal State is
no mere day-dream. Many states may fall short of the high
standards which he has laid down, but it does not follow that
these standards are impossible to reach. Thus he concludes:

> Difficult it may be, but possible, though only on the one
> condition we laid down, that genuine philosophers—one or
> more of them—shall come into power in a state; men who
> will despise all existing honours as mean and worthless,
> caring only for the right and the honours to be gained from
> that, and above all for justice as the one indispensable thing
> in whose service and maintenance they will reorganize their
> own state.[3]

Such, in outline, is Plato's theory of the Ideal State. It is clearly
a *moral* theory, i.e. a theory of how the state ought to be organized
and governed. And its main principle is that the few specially
gifted citizens who, in any state, are capable of discerning the
nature of goodness, and have the strength of character to follow
the rule of right despite all temptations to the contrary, should
be given absolute power over their fellow citizens. Only on this
condition will the life of the community be morally sound.

In the past Plato's theory has been widely respected as a
brilliant and impressive vindication of the place of moral principles in politics, but it does not either anticipate or answer the
arguments upon which Empiricist Theories of Morality have in
modern times been based. Judged by contemporary standards of
philosophical criticism, Plato's arguments are in many cases
either obscure or dogmatic or based upon doubtful assumptions.
None the less, it must be conceded that he raises and attempts
to solve some of the most fundamental issues which have subsequently dominated political philosophy. In particular, his basic

[1] ibid., VII, 521.   [2] ibid., VII, 521.   [3] ibid., VII, 540.

theme—the nature of justice—raises what may well be regarded as the most central of all issues in political philosophy. It is the issue whether force or morality is the foundation of the state; whether the authority of the ruler over the subject is based on power or on right; whether the obedience of the subject to his ruler is based on interest or on duty; whether the organization of a state is the result of an equilibrium of forces—in which the relative strength of the forces is all that counts—or whether it is, in part at least, determined by men's respect for objective moral principles. These are the fundamental questions which the *Republic* raises.

It is clear that Plato had no doubt about the answer to these questions. Against the theory of Thrasymachus he argued that men do not, and against the theory put forward by Glaucon and Adeimantus he argued that men should not, arrange their affairs simply in accordance with their natural desires and powers. The latter, in Plato's view, ought at all times to be subordinated to the pattern set by the Good for the 'right ordering of the state and of the individual'.[1] Hence the direction of the community should be placed in the absolute power of those who, by the circumstances of their lives and the quality of their minds, are least likely to be influenced by personal desires and ambitions and most likely to exercise their power solely in accordance with what they know to be morally right. And hence democracy, in which the opinions of the corrupt and the ignorant may count for as much as the knowledge of the upright and the wise, is the very negation of moral government.

It follows, of course, that if there is an objective distinction between right and wrong (or, as Plato says, between justice and injustice), the state ought to be governed in accordance with the right policy. That conclusion follows necessarily from the fact that 'the right policy' means 'the policy which ought to be pursued'. And Plato is on strong ground when he argues that Thrasymachus's definition of 'justice' as 'what is to the interest of the stronger party' simply does not mean what most people mean by justice. It cannot be what most people mean by justice, because what they call just acts are frequently acts which do not contribute to the interest of the stronger party but go against it. For example, acts described as just often take the form of up-

[1] ibid., VII, 540.

holding the interest of an individual when that interest conflicts with the interest of a far more powerful group. Hence there seem to be good grounds for distinguishing between justice and the interest of the stronger party. But it is not equally clear how the distinction drawn by Plato between merely believing and definitely knowing that a certain act is just can be defended. Plato's own account of this distinction is, as already observed, extremely obscure. He does not appear to regard justice as an ordinary Form but as something 'beyond truth and knowledge'[1] and as that which makes both truth and knowledge possible. A theory expressed in such obscure language is an unconvincing way of establishing the distinction between belief and knowledge about moral propositions. But the purpose of the theory is at least comparatively clear. Plato is trying to justify his belief that moral propositions are *a priori* just like mathematical propositions on the ground that they are based upon the relationship of eternal Forms. If this were not the case he would not regard morality as a possible object of knowledge. It is, he thinks, a possible object of knowledge for those who have been suitably trained just because the goodness of a thing is determined by the Form of the Good, and its goodness can therefore be recognized by those who are acquainted with that Form, or whose knowledge issues from it.[2]

Now it must be conceded that, even if moral propositions are *a priori*, there may not be any way of *demonstrating* this truth to anyone who fails to recognize it. For, as a philosophical proposition, the assertion 'moral propositions are *a priori*' must itself be *a priori*, and it may not be possible to infer it from any simpler *a priori* proposition. And, even if it can be so inferred, it is quite possible that some people may be unable to recognize the *a priori* truth of the more ultimate proposition. Indeed, it is one of Plato's most important contentions that it is far from easy to recognize *a priori* truths and that the majority of mankind are unlikely to do so.

On the other hand, many modern philosophers would hold that Plato assumed far too easily that his own moral beliefs had

[1] ibid., VI, 508.
[2] The peculiarity of the Form of the Good appears to be that not only does its presence in a thing make that thing good but it also enables the mind to apprehend its presence.

a superior status to those which he rejected, and was far too uncritical in reaching the conclusion that morality is a matter of knowledge and not of feeling. They would point to the many controversial subjects, such as capital punishment, corporal punishment, gambling and blood sports, regarding the morality of which there is widespread disagreement, and they would question Plato's assumption that in every case it is possible, at least in principle, for the philosophical mind to recognize, with *a priori* certainty, the right course to take. Some would say with Hume that the incompatible beliefs held about the rights and wrongs of these issues, and the impossibility of deciding between them by reference to some independent standard, justify the theory that such beliefs relate not to objective facts but to subjective feelings and that they are, in fact, descriptions of feelings experienced by the speaker or by some social group to which he belongs.

But, even if Plato was mistaken in his assumption that moral propositions are *a priori*, his theory remains a valuable exposition of the logical consequences of making this assumption—consequences which have not always been so clearly and consistently deduced by others. For if moral distinctions are *a priori*, it follows that there is an unconditional obligation to observe them, and thus to obey without question those who, from their knowledge of morality, can say how human affairs ought to be conducted. In simpler language, if goodness is a possible object of knowledge, then those who have attained to knowledge of it have a right to tell those who lack this knowledge what they ought to do; and the only way of ensuring that a community is rightly governed will be to give absolute power to those who know what is good and can be relied on to apply the rule of right in all they do.

In modern times a society administered in such a way would be called 'authoritarian', and it has to be frankly recognized that Plato's argument for government by 'moral experts' runs counter to the basic assumptions of democracy. For in a democratic society all claims to personal infallibility are rejected, and those who administer policy are answerable to those who have entrusted them with this task. On the other hand, the alleged infallibility of Plato's guardians has a close parallel in the attitude of modern dictators who claim the right to suppress all criticism of, and opposition to, their policies.

Whether the practice of democracy is consistent with the assumption that moral principles are *a priori* is a question which will be examined at length in subsequent chapters. For the present, it is sufficient to note that Plato had no doubt that democracy is, both in theory and in practice, incompatible with the acceptance of a rational morality and, indeed, reduces simply to government by force of the majority. And he saw no reason to suppose that the majority would be always, or even usually, right in what they did.

CHAPTER IV

Aristotle's Theory of the Best Possible State

ARISTOTLE was born in 384 B.C. when Plato was forty-three, and died in 322 B.C. at the age of sixty-two. He was therefore thirty-seven years old when Plato died in 347 B.C. He was sent to Athens at the age of eighteen for higher education, and was a member of Plato's Academy for twenty years. He subsequently spent three years in Asia Minor, where he pursued his scientific interests, particularly marine biology. In 343 B.C. he became tutor to Alexander, Prince of Macedon, afterwards Alexander the Great, who was then a boy of thirteen. There is no indication, however, that he exercised any influence on Alexander's character. The *Politics* makes it clear that he disliked all types of dictatorship and, like Plato, thought that the small city state, which had no political ambitions, provided the most favourable environment for the good life. It is also very noticeable that Aristotle never refers to his pupil's great conquests anywhere in his writings—probably because he had little sympathy with them, and did not regard them as examples of the way in which rulers should use their powers.

When Alexander was called to the Macedonian throne by the murder of his father in 336 B.C., Aristotle returned to Athens. At this time the presidency of the Academy, which had been filled since Plato's death by Speusippus, became vacant, but Aristotle was not selected to succeed him. He may have been offended, for in 335 B.C. he opened a rival school known as the Lyceum, and he was followed there by some members of the Academy. For the next twelve years he was fully occupied by his work in the Lyceum, and he gradually developed a teaching tradition of his own, departing from the Platonic tradition of the Academy by making biology and history, instead of mathematics, the primary subjects of study.

The *Politics*, like Aristotle's other works, takes the form of a treatise, not a dialogue, and its style is quite different from that of Plato's dialogues. This is explained by the fact that, while Plato's lecture notes have been lost, many of his books have come down to us. On the other hand, Aristotle's books have almost all been lost, but many of his lecture notes have survived. Scholars are generally agreed that the 'works' of Aristotle as we know them consist of his lecture manuscripts edited by his pupils after his death.

The argument of the *Politics* is not by any means consistent, and scholars attribute this to the fact that it was probably composed over a period of time during which the influence of Plato's teaching on Aristotle's thinking became weaker. Thus Sabine,[1] following Jaeger,[2] puts forward the hypothesis that Books II, III, VII, and VIII, which are concerned primarily with theories of the Ideal State, were written soon after Plato's death in 347 B.C.; while Books IV, V, and VI, which are concerned primarily with the study of actual states and the conditions governing their stability, were not written until some years after the opening of the Lyceum in 335 B.C. Finally, the hypothesis suggests that Book I was written last of all and intended as a general introduction to the whole treatise. It is certainly true that in Books II, III, VII, and VIII Aristotle is more interested in describing an Ideal State; whereas in Books IV–VI he assumes that the political ideal varies from state to state and argues that the duty of government is to realize that political ideal as completely as possible whatever form it may take.

Apart from philosophy in the strict sense, Plato was mainly interested in mathematics and Aristotle in biology, and their political philosophies in many ways reflect this difference. Thus Plato believed that in politics it was possible to establish principles having the precision and certainty of mathematics, whereas Aristotle believed that in politics, as in biology, careful and patient empirical enquiry was the only way of arriving at reliable generalizations. Plato believed that the apprehension of the Form of the Good would reveal exactly how a community ought to be organized and governed, whereas Aristotle thought that the right organization for any given state could only be discovered by careful examination of its other characteristics. This, at any rate, is what he said in the most consistent passages of the central

[1] *A History of Political Theory*, p. 90.   [2] *Aristotle* (1923).

books already referred to (Books IV, V, and VI). In the Books which are believed to have been written first (Books II, III, VII, and VIII) he makes some statements which imply a conception of the Ideal State closer to that of Plato; but if it is true that Books IV, V, and VI were written some fifteen years later it is reasonable to suppose that they present us with his more mature and considered thoughts on political theory.

Aristotle's Conception of Nature

In Book I (which, as already observed, was probably the last Book of the *Politics* to be written) Aristotle explains the novel sense in which he understands the word 'nature' and the fundamental part which the conception plays in his political philosophy. He understands this word in a very different sense from the Sophists. For them it meant the permanent and objective characteristics of independent reality in contrast to the variable and subjective beliefs and conventions of individuals or communities; but for Aristotle 'nature' is essentially a biological conception. In his own words:

> The nature of a thing is its end. For what each thing is when fully developed, we call its nature, whether we are speaking of a man, a horse, or a family.[1]

Thus for Aristotle the nature of a thing is not what the thing *is* but what it is *capable of becoming*. Its nature is not a static but a developing conception. And just as in biology the 'nature' of a seed can only be discovered by the observation of its growth, so in politics the nature of a state can only be discovered by observation of its development and tendencies. In practice, this means the study of its history and the observation of its dominating tendencies, whether these be to autocratic or democratic forms of government, to an expanding or stable economy, and so on.

After defining the nature of a thing as its 'end' Aristotle adds the important proposition that 'the final cause and end of a thing is the best'.[2] By this he seems to mean that the destined end of a thing's development is necessarily a good end. It is not clear whether this proposition is intended to be analytic or synthetic—whether Aristotle is implying that the 'nature' or destined end

[1] *Politics*, Book I, Chap. 2. (Translation by Jowett.)   [2] loc. cit.

of a thing is what is *meant* by its 'good', or whether he only means that that end is, as a matter of either fact or necessity, always characterized by goodness. There are many passages in the *Politics* which suggest that Aristotle recognized a standard of moral value quite distinct from the natural tendencies of the state, and thought of it as external and independent. But in the passages where he speaks of 'the natural' as *ipso facto* 'the good', he seems to imply that the terms are synonymous, that, in *his* sense of the word, 'the natural' is what is meant by 'the good', i.e. that the attainment of an organism's destined end is its supreme good and defines the standard by which its actual evolution must be approved or condemned.

It would, however, be untrue to say that the *Politics* as a whole justifies this interpretation of Aristotle's conception of morality. Most of his references to the subject suggest that he accepted the 'non-naturalistic' theory of morality, although at the same time he recognized the relativity of moral judgments to the actions or situations being judged and the consequent impossibility of making these judgments without knowledge of the characteristics of the actions or situations in question. This means, in modern terminology, that he regarded moral judgments as synthetic, and consequently thought it impossible to discover moral truths without knowledge of the concrete situations which exemplify them.[1]

Having defined the sense in which he uses the word 'nature', Aristotle claims that 'it is evident that the state is a creation of nature, and that man is by nature a political animal'.[2] For 'the proof that the state is a creation of nature and prior to the individual is that the individual, when isolated, is not self-sufficing; and therefore he is like a part in relation to the whole'.[3]

Aristotle is here stating what has since been designated as the Organic Theory of the State. It has been so called because it conceives of the state as a kind of organism. According to the theory, the state is not a mere collection of its parts but an organic combination of them, so that none of these parts would be what it is if separated from the rest. The essential features of an organism are most simply illustrated by the human body. These are that (*a*) the parts (e.g. a heart and a foot) no longer

---

[1] Attention has been drawn in Chapter I to the difficulty of combining this position with a non-naturalistic interpretation of morality.
[2] *Politics*, I, 2.   [3] ibid.

exist in the same form if separated from the body; (*b*) that the health of the whole depends upon the health of the parts and *vice versa*; and (*c*) that some parts (e.g. the heart) have a more essential function to perform than others (e.g. the appendix). According to the Organic Theory, all these propositions are true of a political society. It is not a mere collection of individuals, but has an organic unity of its own. For this reason, there can be no real conflict between its interest and the true interests of its constituent members. And, finally, different members, or classes of members, have different functions to perform and different levels of importance.

The Relativity of Moral Standards

One of the most important implications of Aristotle's theory is that the moral standards of a society are relative to its 'nature' and thus liable to variation from state to state. Thus Aristotle says:

> Laws, when good, should be supreme. . . . But what are good laws has not yet been clearly explained; the old difficulty remains. The goodness or badness, justice or injustice, of laws varies of necessity with the constitutions of states.[1]

Unlike Plato, who set himself to describe an Ideal State, Aristotle believes that the best possible state may take a variety of different forms. He does not think that it would be true to assert as a universal principle that the power of government is always best exercised by a single man, or by a minority, or by the community as a whole. It is possible for any of these alternatives to provide the best form of government for a community, and it is also possible for any of them to provide a bad form of government. Whether the government is good or bad does not depend upon whether it is exercised by a single person, or by a minority, or by the people as a whole, but upon the way in which it is exercised. It will be a good government if it is exercised in the interest of the community as a whole, and a bad government if it is exercised by the governing body for its own selfish purposes. This principle follows simply from the Organic Theory, for on that theory the interest of the organism is always more

[1] ibid., III, 11.

important than the interest of any one or any group of its constituent elements. Indeed, since the latter are organic constituents of the whole their *true* interest must coincide with the interest of the whole.

Good and Bad Forms of Government

Aristotle then classifies the various possible forms of government according as to whether the power of government is exercised by one, or by the few, or by the many, and according as to whether the government, however constituted, aims at promoting the common interest (in which case it is a good government) or at promoting the special interest of the governing class (in which case it is a bad government). The classification based on these two principles is as follows:

	Good Governments	*Bad Governments*
Government by one	Monarchy	Tyranny
Government by the few	Aristocracy	Oligarchy
Government by the many	Polity[1]	Democracy

Aristotle sums up the defects of the bad forms of government as follows:

> Tyranny is a kind of monarchy which has in view the interests of the monarch only; oligarchy has in view the interest of the wealthy; democracy, of the needy; none of them the common good of all.[2]

Aristotle points out that, as a matter of fact, government by the few is government by the rich, and government by the many is government by the poor since 'the rich everywhere are few and the poor numerous'.[3] He thinks that the principal difference between oligarchy and democracy lies in their different conceptions of justice. Democrats believe that men are equal by birth and that they should therefore have equal political rights, whereas oligarchs believe that these rights should be in proportion to wealth. Aristotle thinks that these different conceptions of justice reflect the biassed judgment of men who are primarily

---

[1] This is a transliteration of the Greek word meaning 'constitutional government'.
[2] *Politics*, III, 8.   [3] loc. cit.

concerned to advance their own interests, and overlook the
fundamental principle that 'a state exists for the sake of a good
life, and not for the sake of life only'.[1] He concludes that political
rights should be awarded to people in proportion to the contribution which they make to the moral purposes of the state,
one of which is that the general (as distinct from any sectional)
interest should be the object of all political action.

Aristotle next considers whether the few or the many are likely
to be the better rulers. He recognizes that the few are more likely
to possess outstanding ability, but observes that there are also
advantages in the rule of the many as they bring varied points
of view to bear on issues of policy, and are therefore less likely
than the few to approve a wrong policy. This does not mean that
in a polity there is no place for the expert, but it does mean that
in such a constitution he is not the final judge of his work. The
expert is necessary to formulate and apply a policy, but the people
whom it is intended to benefit are better fitted than he to judge
whether it is a good policy. Aristotle illustrates this principle by
some simple analogies:

> There are some arts whose products are not judged of
> solely, or best, by the artists themselves. . . . The user or,
> in other words, the master, of the house will even be a
> better judge than the builder, just as the pilot will judge
> better of the rudder than the carpenter, and the guest will
> judge better of a feast than the cook.[2]

The principle that 'the guest will judge better of a feast than
the cook' has, indeed, become a basic principle of modern
democracy. Modern communities are too vast to permit of
government by popular assembly, which was the form of democracy that Plato knew and condemned, nor do they claim that,
even if this difficulty could be surmounted by some from of
referendum, it would be desirable. The need for experts to
formulate and execute policy is generally recognized, but democratic peoples claim the ultimate right to approve or condemn
that policy, and to select other rulers if they are dissatisfied with
the achievements of their existing government.

In discussing the differences between good and bad forms of
government Aristotle draws attention to another fundamental

[1] ibid. ,III, 9.   [2] ibid., III, 11.

principle now commonly regarded as essential in a democratic state. This is the principle of *government by consent*. Thus he says of bad forms of government: 'They are despotic, whereas a state is a community of freemen.'[1] By this he means that a good government, which attempts to promote the interest of the community as a whole, will receive the willing consent of the whole people, whereas a government which attempts to promote the interest of only a particular section of the community will find it necessary to govern the rest of the community by despotic measures. This appears to be true in practice, for modern democracies have generally been most successful where there has been a consciousness of common interests underlying sectional differences, and where the government has sought to achieve an acceptable compromise when the interests of different classes have appeared to conflict. On the other hand, where sectional interests have been in sharp conflict, and the government has clearly identified its policy with the interests of one of the sections, democracy has usually tended to give way to government by force.

Aristotle believes that one of the most important safeguards against the bad forms of government is respect for impersonal law. This law is not, as Plato thought, revealed by immediate insight to a gifted few, but is gradually discovered in and through experience. Such, at least, is Aristotle's view when he expresses his own most mature thought. When he is subject to the influence of Plato's teaching he sometimes writes as though the law were something standing outside and independent of the state. Thus the influence of Plato is obvious at the end of Book III, where Aristotle says that if a perfectly virtuous man could be found it would be right to give him supreme power. This is an admission that the theory of Plato's *Republic* would be justified if only perfectly virtuous men could be found. On the other hand, if political ideals are definable in terms of 'natural' development, the law must necessarily vary with the circumstances of the community to which it applies.

Aristotle's Analysis of Actual States

In Book IV Aristotle directs his attention to the nature of actual states since, as he says, the best is often unattainable and

[1] ibid., III, 6.

the statesman should therefore acquaint himself not only with what is best in the abstract, i.e. theoretically, but with what is best relatively to circumstances, i.e. practically. Books IV, V, and VI are all devoted to an examination of the best practicable states in different sets of circumstances and constitute an empirical study of the kind which is a necessary foundation for sound policy if the assumptions of Aristotle's Organic Theory are true. For on those assumptions the best constitution for a specified state can be determined only after a study of its history, traditions, economic and geographical circumstances, and so on. In these Books Aristotle accepts the implications of his doctrine that the natural end of a state is its ideal, and he seems to regard its natural end as a stable and harmonious condition in which all individuals and groups occupy the place for which they are best fitted.

The general conclusion which Aristotle reaches after considering the various forms which government in practice may take is that for the average city state a compromise between oligarchy and democracy, with the middle class holding the balance of power, will prove most satisfactory. If too much preponderance is enjoyed by either the rich or the poor the one class is almost certain to be oppressed by the other. And this is likely to precipitate a revolution. Indeed, Aristotle thinks that the exploitation of one class by another is the usual cause of revolutions. This danger can be avoided only if general instead of sectional interests are made the determining principles of government. Aristotle thinks that this implies that the weaker classes must not be exploited; that good relations must exist between ruler and ruled; that no individual or class should become too powerful; and that the magistrates should be free from all forms of corruption.

In short, Aristotle reaches the conclusion that a state whose government is a mechanism for exploiting rival forces will be unstable and likely to break down in revolution, while a state in which these forces are evenly balanced, and the government's decisions are determined by moral principles embodied in a legal code which applies to all, will be stable and happy. All this is consistent with, and indeed, follows from, Aristotle's underlying hypothesis of an Organic State. For if the state is an organism it cannot be a healthy one unless its various forces are balanced and harmonized, and only on these conditions will it fulfil its ultimate purpose of providing its members with the conditions for the best possible life.

Defence of Slavery

Aristotle, like Plato, recognizes as a natural implication of the Organic Theory that different classes of citizen have functions of differing value and importance. Thus he sees nothing inconsistent with his principles in defending the contemporary institution of slavery, which everyone in Ancient Greece accepted as a normal and essential element in social life. He defends slavery on the ground that 'from the hour of their birth, some are marked out for subjection, others for rule'.[1] He admits that sometimes a natural master may be found living in a condition of slavery, but he denies that this is any ground for condemning slavery in general. It only shows that individuals are not always found in their proper classes. But he is quite satisfied that men do fall naturally into two classes—those who possess reason, and those who do not possess it and can only respect it. In his view, natural slaves are capable only of an inferior kind of existence, and are not capable of undertaking the responsibilities of citizenship. They are, indeed, nothing more than animate tools.

Aristotle's belief in the inherent inferiority of a large proportion of human beings stands in sharp antithesis to the modern belief in the rights of man, yet it differs in degree rather than in nature from the assumptions of intrinsic inequality which, in one form or another, have been common in the political and social outlook of practically every community. Moreover, even the modern world is not without examples of racial discrimination which are defended by essentially the same arguments as those employed by Aristotle. There may, conceivably, be some moral justification for such discrimination, but empirical philosophers could readily account for it as the natural effect of social and economic conditions in which such discrimination has proved advantageous to the possessors of power and privilege. And even those who accept objective moral distinctions might well regard this causal explanation of the condoning of political inequality as highly plausible.

[1] ibid., I, 5.

The Ideal Life

Aristotle's approval of slavery is closely connected with his conception of the ideal life. This he conceives differently from Plato, who thought that the ideal life for anyone was that in which he made his natural and proper contribution to the welfare of the community, whether as producer, auxiliary or guardian. And such, indeed, is the logical implication of an Organic Theory, since it implies that the welfare of the whole transcends, and indeed ensures, the welfare of the parts. But in Book VII of the *Politics* Aristotle advances the view that the highest virtue consists not in action but in contemplation, not in the exercise of power but in the pursuit of truth. For such a mode of life leisure is obviously necessary. No one absorbed in the exacting business of practical administration can, in Aristotle's view, at the same time engage in the disinterested pursuit of truth, which is both of supreme value in itself and of indirect value if the right principles are to be applied in practical life. Hence those who are capable of the highest intellectual activities must be given the leisure and freedom to pursue them without distraction, and have their practical needs supplied by those who are inherently incapable of those disinterested pursuits.

Aristotle has a strong case for maintaining that the disinterested activities of life have the highest value. For the practical life consists of activities which are a means to the end of living—the securing of food, shelter, clothing, security of person and property, etc., but the attainment of these leaves unanswered the question of the ultimate purpose of life. Aristotle believes that the ultimate purpose of life is the enjoyment of pursuits which are valuable in themselves, and not merely as a means to something which is valuable in itself. Such activities as the creation or enjoyment of music and the pursuit of knowledge are, in Aristotle's opinion, intrinsically valuable in this way, whereas the mere attainment of the necessary conditions of living has no value in itself, but derives its value from being a necessary condition of these higher activities.

The Ideal State

In Books VII and VIII (which, as already observed, were probably written some fifteen years before Books IV, V, and VI)

Aristotle outlines a conception of the Ideal State which is strikingly similar in some respects to the conception put forward by Plato, particularly in the *Laws*. Aristotle argues that the Ideal State should be as small as is consistent with independence. Independence is of prime importance, since otherwise the state will depend on foreign trade and this will have to be protected by armed forces who will make heavy inroads on the available resources of manpower and wealth. Aristotle would clearly have regarded the people of modern Britain as very unfavourably placed for the pursuit of the ideal life in view of their dependence upon foreign trade and the extent to which their energies and resources must therefore be directed to industrial production and national defence. He would have regarded a sparsely populated and relatively self-sufficient country such as Eire as a far more favourable environment for the pursuit of the disinterested values of life. Although Aristotle was writing with reference to conditions in Ancient Greece he raises a fundamental question which has a direct relevance to modern conditions, namely the question whether the complex organization of a modern industrial community is compatible with the survival of the disinterested activities to which he attached supreme value. It is already clear that the close dependence of such a community upon trade with its neighbours makes it peculiarly vulnerable to economic and political disturbances elsewhere, and that when war comes to it the normal activities of every section of the community are likely to be disturbed.

Theory of Education

Aristotle's theory of education is set forth in Book VII, chapters 13–17, and Book VIII of the *Politics*. Like Plato, he believes that education has primarily a civic function: 'The citizen should be moulded to suit the form of government under which he lives.'[1] Moreover, 'the training in things which are of common interest should be the same for all.'[2] Hence the education of the young should be the responsibility of the state and should not be left in private hands.

Aristotle's discussion of the purposes of education is dominated throughout by the distinction already drawn between the means and the end, between action and that which action seeks to

[1] ibid., VIII, 1.   [2] loc. cit.

achieve. As the end of all action is leisure, Aristotle thinks that the right use of leisure should be the ultimate end of education, although it must naturally also cover pursuits which are essential means to attaining this end. As he says:

> There are branches of learning and education which we must study merely with a view to leisure spent in intellectual activity, and these are to be valued for their own sake; whereas those kinds of knowledge which are useful in business are to be deemed necessary, and exist for the sake of other things.[1]

In modern language, Aristotle is saying that education should not be confined to vocational training, but should cover those activities, such as the composition and enjoyment of music and the disinterested pursuit of knowledge, which are valuable in themselves and not merely as a means to some further end. And he specifically states that mere 'amusement' is not a proper occupation for leisure since it has no value in itself but merely acquires value by serving as a relaxation from work.

Aristotle does not fulfil his promise to consider in detail the form which education in the right use of leisure should take,[2] but it is clear that he considers the composition and enjoyment of music and scientific and philosophical research to be appropriate methods of enjoying it. His conception of the earlier stages of education is very similar to Plato's. He stresses the importance of influencing children by the right kind of stories, pictures, and plays. He believes that education should first be directed to the cultivation of the body, secondly to the control of the appetites, i.e. character training, and finally to the development of the mind. The latter is the ultimate end to which the earlier stages of education are means:

> The care of the body ought to precede that of the soul, and the training of the appetitive part should follow: none the less our care of it must be for the sake of the reason, and our care of the body for the sake of the soul.[3]

The difference between the educational theories of Plato and Aristotle is thus subtle but important, and originates in Aristotle's belief that 'to be always seeking after the useful does not become

[1] ibid., VIII, 3.   [2] ibid., VIII, 3.   [3] ibid., VII, 5.

free and exalted souls'.[1] For Plato the purpose of education is to fit the individual to make his appropriate contribution to the life of the community, whether he be producer, auxiliary, or guardian. Thus even the higher studies which the guardians pursue in the intervals of administrative activity are undertaken essentially for the purpose of acquiring a more accurate vision of the moral principles by which such activity should be directed. But Aristotle conceives of the ultimate purpose of education in more individualist terms. He recognizes that it is essential, in the first place, to produce citizens who will contribute to the formation of a stable and harmonious society; but he regards this as a mere means to making possible the higher and disinterested activities which have a value in themselves.

Assessment of Aristotle's Political Philosophy

The argument of Aristotle's *Politics* is not based on any simple and central idea like that which runs through Plato's *Republic*, and it is impossible to identify the principles of his political philosophy with a single and consistent theme. In part this is due to the fact that the *Politics* was composed over a period of some fifteen years during which Aristotle's thinking gradually became more independent of his teacher's. But the more important point to notice is that, when Aristotle achieved this independence of Plato, he found himself impelled to reject the rationalist in favour of an empirical conception of political ideals. In the *Republic* such ideals had been identified with *a priori* principles, while in Book I of the *Politics* they are identified with the laws governing the natural development of a political society.

As already observed, Aristotle appears generally to adopt a point of view which is something of a compromise between these two extremes. He regards moral laws as objective yet he lays great stress upon their relativity to the potential development of the individual or society to which they relate. In so far as the *Politics* has a dominating theme it may therefore be described as that of ascertaining and defining the principal forms of the 'best possible state' in the light of the various circumstances which condition it.

To a modern philosopher, of course, Aristotle stops short of asking the fundamental question whether, once the synthetic

[1] ibid., VIII, 3.

character of moral judgments is admitted, it is consistent to regard them as *a priori* or even objective. But, as noted in Chapter I, this is a controversial issue on which modern philosophers are themselves by no means agreed. And Aristotle must at least be given credit for the formulation of a theory which from many points of view seems to account for widely held convictions regarding the basis of political obligation.

Perhaps the most striking feature of the *Politics* is the extent to which, notwithstanding the very different political and social environment of Ancient Greece, Aristotle succeeded in formulating the principles which are now generally accepted as the moral basis of democratic government. In so doing he demonstrated his greatness as a philosopher, for it required insight of a high order to recognize, within the narrow confines of the city state, the operation of the principles which, many centuries later, have come to be accepted as the essential foundation of the democratic way of life.

CHAPTER V

Political Philosophy between Aristotle and Machiavelli

IT IS obvious that only the most general outline of the development of political thought over a period of fourteen centuries can be given in a single chapter, but such a survey should help to preserve a sense of continuity, and may be sufficient to indicate the limited significance for philosophy of a period that was largely dominated by an uncritical dogmatism which is the very antithesis of philosophy in the proper sense.

During the latter part of Aristotle's life, and after his death in 322 B.C., the city states, which had so greatly coloured the political philosophy of Plato and Aristotle, ceased to be the centres of political life and became small units in the vast empire created by Philip of Macedon and Alexander the Great. This change in their status had far-reaching consequences in the development of political thought. For it was obvious to everyone that the independence and power of the city states had gone and that they would henceforth be small and relatively impotent units in a vast empire. Hence the citizens of these states felt that they had little stake in the shaping of their political destiny and sought within the ambit of their personal lives the keys to fulfilment and happiness.

Epicureans and Stoics

This change of outlook was reflected, soon after the death of Aristotle, in the doctrines of two philosophers who advocated highly individualistic creeds and who sought to make human happiness and virtue independent of the political environment. Thus Epicurus (340–270 B.C.), who came to Athens from the Island of Samos, taught that the conception of the state as a means to the good of the individual was no longer applicable, and that the rational man must find in his own resources the conditions of the ideal life. He argued that the pursuit of personal pleasure or satisfaction of some sort is the proper end of man and that men should seek to make themselves as independent as possible of their political and social environment. Sometimes this ideal took the form of self-realization, at other times it was little better than a pretext for self-indulgence, but common to all its expressions was the object of finding the ideal from within, whatever the nature of the social and political background might be.

The other individualistic creed of this period was known as Stoicism and was founded by Zeno (340–260 B.C.) who, like Epicurus, made Athens his home although he had been born and brought up in Cyprus. Zeno reacted to the political impotence of the individual by representing him as a member of a universal human society independent of all political changes and subject to a universal law of nature superior to all political enactments. This type of individualism proved much more influential than Epicureanism, for it appealed strongly to the Roman temperament and outlook and, indeed, found direct expression in the Roman ideas of universal law and universal citizenship. At a later stage these ideals assumed a new form in the Christian conceptions of membership of the Church and the will of God. Thus although Stoicism originated as an individualistic creed, its basic principles were ultimately embodied in both Roman imperialism and the Christian religion.

Cicero and Seneca

During the period of Roman domination before the foundation of Christianity, Cicero (106–43 B.C.) was one of the most influential thinkers. He recognized universal or natural law in the sense defined by the Stoics as the basis and justification of Roman law. He maintained that this law was at once the law of God and the law of man in view of the rational faculties which made man akin to God. Cicero also accepted the Stoic principle of equal membership of a universal state in his theory that all men are equal, not necessarily in intelligence or wealth, but in their rational powers of judging between good and evil. Thus Cicero held that the state is a moral community consisting of individuals who freely judge by their own reason what its moral purposes ought to be.

The commonwealth, then, is the people's affair; and the people is not every group of men, associated in any manner, but is the coming together of a considerable number of men who are united by a common agreement about law and rights and by the desire to participate in mutual advantages.[1]

This definition of a commonwealth shows clearly how the principles of universal law and individual equality are combined in Cicero's conception of the state. In his development of the basic principles of Stoicism, Cicero laid down the principles of democratic sanction, the rule of law and the moral basis of government which have been so influential ever since and which are still regarded as essential conditions of liberal democracy.

The other important source of Roman political thought was the statesman and philosopher, Seneca (3 B.C.–A.D. 65) who was a Consul in the reign of Nero (A.D. 37–68), and was for some time able to exercise a moderating influence on the tyrant, although ultimately forced to commit suicide. By the time Seneca was born the Republic had given place to the Empire and he did not question that some form of absolute government was inevitable. But he thought it of great importance that absolute power should be placed in the hands of the right individual or class.

Largely because of the corrupt and tyrannical political conditions of the age in which he lived, Seneca was attracted by the original Stoic theory that a man is a member of two commonwealths, the civil state of which he is nominally a citizen, and the greater state composed of all rational beings to which he belongs by virtue of his rationality. By emphasizing this dual status Seneca tried to console those who were embittered and dismayed by the political conditions of the time and to assure them that they were all members of another and greater commonwealth in which virtue and happiness could be attained. Thus Seneca taught that the man who as a teacher or writer influences his fellow beings by appealing to their rationality was performing a more important task than a statesman. In this way Seneca defined clearly the conception of membership of two worlds which was to play such a dominating part in Christian thought and was to inspire and console mankind so greatly during the Dark Ages which were to follow. Man, according to Seneca,

[1] *Republic*, I, 25.

must seek his true good in the higher commonwealth of rational beings, and must not expect the rulers of this world to do more than restrain the sinful tendencies of human nature or, as he put it in a famous phrase, provide a 'remedy for sin'. Thus Seneca's attitude to the state is the complete antithesis of Plato's and Aristotle's. To the latter the state was a necessary condition of the good life, but to Seneca it was simply a coercive authority struggling against human sinfulness and at most suppressing the evil forces which would otherwise make a virtuous life impossible.

The Influence of Christianity

Jesus Christ was born during Seneca's lifetime and the rise of the Christian Church was destined to be the most important influence in the development of political thought during the next fourteen centuries. Christianity endorsed the conception of a dual life, and those who accepted the faith automatically assumed that they were members of a heavenly as well as of an earthly kingdom. Some of the well known sayings of Christ clearly defined this dual outlook. 'My kingdom is not of this world' and 'Render unto Cæsar the things that are Cæsar's, and unto God the things that are God's' were pronouncements which obviously implied that the Church was an organization distinct from the state and superior to it. The superior authority of the Church was even more explicitly expressed by St Paul when he said 'The powers that be are ordained of God.' This outlook naturally led to the conception of a ruler as a Minister of God, although this was later replaced by the theory that it was the office rather than its temporary occupant that possessed authority and was entitled to obedience and respect.

The dual loyalty involved in the Christian conception of man's twofold destiny naturally led to conflict. And the insistence of the Roman Empire on the performance of rights and services inconsistent with the teaching of the Church led to increasing friction and ultimately to open antagonism. This culminated in the general persecution of the Christian Church and its adherents which was initiated by the Emperor Decius in A.D. 251 and continued until the persecuting edicts were withdrawn in 311. In 313 Christianity was recognized by the Emperor Constantine as one of the legal religions of the Empire, and in 392 the Emperor

Theodosius closed the temples and prohibited all other forms of worship.

The end of the persecutions did not, however, lead to a cessation of rivalry between Church and State, which continued in varying forms for many centuries. But the triumph of Christianity over the persecutions at least strengthened the feeling that the resolution of the conflict between the two bodies must be found in compromise rather than in the complete triumph of one side or the other. Different solutions were in fact reached in the eastern and western halves of the Roman Empire, for in the east the union of temporal and spiritual authority was recognized in the personality of the Emperor, while in the west the insistence of the Church on its supreme authority in ecclesiastical matters tended to perpetuate controversy regarding the respective functions of Church and State. In practice the relative power of the two bodies was at any given time largely determined by the relative power and influence of Pope and Emperor.

The sack of Rome by the Goths in the year 410 was the major event of the century following the end of the general persecutions and it naturally tended to discredit the Empire and enhance the prestige of the Church. This calamity was the immediate occasion of St Augustine's great book *City of God*, which was written largely with the object of rebutting the charge that the Christian Church had been responsible for the decline of Roman power and its destruction by the Goths. St Augustine (A.D. 354–430) argued in this work that the fall of Rome was a vivid illustration of the principle that all earthly kingdoms are transient and unstable and that security and permanence must be found in a spiritual commonwealth. Thus he distinguished sharply between the City of God and the city of this world. The City of God consists of the redeemed in this world and the next. The city of this world is the kingdom of the devil and of those who follow him. The two cities are mingled in this world but will be separated on the Day of Judgment.

St Augustine therefore believed that man's salvation depended upon his membership of the Church conceived as an organization of all Christian believers through whom the spirit of God began to influence the course of human history. Before the foundation of the Christian Church this spirit had no opportunity of making its influence felt and the foundation of that Church was, therefore, an event of profound importance to the human race. These considerations implied that no states were truly good before the advent of Christianity. To be good a state had to consist of men and women who had accepted the Christian faith and who recognized that they belonged to a religious community which was eternal and independent of the vicissitudes of worldly politics.

St Thomas Aquinas

It would be out of place in a general survey of this period to trace in detail the complex controversies about the relative authority of Church and State which continued during the following centuries. The only figure of real philosophical significance who emerged during the period in question was St Thomas Aquinas (1227–1274), who sought to combine and harmonize the teaching of divine revelation on the one hand and that of philosophical and scientific enquiry on the other.

The need for such an enquiry was directly occasioned by the rediscovery of Aristotle's works in the early thirteenth century and the translation of the *Politics* from the Greek text about the year 1260. Aristotle had proceeded on the assumption that human reason is the final arbiter of truth and that the discoveries of the special sciences are co-ordinated and harmonized in the final synthesis provided by philosophy. St Thomas did not dispute the validity of these scientific and philosophical principles, but he argued that they have to be supplemented by divine revelation if the universe is not to remain an ultimate mystery. The findings of revelation do not, however, conflict with the principles of science and philosophy. All three sources of knowledge are necessary for a complete and synoptic understanding of the universe and man's place in it.

Like knowledge, the universe itself constitutes a hierarchy reaching from God at the top to the lowest of living creatures All have their natural end or function, and each living creature in striving to achieve its natural end contributes, in a greater or less degree, to fulfilling the purpose of the universe. Man's own position is of special importance since he is at once akin to the lower animals in virtue of his body and to God in virtue of his soul. It is this dual status which creates the conditions of the moral life, and gives rise to the laws and institutions through which the moral law is expressed.

Finally, that part of the universe constituted by human society is also a hierarchy, for it consists of different classes having ends and functions arranged in such a way that the lower serves the higher and the higher directs the lower. The common good is what defines and determines the rights and duties of both. In particular, the authority of a ruler over his subjects is not arbitrary but exists only in so far as it promotes the good of the community as a whole. It is, in fact, a ministry derived from God. Lawful authority is quite different from the arbitrary exercise of power, and there may be occasions when it is justifiable for a people to resist their rulers. It is, in fact, justifiable to do so whenever resistance is less harmful to the common good than the tyranny which it seeks to remove.

St Thomas devoted much thought to analysing the conception of law, and the fourfold classification which he arrived at throws further light on his theory of 'lawful authority'. He distinguished the following senses of the word:

(a) *Eternal Law* is the expression of the reason of God and embodies the laws which determine the nature of the universe as a whole.

(b) *Natural Law* is that part of Eternal Law which determines the nature of living creatures. It is illustrated by the natural tendencies to avoid death and to reproduce the species, to seek good and avoid evil, and to achieve the destiny natural to the species in question. In human beings Natural Law is specially manifested in the desire for a virtuous and rational life.

(c) *Divine Law* consists of those moral principles brought to man's consciousness through Revelation (such as the Decalogue or the rules of Christian morality).

(d) *Human Law* consists of the laws enacted by human authorities for the direction of human beings.

It is the relationship between Natural Law and Human Law which determines whether a political authority is lawful or not. For Human Law is justified only in so far as it is a faithful expression of the underlying Natural Law, which is in turn an expression of the reason of God. And since Natural Law applies to all rational creatures, rulers as well as subjects must obey it.

St Thomas believed that God had implanted in the human mind a knowledge of Natural Law and a disposition to obey it. It is from this knowledge and disposition that virtuous acts result, but man's fallible judgment is liable to error, and it is therefore important to give Natural Law an authoritative expression in Human Law, such as the civil laws of a state, to ensure that it is recognized and that imperfect men are restrained from evil acts. What St Thomas never does is to define an objective criterion for distinguishing those human laws which faithfully express Natural Law from those which do not; but this, of course, is something which philosophers have yet to do. And his theory offered a justification for the belief—universal in his day and still accepted by the vast majority of people—that the moral law, whether clearly recognized or not, is objectively grounded in the structure of the universe.

But, however important and illuminating St Thomas's theory of law may have been, he was only restating the doctrine of Natural Law which had been conceived of in all essentials by the Stoics many centuries before. His more original and lasting claim to fame was his attempted reconciliation of philosophy and religion, and his rejection of the reactionary doctrine that the authority of the Church should extend to matters of scientific research. St Thomas taught that the Church stood in no danger from scientists and philosophers, as the truths which the latter discover belong to a different sphere. Where the literal interpretation of scripture is contradicted by the discoveries of science that literal interpretation must be rejected as false, but this leaves unimpaired the essentially religious message which science can neither refute nor demonstrate. Such has become the official attitude of the Roman Church to the discoveries of science, and its members have in consequence avoided the necessity for an embarrassing adjustment of beliefs of the sort which the Protestant Churches have had to make from time to time. In particular, the Roman Catholic Church found it relatively easy to adjust its theology to the teaching of the Darwinists although the latter caused widespread consternation among Protestants.

One result of the writings of St Thomas was that Roman Catholics gradually abandoned the theory that religion, acting through the machinery of the state, should dominate science and philosophy. In the political sphere the same tendency was manifested by the gradual weakening of papal claims to appoint and depose kings, and by the substitution of nationalist sentiment for ecclesiastical authority as the dominating force behind government. Thus it is true to say that St Thomas contributed in no small measure to the evolution of the modern nation-state built on a secular foundation.

The followers of Martin Luther (1483–1546) and John Calvin (1509–1564) were, by contrast, strongly inclined towards theocratic systems of government, and Calvin actually established a theocratic state in Geneva. Several of the Protestant states of Northern Europe have created 'established' religions which have helped to maintain a close harmony between Church and State, and to ensure that no really independent criticism of political rulers is made by the ecclesiastical authorities, and that the aims of government do not conflict in any essential respect with the principles of the established faith. But today, under the powerful influence of the popular franchise, the policy of democratic governments is gradually becoming less subject even to the 'established' faith; and the modern version of the theocratic state is rather to be found in the totalitarian countries where, although religion in the traditional sense may count for little, the policy of government is subordinated to what is, in all essentials, a religious creed.

Rise of the National State

It was in the fourteenth century that the national state was firmly established, and that national kings began to claim a sovereignty which inevitably led to conflict with the Papacy. The claims of the latter were most forcibly expressed by Pope Boniface VIII in his famous Bull *Unam Sanctam* (A.D. 1302). The counter-claims of the national kings were advanced by John of Paris and others, but most notably by Marsiglio of Padua (1278–1343). From many points of view Marsiglio was the most revolutionary thinker of his time. Not only did he advocate that the Church should be subservient to the State, but he advanced what was then the highly original theory that neither Popes nor kings held their authority by divine right but received it from the sovereign people. This suggestion was too far in advance of contemporary thought to be accepted by either Church or monarchy during Marsiglio's lifetime, but it was eagerly welcomed two centuries later by the political theorists of the Renaissance.

Marsiglio maintained that the chief end of government is peace, and that a monarchy is in general more effective for achieving this than a republic; but he insisted that monarchs do not possess any superhuman or divine authority. Their authority is derived solely from the people over whom they rule, and is exercised subject to popular control and to any legal limitations which the people may decide to impose.

Marsiglio advanced a similar theory of ecclesiastical authority. To him the Church consisted not of the clergy alone but of the whole body of Christian men and women, and the supreme authority therefore resided neither in clerical synods nor in the Papal Curia but in a general council consisting of both clergy and laity. In short, Marsiglio argued that both in Church and State, which are simply different associations of the same people, sovereignty ultimately resides in the people, although responsibility for its actual exercise may be delegated to others.

Marsiglio's views were, as already remarked, revolutionary and had little immediate influence. The assessment of the influence which they subsequently exercised belongs properly to the next chapter, where the conception of the national state, as expounded by Machiavelli, will be examined. But it is interesting to observe at this point that the first serious challenge to the doctrine of universal law was made by a thinker who was born only four years after St Thomas Aquinas died.

Reason and Revelation

It is clear that the lengthy period of human history which has been briefly reviewed in this chapter was mainly dominated by the powerful influence of the Christian faith and the general acceptance of it as the ultimate authority defining man's place in the universe and his moral duties. The Greek conception of human reason as an adequate and final key to the understanding of the universe was abandoned and the need to supplement it by an entirely different mode of insight accepted. Reason and revelation were, in short, set forth as different but complementary sources of human understanding which could not contradict each other. While the acceptance of such a dual authority raises many difficulties there is much in the most recent philosophical developments which tends to justify it. For if the conception of reason which was put forward by David Hume, and has more recently been accepted by the Logical Positivists of the twentieth century, is accepted then reason, as shown in Chapter I, is incapable by itself of establishing any matter of fact or ideal of conduct. Its application to the real world is hypothetical and categorical directives must be sought elsewhere. If religion can provide such directives then it must be accepted as an alternative source of guidance which reason, from its very nature, cannot challenge. That may not be regarded as a wholly satisfying conception of the status of religion, but it is the conception which was defended by St Thomas Aquinas and which seems to be implied by much in current philosophical thought.

If such a view of the rôle of religion is accepted it follows that religion has not, strictly speaking, made any contribution to political philosophy, although it has greatly influenced the development of political ideas and provided much of the moral content of political ideals. It has, in other words, been largely responsible for the form and content of the moral assumptions upon which political theories have been based and for the political institutions which have consequently evolved. In particular, Christianity has given a new meaning and greater strength to the Stoic conceptions of universal law and universal citizenship which are inherent in the political and legal framework of all liberal democracies. But it has stopped short at the essentially philosophical questions of what these moral assumptions imply and what their status is in the hierarchy of knowledge.

CHAPTER VI

Machiavelli on the Science of Government

THE TIME which elapsed between the death of Marsiglio in 1343 and the birth of Machiavelli in 1469 saw the beginning of the great intellectual and spiritual revolution known as the Renaissance. During this period both the Empire and the Papacy lost much of their power and prestige; the modern type of sovereign state came into being, and strong monarchies were established in France, Spain, and England. It was unlikely that these tremendous changes would take place without important repercussions in political philosophy, and Machiavelli worked out a theory of government which marked a complete break with the theories based upon the principle of Natural or Moral Law which had dominated political thought during the preceding fifteen centuries of the Christian era.

Niccolo Machiavelli was born in Florence, the son of a jurist, and entered public life in 1494, the year in which Charles VIII of France invaded Northern Italy and the Medici were expelled from Florence. His first post was that of Clerk in the Second Chancery of the Commune and in 1498 he was promoted to the rank of Second Chancellor and Secretary and continued in this office till the year 1512. While thus employed he undertook a large number of diplomatic missions both to the petty courts of Italy and to other countries, and it was the experience of these missions which was largely responsible for forming the views which he subsequently expounded in his political writings. He was specially influenced by his mission to the camp of Cesare Borgia, Duke of Valentinois, in 1502. Although Machiavelli had undertaken this mission unwillingly, he soon conceived an intense admiration for Cesare's resourcefulness in resorting alternatively to diplomacy and force as instruments of government and for his firm administration of conquered provinces. He showed a rare judgment in handling both friends and enemies for the furtherance of his own purposes. His methods of conquest were ruthless, but he governed those whom he had conquered with justice. Although Cesare ultimately fell from power Machiavelli idealized his achievements to the end, and obviously thought that Cesare had attained, more nearly than any other public figure of the time, to the embodiment of the perfect ruler.

Soon after the battle of Ravenna (1512), in which Spanish and Italian forces sought to relieve Ravenna from siege by the French, Giovanni de Medici brought a Spanish army into Tuscany, the government on which Machiavelli depended fell, and the Medici once again assumed control in Florence. In November 1512 Machiavelli lost his post and was exiled from Florence. In 1513 he was imprisoned and tortured for his alleged complicity in a plot, but was soon released and retired to a farm near San Casciano. In the last year of his life he undertook some official missions at the request of Pope Clement VII, but he died after a short illness in June 1527.

Machiavelli's writings belong to the period after his fall from office in November 1512, but their substance is clearly determined by his first-hand experience of political and diplomatic life during the two previous decades. His reflections are set forth in two complementary works, the *Discourses* and *The Prince*, which were published posthumously in 1531 and 1532. The *Discourses*, of which the full title is *Discourses on the First Decade of Titus Livius*, are ostensibly a commentary on Livy's History of Rome, but really take the form of a fundamental enquiry into the origin and maintenance of states. *The Prince* has the more limited purpose of defining the principles by which the ruler of a state already formed can most effectively cement and strengthen it. The *Discourses* are therefore a study in political science, while *The Prince* is a manual for the guidance of rulers based upon the principles set forth in the *Discourses*.

The Science of Government

Machiavelli cannot be described as a profound philosopher, but his works have a special interest for the philosopher as an attempt to solve the problems of politics in purely scientific terms. Most political philosophers have tried to find a moral justification for the ideals of government, but Machiavelli is a political thinker who treats moral convictions simply as psychological forces which play their part, along with other influences, in shaping the history of nations. He denies that these moral convictions have any foundation of an objective character, or provide any rational principle by which human conduct can be justified or condemned. As a political scientist Machiavelli is not interested in what men ought to be, for to him this is a question to which no objective or rational answer can be given. He is only interested in what men are, although this of course includes the nature of the moral convictions which they actually hold.

Thus Machiavelli contemplated the political scene with the detached vision of a scientific investigator. He was not concerned to solicit support for any moral convictions about the proper ends of government, for he had none. He thought that government should aim at doing what it would ultimately be compelled to do —achieve the purposes for the sake of which men accept the obligations and restrictions which it imposes on them; and he thought that the primary object of the political scientist was to discover and define these purposes and then proceed to show, in the light of experience, how they can be most effectively achieved.

Machiavelli's theory of the origin of government is remarkably similar to that which the British philosopher, Thomas Hobbes, was to propound more than a century later.[1] Men, according to Machiavelli, are 'ungrateful, fickle, deceitful, cowardly, and avaricious'.[2] Their social qualities are expressions of self-interest in disguise, and result from a calculation that a socially organized life affords, on balance, more benefits than drawbacks to the individual. That is the only possible justification of the restraints and limitations imposed by government. They have no value in themselves and cannot be justified as the expression of any kind of 'natural law'.

What the individual demands above all things is, according to Machiavelli, security of person and property so as 'to enjoy freely his own without suspicion, not to doubt of his wife's or daughters' honours, not to be in fear for his sons, or for himself'.[3] Once this basic demand has been satisfied, the individual may seek, in addition, wealth and honour. But he seeks these things only for himself and for his family, and he co-operates with other members of his state only because he realizes that if everyone

---

[1] In the *Leviathan*, published in 1651.
[2] *The Prince*, Chapter XVII.   [3] *Discourses*, I, 16.

were to seek these benefits for himself there would result what Hobbes was later to call the ' war of everyman against everyman', and the attainment of security would be as remote as ever. Experience, according to Machiavelli, shows that security, wealth, and honour can only be enjoyed by the individual who co-operates with others to realize these ends, and in practice the security of the individual is found to depend on the security of the state to which he belongs. This is the real origin of those moral distinctions between good and bad, or just and unjust, which are so influential in human life. What is good or just is what contributes to the security and prosperity of the state and all its members; what is bad or unjust is what has the contrary effect. On this principle, and this principle alone, is it rational to praise or blame, reward or punish, the individual for his conduct. Occasionally the interest of the state may result in the sacrifice of the individual, but on the whole and in the long run what benefits the state will benefit its individual members also.

Sovereignty of the People

If, as Machiavelli holds, the state is formed in order to satisfy the basic demands of the individual, it follows that the citizens of a state are the ultimate holders of sovereign power. The actual exercise of this power may be largely or wholly delegated to a single individual, or to a small group of individuals, but its ultimate source must necessarily be the people as a whole if their demands constitute the ultimate reason why the state exists at all. Machiavelli accepts this implication of his theory. Indeed, he subscribes with enthusiasm to Aristotle's opinion that on broad issues the judgment of the community is less likely to be in error than the judgment of a single individual or a small group of individuals. As he says:

> As touching wisdom, and settled stayedness, I say that the People is wiser and more staid, and of more exact judgment than a Prince. And therefore not without cause the People's voice is likened to God's voice; for we see that the universal opinions bring to pass rare effects in their presages, so that it seems by their secret virtues they foresee their own good or evil.[1]

[1] *Discourses*, I, 58.

Thus, contrary to the impression often formed by those who read *The Prince* alone, Machiavelli is no advocate of absolute monarchy. On the contrary, he believes that only in those states in which government is ultimately based upon a democratic foundation is it safe to assume that the power of government will not be abused. He admits that a limited monarchy may sometimes be necessary for a period, but he insists that a sound basis for government will be achieved only when the ultimate responsibility is assumed by the people themselves.

There is one important respect in which, Machiavelli believes, the state as a whole differs from most of the individuals who constitute it. The majority of citizens are content with security of person and property and only a small minority seek power over their fellows. But states as a whole are dominated by an insatiable appetite for power and those which do not try to extend their power are bound in the long run to lose it. There is no stability or contentment in the field of international relations. One state can achieve the predominance which all desire only at the expense of another, and that other is bound to be dissatisfied with its inferior status. National security, in other words, can only be achieved by national superiority, and the superiority of one nation implies the inferiority, and thus the insecurity, of another. The vicious circle thus created has been a familiar feature of international relations in modern times.

Argument of 'The Prince'

While the *Discourses* set forth Machiavelli's considered conclusions on the motives of human action and the basis of government, *The Prince* is concerned with the more practical question of the methods which a 'prince' or monarch must employ in order to govern a community effectively. Machiavelli thought that a monarchy or dictatorship can be justified for two purposes only— the making of a state out of smaller units or the reforming of a corrupt state. *The Prince* is therefore essentially a manual of worldly wisdom prepared for the guidance of a ruler faced with one or other of these situations. And it was specially written with a view to showing how Italy could be welded into a strong and unified state out of the five principalities—the territory of the Roman Church, the Kingdom of Naples, the Duchy of Milan, and the Republics of Venice and Florence—into which the country was divided at the beginning of the sixteenth century.

The outstanding characteristic of *The Prince* is the complete absence of moral principle in its argument. It lays down, with scientific detachment, the general principles by which, Machiavelli believes, a state can be most effectively unified and strengthened. Whether the means thus prescribed are, in the usual sense of the word, 'moral' is of no concern to Machiavelli. He is only interested in the question whether they are effective for the end in view—the creation and maintenance of a strong, united and expanding state. For the reasons set forth in the *Discourses* this end is assumed to be the primary object of politics, and to be dictated by men's fundamental demand for personal security. Whether it is a 'good' end or not is to Machiavelli a meaningless question unless 'the good' is equated with 'the desired'.

The successful 'Prince' must, Machiavelli thinks, have a reliable army, composed of native troops rather than foreign mercenaries, for all government ultimately rests on force and would soon collapse without it. He must be feared, but not hated, by his people, and must respect the integrity of their property. While he should resort, whenever it seems likely to be useful, to violence, cruelty and deceit, he should, as far as possible, give the appearance of a noble and exalted character, so that his unscrupulous methods may be all the more effective when they are employed. The common faith in religion and morality, and the fear, greed, and credulity of human nature, should all be ruthlessly exploited wherever they can contribute to the purposes of government. This cynical attitude to morality is nowhere better illustrated than in the eighteenth chapter of *The Prince*, where Machiavelli extols the deliberate employment of deceit in exploiting the simple credulity of the average man. Thus he writes:

> Therefore a wise lord cannot, nor ought he to, keep faith when such observance may be turned against him, and when the reasons that caused him to pledge it exist no longer. If men were entirely good this precept would not hold, but because they are bad, and will not keep faith with you, you too are not bound to observe it with them. Nor will there ever be wanting to a prince legitimate reasons to excuse this non-observance. . . . But it is necessary to know well how to

disguise this characteristic, and to be a great pretender and dissembler; and men are so simple, and so subject to present necessities, that he who seeks to deceive will always find someone who will allow himself to be deceived. . . . Therefore it is necessary for him to have a mind ready to turn itself accordingly as the winds and variations of fortune force it, yet . . . not to diverge from the good if he can avoid doing so, but, if compelled, then to know how to set about it.

Machiavelli's Political Background

Machiavelli's disdain for moral principles is largely explained by the circumstances of his time, since with the breakdown of faith in Christian principles men were left without any generally accepted moral creed, and the tangible ideals of security and happiness became the dominating motives of their conduct. In Italy this tendency was strengthened by the weak and divided state of the country, and the danger to which it was exposed by the ambitions of powerful nation-states like France and Spain. The respect which the Roman Church had formerly enjoyed had largely disappeared because of the part which the Pope had played in opposing the unification of Italy and inviting foreign intervention. And murder and cruelty were gradually coming to be regarded as normal and legitimate agents of effective government. Thus Machiavelli's cynicism was a reflection of the age in which he lived, and the principles which he advocated would have been generally endorsed by his political contemporaries. He stands out from them simply because he gave clear and candid expression to those views in writings which have survived the age to which they directly relate.

Yet although Machiavelli's writings were in large measure a reflection of contemporary conditions, they possess a more permanent significance. The very fact that his name is still the basis of an epithet which is often applied to methods of organizing and directing political power shows that methods similar to those which he extolled may still be practised despite the moral opprobrium which they may excite. Indeed, since politics both in the national and in the international sphere consists so largely in the organizing of power for the achievement of specified ends, the employment of methods which experience shows to be effective for this purpose is to a large extent inevitable. This is most obviously seen in the record of modern dictatorships where violence, deceit, and the exploitation of human credulity have been familiar features of the technique of government. In democracies, where the rule of law is respected, and government policy is exposed to the scrutiny of an educated and critical public, there is much less scope for the exercise of Machiavellian methods. Yet anyone with a direct experience of party politics would probably agree that in the organization of political power the end often takes precedence over the means, and the means are often assessed primarily by their effectiveness in furthering the end in view.

Science and Morality

For the political philosopher the main interest of Machiavelli's writings lies in the assumption that a scientific approach to the problems of politics is alone rational, and is fully adequate. He nowhere justifies this assumption, and it could not be justified without a demonstration, such as has been attempted in more recent times, that the facts of morality are empirical, and that the study of morality is therefore a science. If, in other words, it can be shown that moral experience consists exclusively of feelings or desires—possibly of a specific character—and judgments about those feelings or desires, and that a moral fact is therefore never a reason why something ought to be done but at most a cause why it is done, then Machiavelli's purely scientific analysis of political problems can be justified. For moral beliefs will, on such an analysis, simply rank as one of the many influences which help to determine the conduct of individuals and nations. And it is quite clear that Machiavelli did, in fact, regard moral experience in this light. He reversed the Schoolmen's dictum *quidquid petitur petitur sub specie boni* and argued that ends are called good because they are desired, and not desired because they are judged to be good. On this assumption a scientific approach to politics is the only rational one, and those who seek to solve political issues by applying an objective standard of morality are simply complicating the problem by intruding their own subjective prejudices, and thus failing to provide a solution in the scientific manner, which is alone rational.

The scientific solution of political problems which Machiavelli advocated consists in the dispassionate determination of the ends which government is created to achieve, and the dispassionate employment of the means which experience shows to be most effective for this purpose. Whether the ends are 'good' in any other sense than that they are desired is to Machiavelli a meaningless question; and so is the supplementary question whether the means employed to achieve these ends are 'legitimate'. The business of the rational politician is to determine the nature of the ends desired by a scientific study of human nature, and to select the means by a scientific study of political history. In short, Machiavelli thought that the ideal statesman would be a scientist, unlike Plato, who thought that he would be a philosopher.

Whether this conception of the statesman's nature and functions can be accepted depends, as has been shown, on the nature of moral experience. Machiavelli never sought to deny the reality or influence of that experience, but he thought that its place both in political theory and in practical politics had been generally misconceived. It had been thought of as providing a rational directive by which all practical issues could be solved, whereas to Machiavelli it was itself part of the irrational material which the rational statesman can neither justify nor condemn, but which he must necessarily recognize if his plans and calculations are to be successful.

Religious beliefs have, in Machiavelli's view, the same status and functions as moral principles. They are without objective significance, but may prove valuable allies of the statesman if they can be used to influence people to pursue the ends which he is seeking to achieve. It is, for example, likely to be of great help to a national leader if a war which is really being fought for purposes of national survival or aggrandisement is generally believed to be a war against the forces of evil and the devil.

Thus Machiavelli's attitude to politics was remarkably similar to that subsequently adopted by Karl Marx. Both believed that political forces are essentially 'material' or irrational forces, and that the moral judgments frequently evoked by these forces are themselves the expression of forces which are equally irrational. Both held that rationality is achieved only by the detached observer who studies all these forces in a scientific spirit, and directs them in the way best calculated to achieve the end in view. And in politics the only end which can be consistently pursued is the end which government is created to achieve, for the power of government depends upon the support of those who create and sustain it.

Machiavelli's Principles in Contemporary Politics

Some of Machiavelli's principles have found a ready application in the totalitarian systems of modern times. Yet it is clear from the argument of the *Discourses* that dictatorship was not to Machiavelli the best form of government, and was only justified as an expedient in special circumstances. Indeed, in so far as totalitarian systems have accepted an organic conception of the state, and have subordinated the interests of the individual to the pursuit of an 'ideology', they have not conformed to Machiavelli's conception of good government as set forth in the *Discourses*. For it is clear from that work that Machiavelli found both the origin and justification of government in its power to promote the security and happiness of the individual. Its power to govern depends upon the willingness of those whom it governs to obey, and this willingness to obey will not continue if government fails to achieve the purposes for which it was established. Thus it is in the democratic rather than in the totalitarian systems of the present day that Machiavelli's theory finds its fullest application, for only in the democracies is the individual's will, expressed collectively in the will of the majority, the real determinant of policy.

It may be said that Machiavelli's psychology was perverse, and that human beings look to their governments for more positive and less selfish benefits than the provision of personal security and happiness. Today this is undoubtedly the case, but it is only because modern governments ensure the personal security of the individual as a matter of course that they are permitted and encouraged to devote a large part of their energies to more positive ideals. If personal security—or, as we should now say, the 'rule of law'—were not already firmly established, it is safe to say that the more positive aims of modern governments could not be pursued.

It is clear, therefore, that Machiavelli's theory cannot be dismissed as a mere compendium of maxims for the successful dictator if the *Discourses* as well as *The Prince* is taken into account. When viewed as a whole his political theory belongs to the distinguished tradition of thought to which Hobbes, Hume, Ben-

7

tham, and Marx were subsequently to make their contribution. It is the tradition which finds in science, instead of in morals, the key to a rational understanding of political forces and the successful achievement of the ends of government. And it is a tradition which has acquired a new importance in the present century with the development of logical doctrines which claim to prove that moral experience cannot, from its very nature, provide rational directives for human conduct.

CHAPTER VII

Hobbes's Theory of the Rational State

THOMAS HOBBES was born at Malmesbury in 1588 and died in 1679 at the age of ninety-one years. After completing his school and university education he became tutor to the Cavendish family, with whom he remained until 1628 when his pupil, the second Earl of Devonshire, died. He subsequently became tutor to the Clinton family until 1631, when he returned to the Cavendish family to act as tutor to the third Earl. In 1640 the summoning of the Short Parliament provoked him to circulate a pamphlet defending the absolute rights of the King, but this evoked considerable hostility, and he deemed it prudent to remove to Paris, where he stayed for the next eleven years. During this period he wrote his principal work, *Leviathan*, which was published in London in 1651. It met with widespread opposition, because his attempt to justify the absolute rights of whatever government happened to be in power was repugnant to the Royalists (who believed in the Divine Right of Kings), his atheism was condemned by the Church of England, and his subordination of ecclesiastical to civil authority was unacceptable to the Roman Church. The exiled Royalists in Paris particularly disliked a doctrine which, if true, would have justified their permanent exile, and Hobbes was consequently banished from their Court. In these circumstances he thought it wise to make his peace with the Council of State of the 'Rump Parliament'. After the Restoration of the Monarchy in 1660 Hobbes was pardoned by the King and gradually came into favour at Court. But the *Leviathan* continued to evoke hostility in ecclesiastical circles, and a Parliamentary Committee was appointed to receive information about it. No action, however, resulted, and Hobbes spent the rest of his life quietly in England.

A recital of the principal political events which occurred during Hobbes's long life is sufficient to indicate the troubled and uncertain character of the times. The First Civil War between King and Parliament (1642–1645), the Second Civil War (1648), the execution of Charles I (1649), the rule of the 'Rump Parliament' (1649–1653), Cromwell's Protectorate (1654–1658) and the Restoration (1660) all took place within that period. It is therefore hardly surprising to find that in his political theory great stress is laid upon the advantages of strong and stable government, and the importance of submission to its authority.

Hobbes's Analysis of Human Nature

Hobbes's theory of the state is no exception to the generalization that political theories are, as a rule, expositions of the author's conception of the Ideal State. In the case of Hobbes's theory the word 'ideal' has a special and unusual significance; but it is none the less true that he distinguishes between states as they are and states as he thinks they ought to be, and devotes a large part of the *Leviathan* to expounding and defending his conception of the Ideal State. For this reason it is misleading to describe Hobbes's political theory as a 'mechanistic' theory, for that suggests that he believed that the characteristics of actual states could be inferred from the principles of human psychology. Up to a point Hobbes does regard the actions of human beings as determined by their nature and environment, but he also recognizes that they have a faculty of *reason* by which they try to calculate the most effective means of realizing their desires; and as their calculations may be either valid or fallacious, the use of reason introduces an indeterminate element into what would otherwise be a completely determined system.

Hobbes's analysis of human nature is based on four important empirical generalizations:

(i) In the first place, he thinks that the basic motives of all voluntary action (which he distinguishes from involuntary bodily processes such as breathing) are *desire* and *aversion*. He thinks that desire and aversion are two opposite forms of *endeavour*, by which he means a combination of *feeling* and *willing* (which he does not distinguish in the manner of modern psychologists). Endeavour takes these opposite forms according as it is directed towards or away from that which causes it. Hobbes uses the word 'contempt' to signify the attitude of indifference felt towards objects which excite neither desire nor aversion.

(ii) Secondly, Hobbes thinks that <u>men desire not only imme</u>diately attainable objects but the assurance that they will be able to gratify future desires. In his own words:

> The object of man's desire is not to enjoy once only, and for one instant of time; but to assure for ever the way of his future desire.[1]

Put more shortly, a fundamental object of human desire is power, which Hobbes defines as 'present means to obtain some future apparent good'.[2]

(iii) In the third place, Hobbes believes that, when physical and mental capacities are both taken into account, <u>men have, in general the same ability to attain their ends.</u> Lack of physical strength is usually compensated by mental ability and vice versa.[3]

(iv) Finally, Hobbes believes that <u>men have a faculty of reason</u> by which they 'acquire the knowledge of consequences, and dependence of one fact upon another'.[4] Such knowledge is acquired by generalization from experience, and it enables men to calculate the most effective means for attaining the objects of their desires.

If a man had no faculty of reason, his actions would, in theory at least, be predictable in any given circumstances from a knowledge of his desires and his environment, since he would react automatically to any given situation. But the operation of reason, which may reach either valid or fallacious conclusions about the best means of realizing these desires, introduces an indeterminate element.[5]

Hobbes speaks as though the desire for power (described under (ii) above) is as fundamental as the other basic desires of human nature. But it seems clearly to be a derivative desire following on the use of reason. To desire the power to gratify one's future desires appears to result from the realization that one always wishes to gratify one's desires, which is in turn a generalization based upon specific experiences of desire.

Hobbes's four generalizations are clearly of an empirical character, and they must stand or fall by the test of experience. There is no *a priori* necessity in the proposition that desire (whether or

---

[1] *Leviathan* (Everyman edition), Chap. XI, p. 49.
[2] op. cit., Chap. X, p. 43.   [3] op. cit., Chap. XIII, p. 63.
[4] op. cit., Chap. V, p. 21.   [5] op. cit., Chap. V.

not conditioned by reason) is the universal cause of voluntary action; or that men are in general equal in ability; or that they possess a faculty of reason. And if these generalizations are untrue the deductions which Hobbes draws from them in working out his Theory of the Ideal State will be invalid.

Hobbes's Analysis of Moral Experience

Hobbes can find no place in his analysis of human nature for specifically moral experience. The words which appear to describe such experience can, he thinks, be defined wholly in terms of non-moral concepts. But they must be differently defined at the pre-social and social stages of development.

At the pre-social stage, when men are not members of any organized society, 'good' simply means 'whatsoever is the object of any man's appetite or desire' and 'evil' means 'the object of his hate and aversion'.[1] Hobbes thus recognizes no independent standard of good and evil. A man's desires and aversions determine what is good and bad for him, and this is the only sense in which anything can be good or bad until the individual transfers his natural liberty to do as he pleases to someone else. As Hobbes himself expresses the point:

> These words of good, evil and contemptible are ever used with relation to the person that useth them: there being nothing simply and absolutely so; nor any common rule of good and evil to be taken from the nature of the objects themselves; but from the person of the man (where there is no commonwealth), or (in a commonwealth) from the person that representeth it; or from an arbitrator or judge, whom men disagreeing shall by consent set up, and make his sentence the rule thereof.[2]

By this Hobbes means that, if a man lives outside a political society, his own desires and aversions will determine his conception of what is good and evil; while if he lives within such a society his conception of what is good and evil will be determined by the person or persons constituting the sovereign power. The reason for this distinction will become clear in the following paragraphs.

[1] op. cit., Chap. VI, p. 24.   [2] loc. cit.

The State of Nature

From the premises that every individual naturally seeks his own good, and that no individual is decisively superior to any other, Hobbes concludes that, apart from the coercive power of a central government, men would live in a condition of war—'of every man against every man'.[1] By this he does not mean that they would be continuously engaged in fighting but that they would be constantly exposed to the danger of attack and have no security except that which their own strength and resourcefulness might provide. Under such conditions Hobbes thinks that the pursuits of civilized life would be impossible, and that the life of man would be 'solitary, poor, nasty, brutish, and short'.[2]

This, Hobbes thinks, would be the condition of man in a 'state of nature', i.e. the condition in which he would live if he did not belong to a political organization. Hobbes believes that this conclusion is strengthened by the observation that, in the absence of such an organization, these consequences are always observed. To illustrate the point, he refers to the life of savages and the conduct of independent sovereign states. The first of these analogies would not now be regarded as a good one. Anthropological research has shown that, even in the most primitive forms of society, there are the elements of a social life and a moral code, and that Aristotle was much nearer the truth in describing man as a 'political animal'. Hobbes is, however, on stronger ground when he refers to the conduct of sovereign states. Until relatively recent times, when an attempt has been made to have international disputes resolved by international authorities such as the League of Nations and the United Nations Organization, states usually claimed the right to judge for themselves what they were justified in doing, and this was usually identical with what they believed to be in their interest. It may also be true that the general observance of a moral code of behaviour by individuals is largely explained by habit and the fear of punishment, and that, without this fear, selfish disregard of others' interests might be far more common.

The Laws of Nature

Hobbes thinks that man escapes from the state of nature by using his *reason*. Reason does not select the ends of action—these

---

[1] op. cit., Chap. XIII, p. 64.   [2] op. cit., Chap. XIII, p. 65.

are determined solely by desire or aversion—but it reflects on the consequences of acts and shows man how his desired ends may be most speedily and fully achieved. The general principles which emerge from these reflections are called 'Laws of Nature'. Hobbes's own definition of a Law of Nature is as follows:

> A law of nature is a precept, or general rule, found out by reason, by which a man is forbidden to do that which is destructive of his life, or taketh away the means of preserving the same, and to omit that by which he thinketh it may best be preserved.[1]

In this definition Hobbes is using the word 'forbidden' in a metaphorical sense. He does not mean that men are forbidden to do what is destructive of their lives by any authority, human or divine. He simply means that men naturally desire to preserve their lives, and that their reason shows them what they *must* avoid doing *if* they wish to preserve their lives. To disobey such a law is not morally wrong but simply irrational, since it involves doing something which reason shows to be inconsistent with the satisfaction of the universal desire to preserve one's life.

Hobbes enunciates several Laws of Nature, of which the first three are specially important. The First Law is the most fundamental of all, since he believes that the others can be deduced from it. It is stated as follows:

> *Every man ought to endeavour peace as far as he has hope of obtaining it, and when he cannot obtain it, that he may seek, and use, all helps and advantages of war.* The first branch of which rule containeth the first and fundamental Law of Nature, which is to *seek peace and follow it*; the second, the sum of the right of nature, which is, *by all means we can to defend ourselves*.[2]

By this law, Hobbes simply means that where a man can live at peace with his neighbours it is rational to do so, but that where this proves impossible it is rational to fight with the most effective means available. And these alternative courses are 'rational' in the sense that they will most effectively promote the peace and security which all men desire.

[1] op. cit., Chap. XIV, p. 66.   [2] op. cit., Chap. XIV, p. 67.

The Second Law of Nature is derived from the First and is expressed as follows:

> That a man be willing, when others are so too, as far forth, as for Peace and defence of himself he shall think it necessary, to lay down this right to all things; and be contented with so much liberty against other men, as he would allow other men against himself.[1]

As Hobbes remarks, this Law can be expressed more simply as the Law of the Gospel: 'Whatsoever you require that others should do to you, that do ye to them.' The Law states, in other words, that if a man wishes others to respect his desire for peace and security he must respect their desire for these same things. If he continues in a state of nature and does whatever he thinks most likely to preserve his life he must expect others to do likewise; and one of the things which every man will then want to do is to limit the power of others to interfere with his liberty. And if everyone is trying to limit the power of others there will result that state of war in which a man's only security will be what his own strength and ingenuity can provide.

Now Hobbes holds that everyone has what he calls a 'right of nature' 'to use his own power, as he will himself, for the preservation of his own Nature; that is to say, of his own Life'.[2] In accordance with his factual analysis of moral concepts, Hobbes does not mean by this 'right of nature' any moral right to use one's power as one thinks best, but simply the liberty to do so. Liberty, in turn, he defines as 'the absence of external impediments: which impediments may oft take away part of a man's power to do what he would; but cannot hinder him from using the power left him according as his judgment and reason shall dictate to him'.[3] All this is just a complicated way of saying that a man can do what he is not prevented by external constraints from doing. The novelty of Hobbes's view lies in his denial that a man is ever prevented from doing something by the consideration that the act is, in an objective and moral sense, wrong. He may be prevented from doing something which he wants to do because he *cannot* do it: he is never prevented from doing it—in a state of nature—by the consideration that he *ought not* to do it.

[1] loc. cit.   [2] op. cit., Chap. XIV, p. 66.   [3] loc. cit.

The Social Contract

But Hobbes believes that a man may voluntarily 'lay down his right to do all things' (as he puts it in the Second Law of Nature). By this he simply means that a man may voluntarily forgo his natural *power* to do all things. Hobbes thinks that a man may do this in either of two ways: he may simply *renounce* it 'when he cares not to whom the benefit thereof redoundeth'[1] or he may *transfer* it 'when he intendeth the benefit thereof to some certain person or persons',[2] i.e. when he deliberately authorizes some other person or persons to exercise the power which was originally his. Hobbes continues:

> When a man hath in either manner abandoned, or granted away his right; then he is said to be *obliged*, or *bound*, not to hinder those to whom such right is granted, or abandoned, from the benefit of it: and that he *ought*, and it is his *duty*, not to make void that voluntary act of his own.[3]

To say that a man who has transferred his natural right, or rather liberty, to do something is *obliged* or *bound* not to prevent its exercise by someone else tends, however, to conceal the real nature of Hobbes's analysis. He is not saying that there is some objective moral sense in which a man ought not to prevent the exercise of the transferred power by someone else, nor is he saying that a man is bound, in the sense of being physically coerced, to allow the exercise of the transferred power by the person to whom it has been transferred. What Hobbes means is that it is *irrational* to prevent the person to whom one has transferred the power from exercising it. As he puts it in the same context, it is an 'absurdity', for it involves the contradiction of attempting, at one and the same time, to transfer and to retain a natural power.

Now if Hobbes is right in assuming that men's actions are determined solely by desire and aversion, a man will transfer one of his natural powers to someone else only if he believes that by so doing his desires are more likely to be satisfied. And his dominating desire is for power. Hence, Hobbes concludes, 'the motive and end for which this renouncing and transferring of right is introduced is nothing else but the security of a man's person in his life, and in the means of so preserving life'.[4]

[1] op. cit., Chap. XIV, p. 67.　　[2] loc. cit.
[3] op. cit., Chap. XIV, p. 67f.　　[4] op. cit., Chap. XIV, p. 68.

The mutual transference of a right (or power) Hobbes calls a *contract*.[1] When one party discharges his part of a contract before the other party it becomes a *covenant*[2] or contract with an obligation extending into the future. Here again it is important to remember that the 'obligation' involves neither a physical nor a moral compulsion, but merely the rational compulsion of doing what one has promised to do in return for something which the other party to the contract has already done or is doing. On the other hand, as Hobbes points out, there is no assurance that men will 'perform their covenants', i.e. keep their promises, 'because the bonds of words are too weak to bridle men's ambition, avarice, anger, and other passions, without the fear of some coercive power'.[3]

'Fear of the consequence of breaking their word'[4] is, Hobbes thinks, what persuades the majority of men to 'perform their covenants', though 'pride in appearing not to need to break it'[5] may occasionally be effective. But, for the great majority, 'covenants without the sword are but words, and of no strength to secure a man at all'.[6]

Yet, if the performance of covenants cannot be relied on, men remain in the state of nature with all its disadvantages and dangers. For this reason, Hobbes argues, men jointly agree to set up a Common Power 'to keep them in awe, and to direct their actions to the Common Benefit'.[7] And he thinks that this Common Power—by which he means what we should call the 'government' of a state—originates as follows:

> The only way to erect such a Common Power . . . is to confer all their power and strength upon one Man, or upon one Assembly of men, that may reduce all their wills, by plurality of voices, unto one will : which is as much as to say, to appoint one Man, or Assembly of men, to bear their Person; and everyone to own, and acknowledge himself to be author of whatsoever he that so beareth their person, shall act, or cause to be acted, in those things which concernt he common peace and safety; and therein to submit their wills, everyone to his will, and their judgments to his judgments.[8]

[1] loc. cit.
[2] loc. cit., p. 69.
[3] op. cit., Chap. XIV, p. 71.
[4] op. cit., Chap. XIV, p. 73.
[5] loc. cit.
[6] op. cit., Chap. XVII, p. 87.
[7] op. cit., Chap. XVII, p. 89.
[8] loc. cit.

To achieve this result Hobbes thinks that every man must make a covenant of the following sort with every other man:

> I authorize and give up my right of governing myself to this Man, or to this Assembly of men, on this condition, that thou give up thy right to him, and authorize all his actions in like manner.[1]

This is what Hobbes calls the *social contract*. It is the origin of the unity which pervades a state or (as he calls it) a commonwealth. The man or assembly of men to which the right of government is transferred Hobbes calls the 'sovereign'. This he defines as follows:

> One person, of whose acts a great multitude, by mutual covenants one with another, have made themselves every one the Author, to the end he may use the strength and means of them all, as he shall think expedient, for their peace and common defence.[2]

All members of a commonwealth other than the sovereign he calls *subjects*.

Commonwealths by Institution and Commonwealths by Acquisition

Hobbes points out that sovereigns, and therefore commonwealths, may be established in either of two ways—by *institution* or by *acquisition*. The type already described, which is established by a group of men agreeing among themselves to submit themselves to a central sovereign power, is a commonwealth by institution,[3] whereas a commonwealth by acquisition is defined as follows:

> A commonwealth by acquisition is that where the sovereign power is acquired by force; and it is acquired by force when men singly, or many together by plurality of voices, for fear of death or bonds, do authorize all the actions of that man, or assembly, that hath their lives and liberty in his power.[4]

In short, a commonwealth by institution originates in a contract freely entered into by a group of individuals, whereas a

[1] loc. cit.
[2] op. cit., Chap. XVII, p. 90.
[3] op. cit., Chap. XVIII, p. 90.
[4] op. cit., Chap. XX, p. 104.

commonwealth by acquisition is established by *force*, e.g. the force of an invader or of successful revolutionaries. A recent example of a commonwealth by acquisition is the military government imposed on Germany by her conquerors at the end of the Second World War, while a recent example of a commonwealth by institution is the new constitution adopted by the French people after the same war.

It is not clear how far Hobbes intends his account of a commonwealth by institution to be regarded as historical. He frequently speaks as though the institution of such a commonwealth is an historical event,[1] but anthropological research has not supported this theory, and has shown that even the most primitive forms of human society embody the division between ruler and subject. In any case, whatever Hobbes may have implied by his theory, its historical assumptions are not, from the philosophical point of view, its most important feature. As a philosophical theory it has to be judged not by its success in explaining why people originally established governments but by its success in showing that they now have good reasons for obeying their governments whether or not it was for these reasons that government was originally instituted. From this point of view, the social contract must be regarded not as the result of an isolated act but as the expression of the continuing belief of members of a commonwealth that it is to their joint interest to maintain a strong and stable government with unlimited powers.

Many of Hobbes's interpreters have held that he regarded the social contract as 'irrevocable', i.e. that he believed that it would be irrational to withdraw the transferred power from the sovereign under any circumstances, and some of his statements certainly appear to imply this. Thus he says:

> That they have already instituted a commonwealth, being thereby bound by covenant to own the actions and judgments of one, cannot lawfully make a new covenant amongst themselves to be obedient to any other, in any thing whatsoever, without his permission.[2]

By this Hobbes appears to mean that the transfer of power made to the sovereign by the social contract is one which it would be irrational to withdraw.

[1] op. cit., Chap. XVII.   [2] ibid., Chap. XVIII, p. 90.

On the other hand, in Chapter XXI he appears to imply that there are circumstances in which it is perfectly rational to break the social contract. Thus he says:

> The obligation of subjects to the sovereign is understood to last as long, and no longer, than the power lasteth by which he is able to protect them. For the right men have by Nature to protect themselves, when none else can protect them, can by no covenant be relinquished.[1]

The latter statement appears to be quite inconsistent with the former, yet it surely represents the position which is implied by Hobbes's general theory. For in his view men enter into the social contract and transfer their natural powers to their sovereign in order to obtain peace and security, and if the sovereign fails to promote these ends he fails to fulfil the purpose for which power was transferred to him. In these circumstances it seems only rational that his subjects should withdraw the power which they transferred to him and transfer it to another sovereign who will ensure peace and security more effectively. The emphasis which Hobbes elsewhere lays on the inconsistency of breaking the social contract cannot therefore be reconciled with the purposes of that contract, and appears to be a somewhat uncritical expression of his intense anxiety to ensure strong and stable government at almost any price.

If Hobbes's theory really implies that it is rational for people to replace a sovereign who has failed to carry out the purposes for which he was elected, the common interpretation of that theory as a defence of absolute dictatorship must be rejected and it must be recognized, on the contrary, as supporting the principle of government by consent.

The truth seems to be that Hobbes did not distinguish clearly between the *absolute* and the *irrevocable* transfer of power. It is one thing to transfer absolute, i.e. unqualified, power to a sovereign, but it does not follow that such a transfer is irrevocable, i.e. cannot—or should not—be withdrawn. The important points which Hobbes stresses are (*a*) that it is the essence of sovereignty to be absolute and unqualified, and (*b*) that a government possessing sovereign powers is the foundation of a stable and orderly community. But this does not imply that such a government

[1] ibid., Chap. XXI, p. 116.

should be allowed to remain sovereign if it does not use these powers for the purposes for which it was set up.

The Truth in Hobbes's Theory

Thus Hobbes's theory lays down two important principles of government. In the first place, it emphasizes the important fact, which loose talk about 'self-government' has tended to obscure, that all government *necessarily* involves the exercise of force by the government upon the governed. It is of the essence of government that a relatively large group of people should be controlled by a relatively small group, or even by a single individual, and this relationship is found even where self-government is said to exist. All that self-government means in practice is that the governed have some measure of control over the selection of those who govern them, and thus, indirectly, over the policy which is pursued. A more direct influence over policy is exercised by the governed in those communities where major issues of policy are submitted to a referendum; but, even where this is done, there usually remains a large range of issues on which decisions of policy remain the government's responsibility. Moreover, one of the principal objections to the use of the referendum is that it limits the responsibility of the government, and gives to those who are not responsible for implementing a policy the power to decide what that policy should be.

Thus except in those countries (e.g. Switzerland) where a referendum is employed as a recognized piece of government machinery, democratic governments have full responsibility for policy so long as they remain in power. They differ from Hobbes's sovereign only in the limitations imposed on the exercise of that power by their limited tenure of office and by the laws or conventions of the constitution under which they are elected.

In the second place, Hobbes's theory emphasizes that in commonwealths by institution the establishment of the government is a voluntary act on the part of the subjects. The government is that which 'men, disagreeing, shall by consent set up'.[1] As previously observed, it is only in special circumstances that commonwealths appear to originate in this way; but if the 'consent' to which Hobbes refers is understood as a continuing instead of an irrevocable consent it describes exactly the foundation upon

[1] ibid., Chap. VI, p. 24.

which democratic government rests. Fot it then means that, for a limited time, and on the understanding that the government observes certain limitations, whether of law or convention, upon its freedom of action, it will enjoy real power to govern as it thinks desirable and will be supported by the large majority of people. Not all that it does will necessarily be acceptable to everyone, but so long as it does not seriously outrage the feelings or principles of a substantial proportion of the people, it will continue to receive general support on the ground that respect for a central government is in the general interest of the whole community, and that this particular government has been elected, and is governing, in accordance with the recognized principles of the constitution.

The Application of Hobbes's Theory to International Politics

Hobbes's analysis of government is particularly plausible when applied to the international field, for the conditions of external security are in principle the same as those of internal security. In both cases the primary need is to eliminate the danger of strife arising from competing interests. In the civil sphere Hobbes believed that this could be done by the transfer to a sovereign body of the individual's natural power to defend his own interests; and in the international sphere it is clear that war would be impossible if all power were transferred to a single and united sovereign body. Because this has not so far been done, and individual nations still retain armed power for the defence of their interests, Hobbes would have said that these nations still live in a 'state of nature'. The fact that they undertake, in pacts and treaties, not to go to war with one another, would have seemed to him no guarantee of peace. As he said, 'Covenants without the sword are but words, and of no strength to secure a man at all';[1] and he would undoubtedly have considered that the two World Wars of the twentieth century had afforded abundant confirmation of this principle.

Important steps have been taken during the present century to establish an international organization for the prevention of war. But neither the League of Nations nor the United Nations Organization has taken over the power of individual nations to defend their interests. It is true that the nations belonging to these

[1] ibid., Chap. XVII, p. 87.

organizations have had a so-called 'moral obligation' not to use their military power except with the approval of the organization in question; but Hobbes would have held that, unless this moral obligation can be enforced by an international sovereign body, it will afford no guarantee whatsoever of international security, and does not merit the name of law. To achieve real security he would have thought it necessary to effect a real transfer of power from individual nations to an international authority by the abolition of all national armed forces (except those required for internal police work) and the allocation to the international authority of an armed force sufficient to make its decisions effective in the face of opposition. In other words, he would have said that nations must consent to transfer their natural power to defend their interests to an international authority, and accept the latter as the sole source of international law and morality.

Now according to Hobbes's analysis the nations of the world will not take this step until they are satisfied that it is to their interest to do so. They have not (he would have said) taken the step so far because they have not been satisfied that an international authority would defend their interests more effectively than they could themselves. But today he might have recognised indications that a change of outlook is gradually developing. The mere establishment of the United Nations Organization with its many and varied activities has indicated a growing conviction on the part of sovereign nations that their conduct should be subject to international agreement in the general interests of themselves and others. The European Assembly has advocated a real sacrifice of national sovereignty on the part of the nations of Western Europe for the sake of their common interests and united strength. And, if experience shows that these developments contribute to a nation's interest, a greater readiness to transfer real power to an international authority may well result.

The Rational State

Hobbes's political theory is, as already observed, no exception to the generalization made in Chapter I that a political theory is an attempt to justify a certain conception of the Ideal State. The novelty of Hobbes's theory lies in his attempt to define the 'ideal' in purely non-moral terms. Whereas the majority of political philosophers have conceived of the ideal as the *moral* ideal,

Hobbes conceives of it as the *rational* ideal, and thus regards the Ideal State as the sort of state which would result if men correctly judged the most effective means for achieving their desires. The purpose of government, in Hobbes's view, is not to realize and maintain the pattern of a morally ideal state but to achieve the fundamental desires of its citizens. And his primary object in the *Leviathan* is to justify his theory that, human nature being what it is, a strong government, to which absolute power has been transferred in accordance with the terms of the social contract, will afford the best assurance of the peace and security which human beings desire above all else. He recognizes that existing states may fall short of this ideal, but he attributes this to the intellectual, as distinct from the moral, frailty of human beings.

Hobbes's political theory is therefore a utilitarian, as distinct from a moral, theory; and it is a utilitarian theory of the basic and non-moral form which attempts to justify the institution of government on the ground of its utility in promoting the realization of men's desires. His theory does not recognize any independent standard by which these desires may be approved or condemned.

Hobbes has, of course, to account for the facts of alleged 'moral' experience, and the propositions embodying moral terms, such as 'right', 'ought', and 'good', by which such experience is described. He does not deny that these moral terms have *some* meaning: what he denies is that they have the meaning which appears to be implied by ordinary speech. It appears to be implied by ordinary speech that they are names for unique conceptions of a special character not definable in terms of desire and interest. Hobbes, on the contrary, believes that they are simply alternative names for conceptions which could be more clearly and less ambiguously described in these terms. And he would claim that the facts of politics—both the characteristics of actual states and the ideals pursued by parties and politicians—can be fully accounted for in terms of desire and interest. It is, according to him, interest, not duty, which accounts for the obedience shown by subjects to their sovereign. There is no *moral* sense in which they *ought* to obey their sovereign, but there is a *rational* sense in which they *must* do so if they desire (as he thinks they do) to enjoy peace and security.

Hobbes would undoubtedly have thought that the history of

politics during the past three centuries had abundantly vindicated his analysis. He could have pointed to the landowner and the manufacturer proclaiming the moral value of private property and the manual worker proclaiming the moral value of social equality; or to the employer organizing for higher profits and the worker striking for higher wages; and he would undoubtedly have claimed that his analysis of human society in terms of interest was abundantly justified, and that the good was a euphemism for what the individual or group in question believed to be its interest.

A naturalistic political theory of this sort avoids the main difficulty which confronts a moral theory, namely, that of establishing the truth of the moral propositions which it accepts. This difficulty arises because there is no agreed basis of moral fact by which the truth or falsity of moral propositions can be ascertained. The only moral propositions which can be verified in a scientific manner are the propositions describing people's moral beliefs—such propositions as that A believes X to be right, or that B believes X to be wrong. Propositions of this sort can be verified or refuted—on the assumption that people do, in general, accurately describe their beliefs on such matters—by such devices as a social survey or a ballot. But it is fallacious to infer from the proposition 'A believes X to be good' the proposition that 'X is good'; or, in general, to infer that the belief has an objective significance.

Hobbes's theory, on the other hand, has a purely factual basis. He claims to account for the facts of politics wholly in terms of the facts of human desires, and the means of achieving them, without reference to any independent moral standard. His theory therefore represents an important alternative to the Moral Theories which most of his predecessors supported. Its potential importance has become all the greater with the general decline in moral faith which has been witnessed during the present century. Should this decline continue, and moral standards become progressively less adequate as a foundation for political society, the alternative principle enunciated by Hobbes may come to be accepted as the true foundation.

CHAPTER VIII

Locke's Theory of the Moral State

HOBBES had maintained that the revolutionary overthrow of an established government would lead to immediate anarchy, but the English Revolution of 1688 had no such catastrophic consequence. Far from finding themselves in a 'state of nature', the people of England in 1688 simply witnessed a change of sovereign and a slight strengthening of Parliament at the expense of the Crown. These changes were of profound importance for the future of government in Britain, but they took place without violence, and were generally welcomed by the majority of citizens. John Locke (1632–1704) set himself to justify this revolution, and to establish the proposition that the authority of government depends upon its conformity to the moral law. His main exposition of this doctrine is found in Book II of his treatise *Of Civil Government*, which is alternatively entitled *An Essay Concerning the True Original Extent and End of Civil Government*. It was published in 1690, just two years after the Revolution.

Locke was educated at Westminster School and Christ Church, Oxford, and subsequently studied medicine. He became personal physician in 1666 to Anthony Ashley Cooper, afterwards the Earl of Shaftesbury, and received important public appointments when Shaftesbury became Lord Chancellor in 1672. Shaftesbury subsequently took part in the plot to place the Duke of Monmouth on the throne and, although Locke did not play any part in this conspiracy, he thought it advisable to leave England for Holland in 1683. In 1684 Charles II deprived him of an academic emolument which he had enjoyed continuously since 1659, and James II tried to effect his extradition. But he was subsequently pardoned and returned to England after the accession of William of Orange. Apart from the *Letter Concerning Toleration*, the treatise *Of Civil Government* and other political writings, he published an important contribution to the theory of knowledge entitled *An Essay concerning Human Understanding*.

Locke's political theory, like that of Hobbes, reflects the circumstances of his time. Just as Hobbes, living in the uncertain and dangerous period of the Civil War, was anxious to justify a strong government with overwhelming power, so Locke, who had suffered persecution under the Stuarts, wished to justify the revolution which deposed them, although it is only fair to add that his views about the morality of revolutions had been arrived at before 1688. Locke argued that governments could be removed by revolution without the dissolution of society, and that any government could be justifiably displaced in this way under certain conditions. These ideas were eagerly welcomed a century later by the American colonists as a justification of their refusal to recognize the British Parliament, and were thus, in some measure, responsible for all the profound consequences, extending to the present day, which have followed from the political independence of the United Kingdom and the United States.

The Law of Nature

Locke's political theory, like Hobbes's, is a theory of the Ideal State, but it differs fundamentally in being a moral theory. While Hobbes thought that the Ideal State is ideal in a *rational* sense, Locke thinks that it is ideal in a *moral* sense. His theory is based on the assumption that there is a Law of Nature, and that this Law is of a specifically moral character. He consequently conceives of the Ideal State as a *morally* ideal state.

Locke, however, makes no attempt to justify the assumption that there is a basic moral law of this sort beyond asserting that it is self-evident:

> The state of Nature has a law of Nature to govern it, which obliges every one, and reason, which is that law, teaches all mankind who will but consult it, that being all equal and independent, no one ought to harm another in his life, health, liberty, or possessions; for men being all the workmanship of one omnipotent and infinitely Wise Maker; all the servants of one sovereign Master, sent into the world by His order and about His business; they are His property,

whose workmanship they are made to last during His, not one another's, pleasure.[1]

He subsequently refers to the Law of Nature as the 'will of God'.[2]

From the start, therefore, Locke's approach to political theory differs fundamentally from that of Hobbes. Hobbes regarded man as a being activated by desire and endowed with a rational faculty capable of showing him how his desires can be most fully satisfied. Locke, on the other hand, regards the individual as a being whose reason reveals an independent law prescribing moral standards to which he ought at all times to conform. Hobbes, in short, regards man as a rational but amoral being, while Locke regards him as essentially moral.

Locke's theory conforms much more closely to the tacit assumptions of the majority of people both in his day and ours, but he does not justify the dogmatic assumptions which he makes about the Law of Nature and what it prescribes. He seems to regard these assumptions as self-evidently true, and to those who agree with him on this point his general theory may appear adequate. But it is unlikely to satisfy those who deny the existence of an independent moral law, or differ from him in their view of what that law prescribes.

The State of Nature

While Locke's conception of the Ideal State thus differs radically from that of Hobbes, his account of the origin of political society has much in common. In the first place, his conception of the state of nature is very similar. By the state of nature Locke understands the state in which men would live if they had 'perfect freedom to order their actions, and dispose of their possessions and persons as they think fit, within the bounds of the Law of Nature, without asking leave or depending upon the will of any other man'[3]—in short, the state of nature is the state in which men would live if they were not subject to a government. The difference between this conception of the state of nature and Hobbes's conception is that Hobbes recognized a Law of Nature only in the *logical* sense of a rational calculation, whereas

---

[1] *Of Civil Government*, Book II, para. 6.
[2] ibid., para. 135.   [3] ibid., para. 4.

by the Law of Nature Locke means an independent moral standard. Or, to illustrate the contrast in their own words, Hobbes thinks that the purpose of reason is to 'acquire the knowledge of consequences',[1] whereas Locke thinks that it 'teaches all mankind who will but consult it, that being all equal and independent, no one ought to harm another in his life, health, liberty, or possessions'.[2] Despite these differences, however, both philosophers conceive of the state of nature as the hypothetical state (which may at some time have been an actual state) in which men would live if they were not subject to a government.

The Origin of Government

Again, Locke offers a similar explanation of the origin of government. Like Hobbes, he believes that men agree to establish a government in order to enforce the Law of Nature. While Hobbes regards this law as rational in character and Locke regards it as moral, both think that it is because men disagree about its practical implications and cannot, in any case, be relied on to observe it voluntarily, that they transfer to a central sovereign body the power to enforce it. As Locke says:

> Civil government is the proper remedy for the inconveniences of the state of Nature, which must certainly be great where men may be judges in their own case.[3]

So far Locke's account of the nature of government bears a close resemblance to Hobbes's. But because he regards the Law of Nature as a moral law he naturally rejects Hobbes's doctrine of absolute sovereignty. Hobbes thinks that if men were rational they would, in their own interest, transfer unlimited power to a sovereign body. Whether or not this would, in fact, be the rational thing to do, Locke thinks that power should always be subject to the Law of Nature, i.e. to morality. As he says, 'Nobody can transfer to another more power than he has in himself, and nobody has an absolutely arbitrary power over himself, or over any other.'[4] He continues:

> A man . . . having, in the state of Nature, no arbitrary power over the life, liberty or possession of another, but

---

[1] *Leviathan*, Chap. V.
[2] *Of Civil Government*, Book II, para. 6.
[3] ibid., para. 13.   [4] ibid., para. 135.

only so much as the Law of Nature gave him for the preservation of himself and the rest of mankind, this is all he
doth, or can, give up to the commonwealth, and by it to
the legislative power, so that the legislative can have no more
than this. Their power in the utmost bounds of it is limited
to the public good of the society.[1]

The Moral Limitations of State Authority

It is clear from these quotations that Locke believes that all
governments are subject to the moral standards defined by the
Law of Nature, and do wrong if their actions conflict with these
standards. No government, in his view, has an absolute right to
govern as it pleases, any more than an individual has an absolute
right to act as he pleases. Locke's insistence on this principle is
primarily directed against the doctrine of the 'Divine Right of
Kings'—the doctrine that a king can do no wrong because his
authority is derived from God and because his acts express the
will of God. Locke thinks that kings are fallible human beings
whose acts are subject to the moral law, and who are liable to
violate it.

Locke's insistence on the moral limitations to a government's
authority is sometimes regarded as standing in sharp contrast to
Hobbes's defence of absolute sovereignty. It is certainly true that
Hobbes recognizes no *moral* limitation to a government's authority
in the sense in which Locke understands the word 'moral'; but
Hobbes does not, as observed in the previous chapter, regard that
authority as irrevocable. He believes that it is to the interest of
individuals to permit absolute power to their government so long
as that government fulfils the purpose for which it has been set
up—the maintenance of public order and security—but he believes that, if a government should fail to do this, its subjects
should, in their own interests, refuse to obey it. Hobbes certainly
lays more stress on the advantages of obedience than on the justification of rebellion, but that was no doubt partly due to his
natural timidity and his experience of the hazards of civil strife.
Thus the difference between the views of Hobbes and Locke on
the extent of governmental authority was one of emphasis rather
than one of principle. They did, however, justify the right of

[1] loc. cit.

rebellion on very different grounds. Hobbes thought that rebellion would be justified on grounds of individual self-interest if a government failed to uphold the rational Laws of Nature, while Locke thought that it would be justified on moral grounds if a government failed to observe the moral Law of Nature. But neither held that a government's authority should be regarded as inviolate under all circumstances.

The fact is that Hobbes and Locke were emphasizing two distinct, but complementary, principles in all government. Hobbes saw that it is the essence of a government to govern, and that for this purpose it must be in a position to enforce its decisions on the governed. Locke saw that it is none the less true that this compulsory power can be exercised only so long as the majority of the governed—who far outnumber the government—consent to submit to this compulsory power; and he argued that they are justified in withholding that consent if the government does not conform to the moral principles which they accept. Hobbes also recognized the voluntary basis of government (except in 'commonwealths by acquisition') when he stressed the voluntary character of the social contract, but he was less concerned than Locke with the circumstances under which this consent should be withdrawn, and he was inclined to think that they would arise only in the most exceptional conditions. These differences of emphasis on the relative importance of consent and authority were doubtless due in large measure to Hobbes's conviction that strong and stable government is the primary interest of all men, and to Locke's anxiety to justify revolt against a monarch who had done him personal injury and whose policy he believed to be inconsistent with the moral law. Hence, while the principle of popular consent to government is implicit in Hobbes's account of the origin of 'commonwealths by institution', it is consent of a much more passive character than that which Locke thought necessary to ensure observance of the Law of Nature by a government.

Locke recognizes, however, that government cannot be based on individual consent, since individuals may disagree in their conceptions of the government's duty. He thinks it obvious that in practice the consent upon which the government's authority depends must be that of the majority since the majority is the decisive political force:

That which acts any community being only the consent of the individuals of it, and it being one body, must move one way, it is necessary the body should move that way whither the greater force carries it, which is the consent of the majority, or else it is impossible it should act or continue one body, one community, which the consent of every individual that united into it agreed that it should; and so everyone is bound by that consent to be concluded by the majority.[1]

In this passage Locke is obviously writing of what we should call a 'democratic' society, for in autocracies a small minority has often dominated the majority by force and fear. But in a democracy, Locke thinks, it is obvious that, if universal support cannot be obtained for a certain course of action, the policy which receives majority support must prevail. And he thinks that everyone who belongs to such a society implicitly agrees to accept the principle of majority rule.[2]

Locke does not, however, appear to recognize the potential inconsistency between the principle of majority rule and the Law of Nature as he understands it. The latter, as already observed, is a moral law which teaches that 'no one ought to harm another in his life, health, liberty, or possessions', but it does not seem impossible that the majority may, on occasion, think it right to harm someone in one of these respects. Indeed, Locke would almost certainly have regarded such modern intrusions upon private property as requisitioning and the imposition of death duties—both of which have been endorsed by Parliamentary majorities in modern times—as a violation of the natural rights of the property owner. The fact is that Locke never squarely faced the dilemma that if the individual's natural rights are indefeasible it is just as wrong for a majority as for an individual tyrant to deprive him of them; while, if the will of the majority is necessarily decisive in determining policy, there can be no assurance that an independent and objective 'Law of Nature' will be upheld.

The truth is that different political societies have conceived of natural rights in very different ways. Today, for example, the natural right of property is conceived of somewhat differently even by the majorities of the United Kingdom and the United

[1] ibid., para. 96.   [2] ibid., Chap. VIII.

States of America; and both understand it in a very different sense from that in which it is understood by the Russians or was understood by Locke. Moreover, Locke gave no valid reasons for his belief that the individual's natural rights must appear to all men as they appeared to him. In point of fact, the prevailing conception of natural rights, which is embodied in a democratic nation's laws, is generally, if not always, the conception held by the majority. In other words, natural rights tend to be defined by the majority view of what these rights are.

Yet even if Locke's assumption that there are self-evident and unchanging natural rights cannot be justified, he lays down a fundamental democratic principle when he insists on the importance of a general acceptance by the community of a common conception of natural rights. For this has become a basic principle of modern democracy. The democratic constitution is distinguished from the totalitarian mainly by the recognition which it accords to a code of individual rights which is accepted by the majority and upheld by their 'greater force' when challenged either by the government or by minorities. Nations in which there is a serious division of opinion regarding the character of individual rights lack the conditions necessary for a stable democracy, for they contain a standing challenge to whichever conception of those rights happens to be upheld by the existing government.

Thus Locke's theory of the state becomes a substantially accurate analysis of a modern democratic constitution once the relativity of 'natural rights' to time and place has been admitted. For the essence of democracy is to accord to the individual certain rights recognized as inviolate, and to defend these rights when they are threatened either by government or faction. Modern democracies may not conceive of natural rights as Locke did, but they agree with him that the first duty of government is to ensure that these rights, however conceived, are never sacrificed to the exercise of arbitrary force.

Force and Morality

The problems raised by Locke's principle of majority rule should not, however, be allowed to obscure the essential foundation of his political theory. Its whole structure is based on the fundamental axiom that there is a moral law to which both individuals and governments are subject and that no individual should be subject to 'the inconstant, uncertain, unknown, arbitrary will of another man'.[1] Thus, in spite of many similarities, Locke's theory of political obligation is really the very antithesis of Hobbes's. According to Hobbes, law—the law enacted by the sovereign power—is the foundation, and the only foundation, of morality; but according to Locke morality—as embodied in the Law of Nature— is the foundation of the only laws which a citizen has an obligation to obey. If the majority agree that a civic law conflicts with the moral law the citizen has, on Locke's theory, no obligation to obey it.

It is because moral motives continue to play a prominent part in politics, as in other spheres of human activity, that Locke's political theory, in spite of its difficulties and inconsistencies, appears so much more adequate than Hobbes's theory as a justification of government. For even in a constitution, such as the British constitution, where Parliament[2] is in theory the holder of absolute power, its actions are judged, both by its members and by the community in general, by a moral standard, and no Parliament which sought to violate that standard in some fundamental way, e.g. by suppressing basic political liberties, would be likely to survive. Parliament enjoys sovereignty only within the limits of a moral code which may vary from genera-tion to generation but which, whatever form it takes, is accepted as an independent standard to which all legislation ought to conform.

The weakness of Locke's theory lies not in the importance which he attaches to an independent moral standard but in his failure to show how that standard is ascertained and defined. As already observed, he refers to it both as the Law of Nature and the 'will of God',[3] and appears to regard it as a self-evident *a priori* principle. If it is, indeed, an *a priori* principle which should be self-evident to everyone, then Locke may be justified in his somewhat dogmatic account of its nature. But there are today so many different conceptions of the nature of human rights that it is difficult to accept Locke's assumption that their nature is *a priori* and self-evident. It seems far more consistent with the facts of comparative morality to admit the essential

---

[1] ibid., Book II, para. 21.
[2] More precisely, the 'King in Parliament'.
[3] *Of Civil Government*, Book II, paras. 6 and 135.

relativity of the moral standards of different communities, and to define these in terms of what the majority of citizens believe them to be.

An analysis of this sort has at least the advantage of providing a link between the moral law and the principle of majority rule which, on Locke's own theory, appear plainly inconsistent. For on his theory there is no guarantee that the majority will not sometimes exploit its superior power and violate the natural rights of the individual citizen. On the other hand, if the moral law is defined as what the majority of citizens believe to be the moral law, then a conflict of this sort is impossible, and democracy can be defined as that form of society in which the majority recognize that individuals have indefeasible rights. But of course such an analysis makes it impossible to condemn, on any moral grounds, a society in which the majority do not recognize such rights.

The Right to Revolt

Whether the Law of Nature be a relative or an absolute principle, Locke's view that revolution is justified when that law is violated by a government appears to be substantially correct both as an account of the causes and as a justification of the act of revolution. So long as a government operates within the limits defined by the prevailing moral code of a community its moral authority is recognized, and the obligation to obey it is accepted, by the bulk of citizens. Those who reject the prevailing moral code of the majority may obey the government from other motives, e.g. to avoid punishment or to maintain national unity; but they constitute potential revolutionaries, and if their views are shared by a large minority civil strife is likely to break out. It was, for example, obviously a disagreement on a fundamental moral issue between the government and a large minority of citizens which led to the revolutionary activities of the Suffragettes in 1913 and 1914 and to the civil war in Southern Ireland before the creation of the Irish Free State. And the fact that those who differ from their government on a moral issue of this character are potential revolutionaries was felt to justify the imprisonment without trial during the Second World War of a number of citizens who appeared to believe that the war with Germany was morally unjustifiable.

Locke's own statement of the principle justifying revolution is as follows:

> There remains still in the people a supreme power to remove or alter the legislative, when they find the legislative act contrary to the trust reposed in them.[1]

The 'trust', Locke adds, is for 'attaining an end', and 'whenever that end is manifestly neglected or opposed, the trust must necessarily be forfeited, and the power devolve into the hands of those that gave it, who may place it anew where they shall think best for their safety and security'.[2] The end of government Locke describes as follows:

> The great and chief end, therefore, of men uniting into commonwealths, and putting themselves under government, is the preservation of their property; to which in the state of Nature there are many things wanting.[3]

And he explains that by 'property' he means 'lives, liberties, and estates'.[4]

In short, Locke thinks that the primary object of government is the preservation of the individual's life, liberty and possessions, and that when it fails, in the opinion of the majority, to fulfil this trust it should be removed and replaced.

Assessment of Locke's Theory

Locke's theory, like Hobbes's, has often been criticised as artificial and over-simplified in view of the way in which he accounts for the origin of the state in terms of the rational and calculating choice of individuals. It is said that he greatly underestimated the part played by irrational factors, such as various manifestations of the 'herd instinct', in creating and maintaining political societies and that his theory, in so far as it claims to be an historical account of the origin of such societies, is wholly false. It must be admitted that Locke often writes as though he did believe that his theory was historically valid. Yet even though this claim must be rejected—and the evidence of history, anthropology, and psychology alike show it to be false—his theory, like

[1] ibid., para. 149.　　　　[2] loc. cit.
[3] ibid., para. 124.　　　　[4] ibid., para. 123.

Hobbes's, can be alternatively regarded as an attempt to justify political society instead of to account for its historical origin. And this, in any case, is its more important aspect as a philosophical theory.

So conceived, Locke's theory, like the majority of political theories, is essentially an attempt to justify, on moral grounds, a certain conception of the purpose of government. He claims that its primary purpose is to preserve men's property, by which is meant their lives, their liberties and their possessions. Government is entrusted with that responsibility, and it can justifiably be removed and replaced if it fails to discharge it. Thus in Locke's view the individual, not the state, is the object of supreme value, and the state is a mechanism established to promote the individual's good.

Locke's exposition of his theory does not make it easy to distinguish what he intended to be factual analysis from what he intended to be the exposition of a moral ideal; and it may well be that he did not always have this distinction clearly before his mind. It is also by no means clear whether he believed that his factual analysis was true of all states whatsoever, or only of contemporary England and states similarly organized. But it is clear that, however the theory is interpreted in detail, an essential part of it is the moral argument that the primary purpose of government ought to be the protection of the individual's life, liberty and possessions—in short, his natural rights—and that a government which does not seek to promote this end forfeits all claim to moral authority.

The influence of Locke's theory has been great just because it has appeared to clarify and correlate so effectively the implicit assumptions about the rights of government and subjects which have prevailed in the English-speaking world since the Revolution of 1688. Its influence has been even greater in America than in Britain since, in the first place, it was widely cited as a justification of the American Revolution and, in the second place, the principle of a natural law to which even governments are subject is embodied in the Articles of the American Constitution. The unwritten British Constitution is in theory closer to Hobbes's principle of unlimited sovereignty, but in practice the British Parliament observes numerous unwritten conventions which have, in practice, the force of moral law, and Parliament is regarded by the community at large as subject to moral standards no less than the individual citizen.

Locke's contribution to political theory may therefore be shortly described as that of defining the moral responsibilities of government. He sought to revive the belief in an independent moral law which had been almost universally accepted throughout the Middle Ages; and in doing so he defined a principle which has been accepted by all modern democracies and is now being extended to the international sphere in the Charter of Human Rights of the United Nations Organization. It was Plato's principle of justice in a new form—a principle which sought to defend the individual against the tyranny of the community; to ensure that the weak are not exploited by the strong; and to insist that the proper function of government is the realization in human affairs of a moral pattern and not simply the organization of power.

CHAPTER IX

Rousseau's Theory of the General Will

JEAN JACQUES ROUSSEAU was born in Geneva, the son of a mad watchmaker, in 1712, and died in 1778. Having left school at the age of twelve, and failed to settle in any of the trades to which he had been apprenticed, he fled from Geneva to Savoy four years later, and began a life of wandering and exile which, apart from twelve years spent in Paris (1744–1756), continued to his death. For part of these early years he was supported by women who befriended him; for part of them he lived the life of a vagabond and earned a livelihood as best he could. In 1743 he became secretary to the French Ambassador to Venice, and appears to have served him well, but quarrelled because he received no salary. In 1750 he achieved fame through winning a prize offered by the Academy of Dijon for the best essay on the question 'Have the arts and sciences conferred benefits on mankind?' Rousseau answered the question in the negative, contending that the arts and sciences create artificial wants and jeopardise the natural morality of unspoiled man. This theme was elaborated in his *Discourse on Equality* (1754), in which Rousseau argued that 'man is naturally good, and only by institutions is he made bad'.

It was in 1762 that Rousseau's two most important works were published—*Emile*, his treatise on education, and the *Social Contract or Principles of Political Right*. The first offended both the Catholic and Protestant Churches by its support of natural religion, and the latter offended both the Council of Geneva and the French Government by its implied denial of the Divine Right of Kings. Rousseau left France and was befriended by Frederick the Great, who gave him asylum at Motiers. After spending three years there, however, he incurred local suspicion which placed his life in danger, and he fled to England in 1765. George III granted him a pension, and he formed friendships with both Burke and Hume. Burke found his vanity intolerable and their association was short-lived. Hume was a faithful friend but in the end Rousseau's delusions convinced him that Hume was engaged in plots against his life. He fled to Paris, where he spent his last years in great poverty, and is believed to have died by his own hand.

The Enlightenment and the Romantic Reaction

Rousseau was one of the leading figures in the so-called 'Romantic Reaction' which followed the 'Age of Enlightenment'. The latter was the name given to the period from about 1650 till late in the eighteenth century when the leading thinkers of both England and France were inspired by a faith in the power of human reason to achieve a final understanding of the universe and to provide a rational guide for human conduct. Other faculties, such as feeling or intuition, were held to be essentially inadequate for this purpose. Hobbes's philosophy was an early expression of this outlook. After the middle of the eighteenth century, however, there was a reaction against this faith in reason, and as this reaction took the form of looking to feeling or intuition instead of to reason for fundamental truth, it came to be known as the 'Romantic Reaction'.

Rousseau was, from certain points of view, a leading representative of this Romantic Reaction, and his works bear all the marks of an intensely emotional faith in the truth of the principles which he advocates. This characteristic made his writings highly effective as propaganda, although they are without the careful logic of the rationalists. Thus it is generally agreed that the central theme of Rousseau's *Social Contract*—man's loss of his natural liberties in the modern state—played no small part in fanning the flames of discontent which culminated in the French Revolution.

As observed in Chapter I, political philosophies are essentially attempts to justify a certain conception of the ideal state, and it is of special importance to bear this in mind when reading the *Social Contract* as much of what Rousseau says is obviously untrue if regarded as a description of actual states. For example, his account of the way in which a political society originates, and the emergence of its 'general will', is intended to be an account of the way in which the *ideal* society *would* develop. Rousseau does not claim that every society has developed in this way, and indeed he thinks that only small and intimate societies like the Greek city states could be expected to do so.

The *Social Contract* is not Rousseau's only contribution to political philosophy, but it embodies his most mature views, and will accordingly be used to illustrate and justify the interpretation of his theory which follows. It was published, along with *Emile*, his treatise on education, in 1762, and his later works, which were largely of an autobiographical nature, added nothing of importance to the theories put forward in these two books.

Rousseau thinks that the outstanding defect of existing political societies is the way in which they restrict the freedom which the individual would enjoy in a state of nature, which, like Hobbes and Locke, he conceives as the condition in which an individual would live if he were not subject to a government. And he thinks that the ideal state would therefore be one in which the advantages of political law and order could be enjoyed without the loss of these natural liberties. Hence he states the fundamental problem of politics as follows:

> The problem is to find a form of association which will defend and protect with the whole common force the person and good of each associate, and in which each, while uniting himself with all, may still obey himself alone, and remain as free as before.[1]

Rousseau argues that the social contract provides the solution to this fundamental problem. By this he means that a political society founded upon a social contract, understood in the sense in which he defines it, will provide its members with both the freedom of the state of nature and the advantages of civil law and order. And he defines the social contract as follows:

> Each of us puts his person and all his power in common under the supreme direction of the general will, and, in our corporate capacity, we receive each member as an indivisible part of the whole. At once, in place of the individual personality of each contracting party, this act of association creates a moral and collective body, composed of as many members as the assembly contains votes, and receiving from this act its unity, its common identity, its life and its will.

[1] *Social Contract*, Book I, Chap. 6.

> This public person, so formed by the union of all other persons, formerly took the name of *city*, and now takes that of *republic* or *body politic*; it is called by its members *State* when passive, *Sovereign* when active, and *Power* when compared with others like itself.[1]

This quotation embodies the essence of Rousseau's political philosophy, but it is stated in a misleading way, as it suggests a description of the way in which political societies do, as a rule, originate and develop. This, however, is not Rousseau's meaning. He is actually describing the origin and constitution of an ideal state, and he would have been the first to admit that this description seldom, if ever, applies to actual states. In other words, he is telling us how a state would have to originate and be constituted in order to meet the claims of both individual liberty and social order.

The outstanding characteristic of such an ideal state would be its *organic* character; it would, as Rousseau says in the passage just quoted, be a 'collective body', a 'public person', and a 'body politic'. For only if it takes this form will there be no conflict between the natural liberty of the individual and the collective will of the state. If the state is a genuine organism there will be no such conflict, for the true will and interest of the individual will coincide with the will and interest of the state, just as the health of a bodily organ depends on the health of the body as a whole. If there appears to be a conflict between the two this is because 'each individual, as a man, may have a particular will contrary or dissimilar to the general will which he has as a citizen. His particular interest may speak to him quite differently from the common interest.'[2]

Rousseau believes that the continuation of this conflict between an individual will and the general will would 'prove the undoing of the body politic'.[3] Accordingly, he thinks that it should be resolved as follows:

> Whoever refuses to obey the general will shall be compelled to do so by the whole body. This means nothing less than that he will be forced to be free; for this is the condition which, by giving each citizen to his country, secures him against all personal dependence.[4]

[1] loc. cit.   [2] ibid., I, 7.   [3] loc. cit.   [4] loc. cit.

To Rousseau there is nothing paradoxical in this conception of being 'forced to be free', for he believes that the citizen is truly free only when he conforms to the general will. In so far as a citizen opposes the general will his 'actual' will cannot be his 'real' will, for his 'real' will is always identical with the general will of the whole community. This follows, indeed, from the assumption that the state—the ideal state—is an organic whole, for on that assumption there can be no conflict between the purposes of the whole and of the part any more than there can be a conflict between the health of a living body and the health of one of its organs.[1] In both cases the true interests of whole and part are identical.

The practice of 'forcing people to be free' has become familiar during recent decades, and has been frequently illustrated in totalitarian communities. Those who have refused to accept and practise the official 'ideology' as defined by the government have been forced to do so by the threat of imprisonment or torture; and the compulsion has been carried out in the name of the 'people's will'. But such states have all differed in one fundamental respect from the ideal state of Rousseau, namely, they have been without any machinery for discovering the free will of the people as a whole. On the contrary, they have always resorted to a powerful mechanism of central propaganda for ensuring, as far as possible, that everyone accepts a uniform code of belief and practice, and the 'will of the people' has therefore in fact meant the will of the government. Rousseau would have regarded such states as a complete travesty of his ideal.

Rousseau distinguishes the *general will* from both the *will of the majority* and the *will of all*. These latter wills are, in Rousseau's opinion, the wills of groups of individuals who happen to agree. The will of the majority is, of course, the will shared by the majority of the members of a community, while the will of all is the will shared by *all* the members of a community. But the general will is the will of an *individual*—of the 'collective body' which the act of association creates in an ideal state. Neither the will of the majority nor the will of all can, in Rousseau's view, provide a moral basis for the state, for they represent mere forces, devoid of moral authority, which may, indeed, overwhelm the

[1] In his *Discourse on Political Economy* Rousseau specifically compared the 'body politic' to a physiological organism.

will of an individual, but which do not thereby make him conform to his 'real' will.

Although this conception of a general will is strange to people with a democratic outlook, and may appear to them quite inapplicable to human society, its general significance is apparent when the analogy with a physiological organism is borne in mind. For such an organism does, to all appearances, exhibit a fundamental urge to survival and reproduction, and the functioning of all its organs is dominated by these primary purposes. Whether a human society can achieve such a unity is far from certain. That its individual members may have a *common* interest or *common* purpose in certain circumstances does not prove that they have a *single* interest or a *single* purpose. Nor does the fact that, following on initial disagreement among its members, a group of people ultimately comes to accept a common policy prove more than that it feels it more important to agree on some policy than on none. Nor, again, does the undoubted fact that an individual's motives and ideals may be largely fashioned by the social influences which surround him prove that his outlook can be explained wholly in terms of these influences. For these and other reasons the democrat is unconvinced that, however much the individual is conditioned by his social environment, his individuality can be explained away, or that it is necessary for it to be absorbed in the will of society as a whole if that society is to be described as good.

Now it is, as previously remarked, with the latter question—the question of the good society—that Rousseau is primarily concerned. Even if no existing society does exhibit a general will Rousseau believes that the ideal society *would* exhibit such a will and that this will would be a good will. As he said:

> The Sovereign, merely by virtue of what it is, is always what it should be.[1]

Rousseau had previously made the same point in his *Discourse on Political Economy*:

> The body politic, therefore, is also a moral being possessed of a will; and this general will, which tends always to the preservation and welfare of the whole and of every part, and

[1] *Social Contract*, I, 7.

is the source of the laws, constitutes for all the members of the State, in their relations to one another and to it, the rule of what is just or unjust.[1]

A general will, in short, is a good will, and defines, through the medium of the law, what a citizen ought to do. But a state itself is not subject to any moral law. For, while the citizen, in his dual capacity as legislator and subject, is subject to the general will which he has assisted to formulate, the Sovereign, i.e. the state in its active capacity, cannot impose on itself a binding law.

> It is in the position of an individual who makes a contract with himself; and this makes it clear that there neither is nor can be any kind of fundamental law binding on the body of the people—not even the social contract itself.[2]

The progress of international co-operation during the past thirty years suggests the possibility that, if a general will can develop in a state, it may ultimately develop in humanity as a whole. But Rousseau explicitly denies this possibility. The general will of a state defines the standard of morality for its citizens, but the state itself is a law unto itself and can do no wrong. There is little doubt that this doctrine, as developed by Hegel and his followers, has been held to justify a theory of 'power politics' which appears quite immoral to supporters of liberal democracy.

Apart from the theoretical objections which may be made to Rousseau's theory, it is difficult to see how it could be applied in practice, for there is no objective way of determining when a general will has been achieved. As already observed, this will is explicitly distinguished both from the will of all and from the will of the majority, and it need not itself be unanimously accepted.[3] Rousseau seems to assume that in a small and compact society, modelled on the pattern of the Greek city states, such a will could be achieved, and that the large majority of people would recognize it when it was achieved; but this is a highly speculative assumption.

Nor is the determination of the general will made easier when its alleged end is taken into account. This end is defined by Rousseau[4] as the 'common good', the implication being that a

[1] *Discourse on Political Economy* (Everyman edition), p. 236.
[2] *Social Contract*, I, 7.   [3] ibid., II, 2, note.   [4] ibid., II, 1.

particular will aims at its own selfish good, which may not coincide with the general good nor, therefore, with the true good of any individual. But the same difficulty arises in determining the common good as in determining the general will. There may in fact be no general agreement about the nature of the common good, and no apparent reason, apart from more general support, why one view of its nature should be preferred to another. And Rousseau specifically denies that the general will is simply the will of the majority, or that 'the majority is always right'. It is therefore very doubtful whether a general will, which is distinct both from a universal will and from a majority will, can exist, or whether the 'common good' at which that will is said to aim can be defined except in terms of what the majority of people believe the common good to be. And the achievement of what the majority believe to be the common good may, and probably will, mean the sacrifice of what the minority believe to be the common good.

As was previously observed, Rousseau's theory of the general will is neither defensible nor even intelligible unless the general will is understood as the will of a collective *individual*. And it is by no means clear that such a collective individual exists. Individuals in the ordinary sense—men and women of flesh and blood with their desires and prejudices and convictions—are easily recognized. It may be true that these desires and prejudices and convictions are largely conditioned by the relationship of such individuals to other individuals, but this is far from saying that a truly collective individual does or could exist. It is not therefore surprising that the nature and existence of the collective individual should be matters of speculation; and that the attempt to make its alleged 'will' the standard of morality for a community should attract those who desire to provide some apparent 'justification' for an exercise of power which is really dictated by quite different motives.

Rousseau's Moral Theory

To modern philosophers the most important question which can be asked about Rousseau's moral theory is whether it is naturalistic. When he says that the general will is necessarily a good will does he mean simply that 'good' means 'general' (in the same way that 'equilateral' means 'with equal sides'), or does he mean that 'generality' and 'goodness' are different qualities, although when one characterizes a will the other always does so as well? If he means that 'goodness' and 'generality' are synonymous, he is defending a moral theory which is just as naturalistic as that of Hobbes, although he differs from Hobbes in identifying 'the good' with 'the general' instead of with 'the desired'. And this interpretation is consistent with much of what he says.

Whatever may have been Rousseau's view of the relation between the goodness and the generality of the will, he thought that its generality could be defined in objective terms:

> Each individual, as a man, may have a particular will contrary or dissimilar to the general will which he has as a citizen. His particular interest may speak to him quite differently from the common interest: his absolute and naturally independent existence may make him look upon what he owes to the common cause as a gratuitous contribution, the loss of which will do less harm to others than the payment of it is burdensome to himself.[1]

> There is often a great deal of difference between the will of all and the general will; the latter considers only the common interest, while the former takes private interest into account, and is no more than a sum of particular wills: but take away from these same wills the pluses and minuses that cancel one another, and the general will remains as the sum of the differences.[2]

Given the appropriate conditions, Rousseau believes that a general will, so conceived, will always emerge:

> If, when the people, being furnished with adequate information, held its deliberations, the citizens had no communication one with another, the grand total of the small differences would always give the general will, and the decision would always be good.[3]

But in a later passage he recognizes that in practice the people may be misguided:

> Of itself the people wills always the good, but of itself it by no means always sees it. The general will is always in the

---

[1] *Social Contract*, I, 7.   [2] op. cit., II, 3.   [3] loc. cit.

right, but the judgment which guides it is not always en-
lightened. It must be got to see objects as they are, and
sometimes as they ought to appear to it.[1]

Rousseau therefore appears to hold that the general will can be
identified as the will which wills the common interest. The particular wills of individuals aim at particular interests, which may,
and often do, conflict with the common interest of the community,
and therefore with the true interest of its individual members.
But a theory of this sort must show how the common interest can
be defined in terms which are not purely arbitrary. Rousseau
himself does not provide any assurance that a general will, conceived as he conceives it, can exist. For there may always be
differences of opinion among the individual members of a community about the nature of the common interest, and the extent
to which their particular interests conflict with it. Indeed, the
last sentence of the passage just quoted, with its reference to
making the general will see objects 'as they ought to appear to it'
raises the obvious question as to why objects ought to appear
differently from how they do appear, and who is to determine
how they ought to appear. The truth is that behind Rousseau's
'romanticism' lies the extremely rationalist assumption that it is
more *reasonable* to desire some objects than others, and that the
general will is really the rational will. Only so is it possible to
conceive of a will which is neither the will of an individual nor
of a majority of individuals, nor even of all the individuals in the
society whose will it is said to be.
It is, of course, necessary to agree with Rousseau that an
important distinction can be drawn between the apparent and
the real interests of individuals—between that which appears
likely to afford them the maximum of satisfaction and that which
would really do so if they took account of all the relevant factors
and calculated rightly. But the fact that this distinction can be
drawn does not imply that there is only one way in which the
real interest of an individual or the common interest of a society
can be defined—unless it is defined, as Rousseau defines it, without reference to the actual wills of individuals, and in terms of a
'rational' will which is not necessarily related to any actual will
at all.

[1] op. cit., II, 6.

Rousseau's Theory in Practice

Apart from these general difficulties inherent in Rousseau's theory it is clear that its application in practice is very limited. For a general will can be achieved only in a community where every citizen participates actively in the work of legislation, and it cannot therefore be achieved in large communities with representative governments legislating on behalf of the people as a whole. It was for this reason that Rousseau considered that the Greek city states exemplified the form which the ideal state must always take. He held that, even if a representative government were to achieve a general will, this would not be the general will of the community but only of the representative government.

Again, Rousseau thought that the existence of associations within the state, such as churches, trade unions, and political parties, is a serious obstacle in the way of achieving a general will for the community as a whole, since they tend to influence the spontaneous expression of the individual's will, without which a general will cannot be formed. Rousseau therefore thought that if such associations are to be permitted at all they should be kept as small and as numerous as possible so as to cancel out each other's influence and not rival the influence of the general will.

The Function of Government

Since Rousseau holds that the general will should be the sovereign power in a community it follows that the function of government is purely executive. As he says:

> Sovereignty, for the same reason as makes it inalienable, cannot be represented; it lies essentially in the general will, and will does not admit of representation: it is either the same, or other; there is no intermediate possibility. The deputies of the people, therefore, are not and cannot be its representatives: they are merely its stewards, and can carry through no definitive acts. Every law the people has not ratified in person is null and void—is, in fact, not a law. The people of England regards itself as free; but it is grossly mistaken; it is free only during the election of members of parliament.[1]

[1] op. cit., III, 15.

It is therefore clear that, whatever parallel may be drawn between Rousseau's ideal state and the totalitarian states of today, Rousseau would have emphatically denied the claim of any government to express the general will of the community. For Rousseau the general will is the spontaneous will of the 'body politic', constituted by the organic union of all citizens, and no government can govern in accordance with that will unless it is continually directed by it. And in the ideal state, modelled on the city states of Ancient Greece, Rousseau believes that the people would always have a general will on all major issues of policy, and would always make it abundantly clear what that will was. There would therefore be no need for a government to interpret it.

All this might possibly be true in a small and intimate community of the sort which Rousseau seems to have had in mind, but the dominating political forces of the modern world are large states in which representative government is, for practical reasons, inevitable and in which, according to Rousseau, it is therefore impossible to achieve a general will, still more to govern in accordance with it. Yet something closely resembling the general will as conceived by Rousseau does seem to operate in liberal democracies. On major constitutional principles, such as the maintenance of a constitutional monarchy, parliamentary government, a free Press, and an independent judiciary there would appear to be virtually unanimous agreement among all sections of the population in modern Britain, and without such a general measure of agreement it is doubtful whether democracy would survive. Within that general agreement about the way in which government should govern there is, of course, abundant scope for disagreement about the policy which it should pursue; but agreement about the way in which government should resolve these disagreements is the condition on which alone democracy can survive, and this general agreement appears in many ways to be a spontaneous expression of a will which is 'general' in the literal sense, and therefore bears an important resemblance to Rousseau's basic conception.

There is, however, a fundamental difference between democratic theory and Rousseau's doctrine, for the former is an individualist and the latter an organic theory of the state. Democratic theory asserts that the general agreement among members of a democracy on broad constitutional issues is simply an important empirical fact which justifies the overriding of conflicting minority opinions on grounds of practical expediency; whereas Rousseau would have said that the unity of an organic state is based upon a general will which is moral in character and justifies the over-riding of minority opinions on moral grounds.

Rousseau would have said that the dissentients from the general will do not know what their 'real' will is and should be 'forced to be free'; whereas the democrat holds that the dissentients are under no delusion about what they want but must, as a matter of practical necessity, be forced to conform to the will of the majority.

On a superficial examination it might appear that modern totalitarian states come much nearer than the democracies to accepting the theory of the general will in the frequent references which are made in them to the 'will of the people' as the justification of governmental acts. But there is the fundamental difference that in such states no machinery exists for the direct and frequent ascertainment of the public will, and Rousseau would have said that without this no general will in the true sense can exist. Indeed, the methods of controlling and organizing public opinion which are such conspicuous features of modern totalitarian states are the direct antithesis of the relationship between government and people which, in Rousseau's view, gives government a moral sanction for its acts.

It is, therefore, in democratic rather than in authoritarian states that a force, which in some ways resembles the 'general will', seems to be found. While Rousseau would have said that no truly 'general' will can emerge in a state with a representative government, there is something remarkably like it to be found in the strong and united expressions of what is called 'public opinion', which are evoked in liberal democracies from time to time, and which usually have a decisive influence on governmental policy. But too much must not be made of this comparison for unless the state is assumed to be a genuine organism these expressions of public opinion must represent the 'will of the majority' or the 'will of all' rather than the general will in Rousseau's sense.

The truth is that Rousseau's refusal to identify the general will with the actual will of any individual or group of individuals shows that it is not an empirical concept at all. It is the rational will—the will which ought to be shared by everybody even if it is actually possessed by none. It is, from another point of view, the good will. But these definitions all emphasize that it is an essentially empty will without specific objects, and thus liable to be applied in criticism of actual wills by anyone who claims to have insight into its nature. It is this characteristic of the general will which has made it so easy for modern totalitarian governments to justify in its name arbitrary acts of force with a considerable measure of plausibility.[1]

The fact is that Rousseau's theory is essentially unintelligible when interpreted in terms of the assumption that the individual's judgment is the ultimate criterion of truth and value. And his exposition of his theory is necessarily inconsistent in so far as he assumes an individualist criterion of truth while defending an organic theory of morality. An organic theory of morality can be defended—if at all—only if it is based upon an organic theory of knowledge generally, and it was left to Rousseau's successor, Hegel, to show how this comprehensive synthesis might be achieved.

[1] Robespierre made a similar use of Rousseau's doctrine when he said of the Jacobins, 'Our will is the general will'.

CHAPTER X

Hume and Burke on the Philosophy of Conservatism

WHILE Edmund Burke (1729–1797) has usually been regarded as the leading philosopher of political conservatism, David Hume (1711–1776) was, by general admission, a more profound philosopher, and his Empiricism is the logical basis of the Conservative creed. Moreover, he did not, like Burke, live into an age when revolution threatened the foundations of society, and when political conservatism was therefore a natural reaction to contemporary conditions. Hume's conservatism was founded on the more permanent basis of logical empiricism and utilitarian ethics, although it was no doubt encouraged to some extent by the stable political conditions under which he lived.

Hume's life was relatively uneventful, although he held the posts of Secretary to the British Ambassador in Paris and Under-Secretary of State during the years 1763–1769. For the rest, he lived the life of a philosopher and historian. After unsuccessful attempts to settle down in the profession of law and in commerce, he went to France in the year 1735, and spent the next few years in study and writing. The three Books of the *Treatise of Human Nature* appeared in 1739 and 1740. This work comprised a full exposition of Hume's metaphysical and moral philosophy, but the originality of his ideas and the complex nature of much of the argument restricted the book's appeal, and, as Hume himsel' said, 'it fell deadborn from the press without reaching such a distinction as even to excite a murmur among the zealots'. Hume felt that this failure to attract attention 'had proceeded more from the manner than the matter', and he set himself to expound his theories in a simpler and more readable style in his *Enquiry into the Human Understanding* (1748), the *Enquiry concerning the Principles of Morals* (1751) and the *Dissertation on the Passions* (1757). He had published in 1741 and 1742 two volumes of *Essays Moral and Political,* which were immediately successful, and these were followed in 1752 by a volume of *Political Discourses.* He also published a *History of Great Britain* and a *History of England under the House of Tudor.* His *Dialogues on Natural Religion* were published posthumously.

Although the *Treatise* was completed when Hume was only twenty-five years of age, it contains all the essential principles of his metaphysical and moral philosophy, and its supreme importance is now generally appreciated. It was the book which awoke Kant from his 'dogmatic slumber' and inspired him to work out his own 'critical philosophy' as an answer to Hume's sceptical conclusions. And it embodies the basic ideas which have very recently emerged in a new guise in the modern doctrine known as Logical Positivism.

The general theory expounded by Hume in the *Treatise* and the *Enquiries* is a form of Empiricism, in the sense in which this term was defined in Chapter I. It is the doctrine that the only propositions which are certainly true are those which describe 'relations of ideas', i.e. are analytic; and that those which proceed beyond the mere analysis of an idea to assert something about its application to reality are without rational necessity and can be justified only by direct observation. Such propositions are synthetic, and Hume's Empiricism can be summed up in the axiom that a synthetic proposition can never be *a priori*.

Hume's Moral Theory

As was shown in Chapter I, Empiricism thus understood implies that the generalizations of both science and morality are empirical and devoid of rational necessity. They may be universally true, but they need not be, and whether they are or not can be ascertained only by observation. There is therefore no ground for assuming that there is a universal 'Natural' or Moral law standing independent of experience and prescribing the form which experience ought to take. The moral norms which apply to experience must be found within experience itself, and must therefore be subject to its contingent character and variations. What ought to be must ultimately be determined by what is, and the sense of duty must ultimately be a kind of feeling or desire.

In Hume's view these conclusions necessarily follow once we recognize that an act is an event, that its occurrence cannot be understood except in so far as it is caused by (i.e. regularly follows) another event, and that an act is always ultimately caused by a 'passion', i.e. a feeling or desire, although cognition and reason may play an important part in determining the form which that passion takes by showing what the conditions and consequences of realising its end are likely to be. Moral feelings of approval or disapproval are recognized by Hume to be among the most important and influential of the passions, but they are no more than passions, and it is for experience to ascertain when, and in what circumstances, they occur. There is no basis for any *a priori* claim that certain acts ought to be approved under all circumstances, for such a generalization is itself simply the empirical proposition that a feeling of approval is excited in someone by all such acts.

Hume thinks that these conclusions necessarily follow from the consideration that moral approval and disapproval influence action, and frequently in a very marked degree. They cannot, for this reason, be acts of apprehension or judgment because the latter cannot, by themselves, influence action in any way. The judgment that 'the fire is out' does not result in any action on my part *unless* it is accompanied by a desire, such as the desire to keep warm. Similarly, the judgment that 'stealing is wrong' would not dissuade people from stealing unless at the same time they desired to avoid doing what is wrong. Moral approval and disapproval must, therefore, in some sense express desires in view of the influence which they have on action. The disinterested contemplation of good and evil could not have any such practical effects.

Hume thinks that it is inconceivable that acts should be directly influenced by reason, although reason may play an important part in determining the nature of the objects which excite desire. He set forth his views on this fundamental question in his important chapter 'On the Influencing Motives of the Will',[1] where he claimed to prove '*first*, that reason alone can never be a motive to any action of the will; and, *secondly*, that it can never oppose passion in the direction of the will'.

Since moral experience must therefore be of an emotional and conative character, moral judgments must be about this emotional and conative experience and cannot, as is commonly assumed, be

[1] *Treatise of Human Nature*, Book II, part iii, section 3.

about external and objective facts. Actions, feelings and characters are not good or bad, right or wrong, in virtue of some quality which they possess but, as Hume puts it:

> An action or sentiment or character is virtuous or vicious . . . because its view causes a pleasure or uneasiness of a particular kind.[1]

The words 'of a particular kind' are of great importance, because they mean that Hume is not advocating a theory of egoistic hedonism. As he says later in the same chapter:

> The good qualities of an enemy are hurtful to us, but may still command our esteem and respect. It is only when a character is considered in general, without reference to our particular interest, that it causes such a feeling or sentiment as denominates it morally good or evil.[2]

Hume does not think that there is any universal law according to which the moral sentiments occur; but he thinks that the majority of those which are not mere expressions of habitual attitudes are based upon estimates of utility. Thus he says:

> These sentiments may arise either from the mere species or appearance of characters and passions, or from reflections on their tendency to the happiness of mankind, and of particular persons. My opinion is, that both these causes are intermixed in our judgments of morals. . . . I am also of opinion that reflections on the tendencies of actions have by far the greatest influence, and determine all the great lines of duty.[3]

Judgments of utility, i.e. of the tendency of an act to promote happiness or diminish pain, are, therefore, in Hume's opinion, the usual basis of the moral principles which we habitually accept, or which we arrive at in cases of dispute. Hume recognizes that this is a purely empirical generalization to which there may well be exceptions, but he thinks that it applies to the great majority of moral laws and is the generalization which gives them a large measure of systematic coherence. He recognizes, however, that

---

[1] op. cit., Book III, part i, section 2.   [2] loc. cit.
[3] op. cit., Book III, part iii, section 1.

in a rapidly changing society moral laws which could formerly be justified on a utilitarian basis may, through the force of habit and tradition, survive long after they have ceased to serve their utilitarian purpose.

Hume's Political Theory

Hume believes that utility is similarly the foundation of the state. The way in which governments originated has, he thinks, no relevance to the utilitarian reasons which now exist for obeying them, and he thinks that the doctrine of the social contract is without either historical or logical justification. As he says:

> If the reason be asked of that obedience, which we are bound to pay to government, I readily answer, *because society could not otherwise subsist*; and this answer is clear and intelligible to all mankind. Your answer is, *because we should keep our word*. But besides that nobody, till trained in a philosophical system, can either comprehend or relish this answer, besides this, I say, you find yourself embarrassed when it is asked, *why we are bound to keep our word*? Nor can you give any answer, but that would, immediately, without any circuit, have accounted for our obligation to allegiance.[1]

All governments have a special responsibility for the security of personal property, and this, too, is based on considerations of utility:

> By the laws of society, this coat, this horse is mine, and *ought* to remain perpetually in my possession: I reckon on the secure enjoyment of it: by depriving me of it, you disappoint my expectations, and doubly displease me, and offend every bystander.[2]

Hume, in short, agrees with Hobbes that the primary function of government is the maintenance of personal security, and that so long as a government fulfils this purpose there are utilitarian grounds for giving it allegiance whether it originally derived its power from force or from consent. And Hume thinks that in practice the allegiance which people give to their government is, as a rule, simply an expression of habit, although such a habit, if

---

[1] Essay XII, *Of the Original Contract.*
[2] *Enquiry Concerning the Principles of Morals,* Appendix III.

challenged, can always be justified on grounds of utility. Thus Hume takes his place on the Conservative side of politics as a respecter of tradition and habit. In his view, radical innovation and violent revolution have consequences which can never be justified on utilitarian grounds, since on balance they diminish the general happiness, and are therefore opposed to the general objective of moral approbation.

Hume believed that there were also sound reasons for support-ing the sort of government which ruled in England during his lifetime. These reasons derive from his theory that the ultimate cause of all action must necessarily be 'passion', i.e. feeling or desire, and that reason, from its very nature, can never be a sufficient motive of any act. But, although passion is therefore the ultimate cause of all action, a distinction can be drawn between acts resulting from the impulse to satisfy a desire and those resulting from a rational calculation how it may be best satisfied. Hence, although reason cannot by itself determine the objectives of action it can influence the course of action by drawing attention to the probable consequences of alternative courses of action and thus altering the action which is taken. A distinction can therefore be drawn between unreflective passions on the one hand and those upon which reason has been brought to bear in the way just described. Hume called the uncontrolled passions 'violent' and those which had been influenced by reason 'calm'.

It is in terms of this distinction between calm and violent passions that Hume tried to defend aristocratic government. For he thinks that experience shows that the calm passions are most likely to replace the violent passions in people whose powers of reasoning have been developed by education and whose economic security makes them less likely to succumb to the temptation of seeking immediate, at the expense of lasting, advantage. Thus he believed that the most general and enduring happiness for all is most likely to be realized in a community where power is placed in the hands of a prosperous and educated minority. He also believed that drastic political changes are likely to disrupt the operation of the social traditions which have proved most useful in the past and to weaken the force of habit which is the main source of allegiance to a government.

Hume's defence of political conservatism is, therefore based directly on his Empiricist Theory of Morality. If he is right in holding that the ultimate object of men's desires is happiness and that moral approval and disapproval are generally based upon an estimate of the extent to which the act which is approved or disapproved tends to promote or diminish the general happiness, then it follows that the form of government which men ought to support is that which experience has shown most likely to promote the general happiness. It is true that the anthropological knowledge on which Hume based his political theory was somewhat limited and that he proceeded on the assumption that the conditions of life in the Britain which he knew were representative of conditions elsewhere and were likely to endure. He did not contemplate a future in which the education and culture which were then confined to a privileged minority would be enjoyed by the entire population, and might thus make the calm passions more general than they were when he lived.

Although Hume's political conservatism is therefore based on assumptions which do not universally apply, it remains an interesting and important example of a theory which attempts to justify a specific form of government on the ground of its utility in promoting the general happiness. Most political philosophers have based their justification of government on an *a priori* set of moral principles and have thus submitted a justification of a categorical nature. As Hume's justification is based on empirical premises it is necessarily hypothetical in character. If people desire the general happiness, and if government by a cultivated minority is the best way of promoting such happiness, it necessarily follows that this form of government ought to be supported. But if the truth of these premises can be disputed on empirical grounds—as it well may be—the conclusion does not follow.

Hume's defence of Conservatism, like his defence of any practical creed, is therefore based on the principle of utility. A respect for tradition, the avoidance of violent change, and the repudiation of all precise and uncompromising dogmas are, in Hume's view, the principles which are shown by experience to be the most effective in promoting the happiness of a community, and are thereby justified. For the general happiness is the ultimate aim of all human activity, and government is therefore justified in so far as it contributes to this end.

Burke's Contribution to Political Thought

Edmund Burke (1729–1797) could be more accurately described as a philosophical politician than as a political philosopher, but his work deserves consideration in view of the influence which he exercised on his contemporaries and the fact that he is usually held to have formulated the basic principles underlying the Conservative tradition in British politics. His exposition of these principles is rhetorical rather than logical, but he was able for that reason to reach a far wider circle than Hume, and beneath the rhetoric it is easy to discern the same empirical principles which were defined so precisely by the Scottish philosopher.

Burke was educated at Trinity College, Dublin, and came to England at the age of twenty-one to keep his terms at the Temple and prepare himself for the English Bar. It was not long, however, before he realized that the study of law would stifle his urge to creative thinking in the field of politics, and he soon decided to abandon a legal career for the more congenial, if more hazardous, profession of letters.

In 1755 Burke achieved fame and acquired friendships by the publication of his *Vindication of Natural Society*. He became Private Secretary to the Marquis of Rockingham, who later became Prime Minister. Burke himself entered the House of Commons in 1766 and held several high offices of State.

Burke belonged to the Whig Party, from which the Liberal tradition subsequently developed, but this does not make it inconsistent to regard him as a defender of Conservative principles, for the Whigs of his time differed from the Tories mainly on details of policy, and Burke's philosophy was applicable to both. In fact, he was not deeply interested in the transient issues of party politics, and was more concerned to defend traditions and principles which he thought vital to the survival of the British Constitution.

Burke's theories are expounded in three principal writings, each of which was inspired by a contemporary issue. His *Thoughts on the Cause of the Present Discontents*, published in 1770, was provoked by the attempt of George III to limit the powers of Parliament and extend the royal influence in politics. Burke sought to mobilize both public men and the nation at large against what he called 'a faction ruling by the private instructions of a Court against the general sense of the people', and his essential argument was that, although Parliamentary government had developed from obscure origins in a way which was not wholly intelligible, the fact that it had so developed could be taken as proof that it fulfilled a function of vital importance. To reverse the course of its development, as George III sought to do, was, in his view, to oppose fundamental developments of vital importance to the community as a whole.

Burke expressed his opposition to all such attempts to interfere with the natural course of constitutional development in a memorable passage:

> Our constitution stands on a nice equipoise with steep precipices and deep waters upon all sides of it. In removing it from a dangerous leaning towards one side there may be a risk of over-setting it on the other. Every project of a material change in a Government so complicated as ours is a matter full of difficulties, in which a considerate man will not be too ready to decide, a prudent man too ready to undertake, or an honest man too ready to promise.[1]

In these words Burke gave vivid expression to his basic conviction that a state is not a man-made machine but an immensely complicated organism, which the efforts of individuals have certainly helped to shape, but whose evolution and destiny cannot be wholly understood by any individual. Burke believed that the way in which a state evolves and develops is largely determined by forces which no individual can fully comprehend, and that when men make changes they should do so with restraint and caution, since the consequences of their actions cannot be foreseen and may conflict with the most fundamental interests of the community as a whole.

Burke's next great work was his *Speech on Conciliation with America* (1775), in which he sought to avert the tragedy of war with the American colonists. In this speech he attacked with vigour the doctrine of natural rights, and argued that considerations of commonsense and expediency were better guides in politics. He agreed that it might be maintained that, as a matter of constitutional right, the British Parliament was the sovereign

[1] *Thoughts on the Cause of the Present Discontents.*

body in relation to the Colonists, and was therefore legally justified in taxing them. But he argued that it was not self-evident
that this theory of sovereign rights should apply in all circumstances, and that in the circumstances of the dispute with the
Colonists its application was likely to have consequences which
both sides would deplore. Burke argued that in such a case of
conflict between two parties taking incompatible views of what is
right, the solution which contributes most to the happiness of
both is a compromise which goes some way to meet the different
points of view. On the other hand, he maintained that an uncompromising insistence by Parliament on what had hitherto been
regarded as its right would result in the loss of the Colonies and
thus ultimately injure the interests of Britain herself. And he
summed up his argument in the famous words, 'Magnanimity in
politics is not seldom the truest wisdom, and a great Empire and
little minds go ill together.'[1] Burke's advice was not, however,
accepted, and the Colonies were lost to the Empire, as he had
predicted.

But the event which made the deepest impression on Burke,
and called forth the most eloquent exposition of his theory, was
the French Revolution. Here, he felt, was a clear example of men
confident in their own insight and judgment and determined to
reconstitute society in accordance with their ideals and without
thought for the lessons of history or respect for the accumulated
wisdom of the centuries embodied in the existing constitution of
France. Burke was not without sympathy for the practical objectives of the French Revolution, but he felt that the violent and
unconstitutional method adopted by the revolutionaries was not
the way to achieve them, and would have disastrous consequences
for the community as a whole. He predicted that, although the
Revolution might temporarily remove some of the more glaring
injustices in French society, it would fail to achieve the real
liberty at which it aimed, and would culminate—as in fact it did—
in a military dictatorship. These views were eloquently expounded
in Burke's *Reflections on the Revolution in France* (1790), which
had a wide sale both at home and abroad, and exercised a considerable influence in confirming the opposition of the vast
majority of British people to the methods, and even the ideals,
of the revolutionaries.

[1] *On Conciliation with the Colonies.*

Burke's writings are, for the most part, variations on a single theme, and were addressed more to the public at large than to those whose interest lay in the philosophical foundations of political theory. Moreover, the exposition of his theory is too diffuse and rhetorical to make it clear exactly what his assumptions and deductions are. Yet it seems clear that the fundamental principle underlying the arguments which he applied to contemporary problems is the principle of utility—the principle that both in public and in private life the greatest happiness of the greatest number is the ultimate standard by which duty and justice must be determined, and that arbitrary assumptions about 'natural rights' must not be allowed to stand in the way of this overriding objective. The stress which he laid on the limitations of the individual's understanding of social and political laws was not, as has been sometimes suggested, because he thought of society as an organic individual with a general will but because he recognized the empirical character of the problem of achieving the greatest happiness of the greatest number, and repudiated all suggestions that it could be solved by some simple and self-evident process that did not need to be tested in practice and could ignore the accumulated wisdom of tradition.

Empiricism and Conservatism

Burke's writings and speeches may therefore be justly regarded as the application of political empiricism to the leading political issues of his age. And it is because Empiricism is the logical and philosophical basis of modern Conservatism that Burke has been commonly regarded as the leading philosopher of the Conservative faith. For Empiricism cannot justify change except where experience gives ground for supposing that change will increase the general happiness. Today, Burke's principles do not appear to be specifically the principles of Conservatism so much as the principles of constitutional democracy in general. He would clearly have opposed the revolutionary methods of modern Communism and extolled the fidelity of both the Conservative and Liberal Parties to constitutional traditions. Whether he would have been equally satisfied by the record of recent Socialist Governments in Britain is more open to doubt. In so far as these Governments have worked through the traditional machinery of Parliament they would have met with his approval, but he would almost certainly have viewed with suspicion, if not active disapproval, their ambitious schemes of social reform and industrial reorganization inspired by the abstract ideal of social equality. When Burke died the industrial revolution had scarcely begun, and these problems had not arisen. If he had witnessed the consequences of that revolution in the nineteenth century he might have adopted a more progressive attitude to social reform than in fact he did. None the less, he would probably still have adhered to his view that 'the nature of man is intricate, the objects of society are of the greatest possible complexity, and therefore no simple disposition or direction of power can be suitable either to man's nature or to the quality of his affairs'. Such cautious Empiricism is in marked contrast to the uncritical dogmatism which Rationalism tends to encourage, and it remains a conspicuous feature of the Conservative outlook at the present day.

CHAPTER XI

Hegel's Idealist Theory of the State

GEORG WILHELM FRIEDRICH HEGEL (1770–1831) was born at Stuttgart, and received his early education in the local grammar school. In the autumn of 1788 he proceeded to the University of Tubingen as a student of theology, but did not achieve any distinction. Subsequently, he worked for a time as a private tutor, first at Berne and later at Frankfort, where he was able to devote considerable time to study, and to work out the outlines of his general philosophy. The death of his father in January 1799 gave him a modest inheritance, and he was able to give up his tutoring and go to Jena. There he became a close friend and collaborator of the philosopher Schelling, and was soon appointed to lecture at the University in an honorary capacity. In 1805 he was appointed to an extraordinary professorship at Jena, but he drew little money from the post, and had to look for other work when Napoleon's invasion in 1806 brought the life of the University to a standstill. After working for a year as a newspaper editor he became Rector of the Aegidien-Gymnasium in Nuremberg, a post which he discharged with considerable success until August 1816.

During the eight years which he spent at Nuremberg Hegel had been working steadily at his philosophy, and the first two volumes of his *Logic* appeared in 1812. In 1816 he seized the opportunity of returning to university teaching as Professor of Philosophy at Heidelberg, and two years later he accepted a similar appointment at Berlin. It was here that he published, in 1821, his theory of moral and political philosophy in the *Philosophy of Right*.

Hegel's fame spread far and wide during his tenure of the Chair at Berlin, and a Hegelian school of disciples soon began to form. In 1830 he was made Rector of the University, and in 1831 he was decorated by Frederick William III. But the revolution of 1830 was a great shock to him, and he viewed the prospect of more democratic forms of government with deep anxiety. His whole philosophy was based on the principle that the state is more important and more real than the individual, and prescribes the ideals of individual conduct. Hegel was not, however, destined to witness the aftermath of the revolution, for he fell a victim to the cholera epidemic which attacked Europe in 1831, and died, after one day's illness, on 14 November in that year.

Hegel's political theory has been variously referred to as an 'Idealist' or 'Metaphysical' or 'Philosophical' Theory of the State. Of these adjectives, the most specific and illuminating is 'Idealist', since it describes one of the characteristic features of the general philosophy upon which Hegel's political theory is based. The adjectives 'Metaphysical' and 'Philosophical' indicate that this political theory depends, in a particularly direct and obvious way, upon a general 'metaphysical' or 'philosophical' theory of the universe; and a brief outline of its essential features must first be given if the foundations of the political theory are to be properly appreciated.

Hegel's Idealism

Hegel's idealism is essentially the logical development of Kant's doctrine of the categories. Kant had been convinced that certain synthetic judgments—in particular, causal and moral judgments —are *a priori*, and had traced this *a priori* character to the operation of the categories in terms of which the mind was, in his view, bound to synthesize the raw material of its experience if that experience was to take a significant form. The validity of the categories had therefore to be postulated as a necessary condition of significant experience. But in Kant's theory the categories were only the *formal* conditions of experience; its *material* conditions were constituted by unknowable things-in-themselves. Hegel rejected the notion of a thing-in-itself, which lies behind and does not enter into experience, on the ground that it is a self-contradictory notion; for it seemed to him obviously self-contradictory to speak of that which, by definition, cannot be known. Hegel therefore concluded that the categories must constitute the material as well as the formal conditions of experience, i.e. must determine both the raw material of experience and its relational characteristics. For if the matter of experience is not determined by something which lies outside experience it must be determined, like the form of experience, by the necessary pattern of experience itself. There can be no external realm of 'things' or 'facts' by which the judgments which constitute experience can be accounted for or their truth confirmed. Indeed, the usual conception of truth as a sort of correspondence between judgment and reality must be replaced by a new conception according to which the truth of a judgment is defined in terms of its relationship to the only entities to which it can be related, namely other judgments. Truth, according to this latter view, means *coherence*, i.e. a judgment is true in so far as it is consistent with other judgments, and more true the wider the range of judgments with which it is consistent. The only judgment which is wholly true is therefore a judgment asserting everything about everything,[1] for only such a judgment embodies, and is thus consistent with, the numerous judgments which, viewed from a narrower perspective, appear to be in some measure inconsistent with each other.

Thus Hegel rejected the distinction commonly drawn between knowledge and reality. Knowledge is reality and reality is knowledge, for if the two were separate reality would be unknowable and knowledge would be illusory. And since this implies that reality could not be other than it is—for it embraces everything in space and time, in imagination and in conception—knowledge could not be other than it is, and the contradictions which exist at the level of finite experience must disappear when viewed from the universal perspective of the Absolute. Hence, in Hegel's famous words, the real is rational.

Identity of Knowledge and Reality

The basic difference between Hegel's Rationalism and Empiricism obviously lies in the denial of a 'reality' outside experience. The possibility of such a reality is denied on the ground that its assertion would be self-contradictory. For, Hegel maintains, reality is necessarily part of experience in so far as any assertion whatsoever is made about it; and, if nothing is asserted about it, it does not in any intelligible sense exist. And from this general premise the Coherence Theory of Truth necessarily follows; for if the truth of a judgment cannot be defined in terms of its relationship to that which is not a judgment, then its truth must be defined in terms of its relationship to another judgment

[1] Or, as Hegel put it, the Absolute's knowledge of itself.

or judgments. It will be true in so far as it is consistent with other judgments assumed to be true, but the truth of these other judgments will in turn depend upon their relationship to yet other judgments, and so on *ad infinitum*. Hegel denied that this process involves a 'vicious circle'; on the contrary, he maintained that if it *were* pushed to infinity by asserting every judgment which is consistent with every other judgment the result would be one coherent system of judgments which could not be other than it is, and which would thus constitute absolute and *a priori* truth—or the Absolute, as he called it. And while it is in practice impossible for a finite mind to achieve this absolute coherence, it is possible, by applying the test of coherence to an ever widening sphere of experience, to approach more closely to it, and thus achieve a higher degree of truth than formerly.

This amounts to saying that the conception of thinking held by the earlier rationalists was fundamentally mistaken. According to them thinking is a process of linear inference from *a priori* premises by *a priori* inferences to *a priori* conclusions. Hume had effectively refuted this theory by pointing out that, where the premises afford grounds for drawing valid conclusions about the nature of the experienced world, they must necessarily assume a synthetic form and thus be without any *a priori* necessity themselves. Kant tried to save something of the older Rationalism by arguing that the more important synthetic generalizations (such as the laws of causality and morality) are necessary in a transcendental, though not in a logical, sense, meaning that their necessity is a necessity of experience though not of logic.

It was, however, left to Hegel to recognize the full implications of Hume's analysis and, in particular, to recognize that since the truth of a synthetic proposition is never an inherent characteristic of such a proposition it must be determined by the relationship of that proposition to other propositions. This, Hegel believed, is the only self-consistent conception of truth which can be applied to synthetic propositions, for any attempt to define their truth in terms of correspondence to 'facts' or other alleged features of 'reality' conceals within itself the very concept which is supposed to be defined.[1] Hegel would have agreed that purely analytic

---

[1] For example, the distinction between what is a fact and what is not a fact can be defined only in terms of the distinction between a true and a false judgment that 'X is a fact'.

propositions are, in a different sense, necessarily true, namely in the sense of being tautologies; but he saw that human thinking cannot be reduced to the repetition of tautologies, and he set himself to show how thinking can be at once rational and constructive. This, as already observed, he claimed to do by giving truth a novel interpretation in terms of coherence, and by arguing that such an interpretation is the only one which can avoid some form of self-contradiction.

Hegel thus claimed to show how thinking can be at once rational and fruitful by defining truth in terms of the logical relationship of propositions to one another and by portraying thinking as a process, not of linear inference, but of dialectical evolution. He thought it obvious that the greater part of human thinking does not consist in the assertion of tautologies but in the opposition of thesis and antithesis, and the evolution of a synthesis which marks a genuine advance on the thesis, and does not merely assert it in different language. But he differed from empiricists like Hume in holding that, although such thinking is not tautologous, neither is it the completely irrational sequence with which they identified it. On the contrary, he believed that the apparently contingent features of the history of thought would, if viewed as a whole by an infinite mind, appear as the partial revelation of a logically necessary whole—the Absolute.

Hegel's theory is therefore something of a compromise between the older type of Rationalism and Hume's Empiricism. Like the earlier rationalists, Hegel believed that 'the real is rational', but he agreed with the empiricists that its rationality is not apparent at the finite level of human experience, and that thinking does not start from self-evident and *a priori* premises. The novelty of his theory lies in his contention that human experience can be made progressively less irrational by making it more comprehensive and coherent, and that beyond it there lies the unattainable ideal of an infinite experience from which the last vestige of irrationality would be removed. If, in other words, we knew everything about everything we should recognize that everything must be exactly as it is.

Fallacies in Hegel's Theory of Knowledge

Hegel's claim that human experience can be made progressively less irrational obviously requires the postulation of an

'Absolute' embodying absolute truth, since otherwise there would be no standard by which to measure the relative truth of judgments made at the level of finite experience. Yet it is just this ultimate postulate which he fails to justify. However comprehensive an experience may become there is no rational ground for saying that it could not have been otherwise. It may, indeed, be conceded that an infinite experience, in virtue of its infinite comprehension, *must* be coherent, but this does not rule out the possibility that it could take an indefinite number of different forms, and could therefore be completely coherent in an indefinite number of different ways. In claiming that the whole truth about anything would be necessarily true Hegel is, in fact, asserting a purely analytic proposition. He is saying that, if the universe is defined as the object A possessing the characteristics X, Y, Z, etc., then the judgment that A is X is necessarily true; but this is obviously an analytic judgment of the form 'A-which-is-X-Y-Z-etc. is X'. Thus Hegel's theory that all truths would be recognized as necessarily true by an infinite mind is nothing more than an assertion of the truism that if the Absolute is defined as the whole truth about everything then it necessarily implies the partial truth about everything. But there is no categorical reason why the Absolute should be constituted as it is constituted.

For these reasons Hegel failed to provide a foundation for experience which is at once synthetic and necessary even at the level of infinite experience. All he showed is that human thinking at the finite level does, in fact, follow a certain pattern and that this is explained by the fact that all thinking takes the hypothetical form familiar in the natural sciences, and proceeds by formulating progressively more comprehensive hypotheses to account for the more primitive judgments known as the 'facts of experience'. This, Hegel believed, was the real nature of all the philosophical systems which had preceded his; hence his famous dictum that 'philosophy is the history of philosophy'. But he failed to show why the history of philosophy should have taken just the course which it has taken, or why the Absolute Spirit should have manifested itself in just the way that it has.

If the foregoing criticism of Hegel's theory is valid it is fatal to his whole system, for it is essential to the latter to maintain not only that the whole of experience implies any part of experience but that from any part of experience it is possible to proceed by dialectical thinking to the whole. And this is what Hegel failed to establish. In so far as his dialectical process extends beyond the limits of analytic inference it is a synthetic process which widens experience only in so far as it proceeds beyond what is necessarily implied on *a priori* grounds. In so doing the dialectical process may constitute a useful and illuminating account of how the Absolute *is* constituted, but it can never show how the Absolute *must be* constituted, and if it cannot do this it cannot provide any real alternative to Hume's Empiricism.

The fundamental inadequacy of Hegel's dialectical method for the task which he sets it to accomplish can be illustrated by an analysis of the very first triad in his deduction of the categories. These 'categories' are the most general characteristics which apply to the whole of reality, and the dialectical method can therefore be applied most plausibly to the deduction of their relationships. If this application is found to be invalid it will be safe to conclude that the method cannot be used to deduce the truth about the more concrete and less general features of experience.

Now Hegel's first triad consists of *Being* as the thesis, *Nothing* as the antithesis, and *Becoming* as the synthesis. Hegel regards *Being* as the original thesis because it is the most general and universal characteristic of everything in experience. Everything in experience necessarily *is* in the most general sense of the word 'is'. But, Hegel argues, something which merely 'is' without further specification would be nothing at all. Everything which 'is' must have some further determination—must, for example, be material or mental, animate or inanimate, and so on. Hence, he argues, mere *Being* would be the same as *Nothing*.

The synthesis of the opposition between *Being* and *Nothing* is *Becoming*. By this Hegel means that *Being* 'passes into' *Nothing* and *Nothing*, in turn, 'passes into' *Being*. Such 'passing into' is not, of course, a temporal but a logical process. What Hegel means is that the thought of 'Being' is identical with the thought of 'Nothing' and that the thought of 'Nothing' is identical with the thought of 'Being'. The two categories are therefore at one and the same time identical and different, and the synthesis of the dialectical triad to which their opposition leads is called *Becoming*. *Becoming* is the unity which contains within itself the difference found within the identity of *Being* and *Nothing*. And because it contains and preserves this difference it is a relatively *concrete* universal—in contrast to the *abstract* universals of traditional philosophy which specifically exclude what is not common to all the members of a class.

This initial triad of Hegel's dialectic introduces two of his most important and characteristic doctrines. In the first place, it shows that Hegel believed that even the most complete opposition—that of *Being* and *Nothing*—has an underlying unity; and, in the second place, it introduces the important doctrine of the concrete universal, according to which universals of the most abstract character contain within themselves, and logically imply, the most specific characteristics of their concrete instances.

It is obvious that this doctrine of the concrete universal is the key to Hegel's whole philosophy, for if it is valid it implies that it is possible to deduce species from genus progressively until the most specific determinations of experience are reached. And this is what Hegel claimed to do. But the very first triad illustrates— though not so obviously as some later triads—the fallacy which vitiates the whole process. It is true that *Being* is equivalent to *Nothing* in the sense that Being in itself has no specific deter- minations such as mental being, physical being, animal being, etc.; but this could not be deduced from reflection upon Being unless we were already aware of some of the concrete manifes- tations of Being. It is only because we have already experienced some of these manifestations that we can say that mere Being is not equivalent to any of them, i.e. is Nothing; but this is an analytic inference from concrete experience and not, as Hegel contends, a synthetic inference from mere Being.

Examination of any of the other triads in the dialectic would illustrate the same point, namely that in so far as Hegel's deduc- tions proceed from the relatively abstract to the relatively con- crete they are invalid unless the relatively concrete is already experienced as that which the relatively abstract characterizes. We cannot infer that mere Being is equivalent to Nothing unless we already know that Being frequently characterizes something; and what it characterizes cannot be logically deduced from it.

One of Hegel's modern interpreters seems to admit as much when he says:

Hegel's solution consists in showing that Being is not an undeduced beginning because its foundation is the Absolute Idea; and the Absolute Idea is not an undeduced beginning because its foundation is Being. Both orders of deduction are, therefore, necessary.[1]

Certainly the Absolute Idea—the most complex of all the categories—is the 'foundation' of Being in the sense that Being can be logically deduced from it; but how can Being be the foundation of the Absolute Idea in this sense? Professor Stace fails to show how the more concrete and more specific can be logically deduced from the less concrete and less specific. His description of the concrete universal as the genus, which 'contains its differentiae and its species within itself, so that they can be extricated from it by a logical deduction,'[2] simply begs the question, for the whole point at issue is how a logical deduction can extricate from a universal what is not already *explicitly* contained within that universal.

Hegel therefore failed to show that the more concrete categories can be logically deduced from the more abstract. The important principle which he did establish is that the truth of a synthetic proposition must be defined in terms of its coherence with other synthetic propositions. The rational foundation of a synthetic proposition is, therefore, necessarily hypothetical. *If* proposition P implies proposition Q and if proposition P is true, it follows that proposition Q must be true; but it is never possible to eliminate the ultimate 'if' unless the dialectical process is valid.

Hegel's Moral and Political Philosophy

These conclusions have an important application in Hegel's political philosophy, which is an attempt to use the dialectical process to demonstrate the comparative morality of different types of political institution. If his logic can be defined as an exposition of the principle that 'the real is the rational', his political philosophy can be defined in corresponding terms as an exposition of the principle that 'the right is the rational'. According to Hegel, the essence of moral conduct is found when the individual acts not in accordance with particular impulses and

---

[1] *The Philosophy of Hegel*, by W. T. Stace, p. 112.
[2] op. cit., p. 84.

desires but in accordance with universal reason—the reason which is shared by all rational beings. Hence Hegel rejects as wholly false all forms of a Utilitarian Theory of the State on the ground that they find the ultimate sanction of policy in the desires and interests of individuals. According to Hegel the 'will of the state' represents the true will of the individual, and only in so far as the latter coincides with the former is the individual acting morally.

Thus Hegel draws a sharp distinction between Civil Society and the state. Civil Society is that form of political organization which follows logically from the disruption of the family due to children growing up and becoming independent persons. At that stage they become dependent for various necessities upon other people, and thus accept a form of organization which embodies appropriate arrangements for mutual support. But Hegel believes that no rational man can rest content with such a form of political organization since it assumes that every individual is seeking his own personal ends and regarding others simply as means to these ends. He can only be finally content with the higher form of organization, called the state, which expresses the rational will of every individual contained within it, and in serving which every individual therefore finds the realization of his true will.

Thus Hegel, like Rousseau, finds the criterion of political morality in the *general* will of the state. He readily admits that some states may not be perfect, and that it would be going too far to respect the authority of every ruler or government; but all contain at least an element of rationality in their fundamental purposes. Thus Hegel comments:

> Although a state may be declared to violate right principles, and to be defective in various ways, it always contains the essential moments of its existence, if, that is to say, it belongs to the full-formed states of our own time. . . . Evil can doubtless disfigure it in many ways, but the ugliest man, the criminal, the invalid, the cripple, are living men.[1]

These observations certainly answer the criticism that Hegel held the will of any state to be a good will. But they give no indication how we may discriminate between good states and bad ones. If the dialectic process were really able—as Hegel thought

[1] *Philosophy of Right*, Section 258 addition.

it was—to provide valid deductions of the more determinate from the less determinate, then it might be possible to deduce from the conception of the state more specific criteria of its rationality. But, for the reasons already given, such deduction does not appear to be possible, and the conception of the 'will of the state' is therefore just as open to arbitrary interpretation and practical abuse as it was in Rousseau's theory.

The Rational Will

The truth is that Hegel is no more able than was Kant to give the good will a 'content', i.e. specific objective, unless it is possible to deduce the more determinate from the less determinate. To say, as Hegel says, that the good will is the 'rational' and 'universal' will does not tell us *what* it wills unless it is possible to deduce from the concepts of 'rationality' and 'universality' the nature of the objectives at which the rational and universal will must aim. And this is impossible unless the dialectical deduction of the relatively determinate from the relatively indeterminate is possible. For the reasons set forth above, Hegel fails to show that such deduction is ever possible, and therefore his whole conception of morality is based on a fallacious assumption. In particular, he fails to provide any criterion for distinguishing between good states and bad ones, and thus makes it possible for the most arbitrary acts of government to be justified as the 'will of the state'.

Hegel, like Rousseau, distinguished the 'general will' or the 'will of the state' both from the 'will of the majority' and from the 'will of all'—in fact, from any actual will. They did so because by the 'general will' they meant the 'rational will', i.e. an ideal will which is not necessarily expressed by the will of the majority or, indeed, by any actual will at all. But while it is easy to talk of such a will it is impossible to define its objectives in a way that is not purely arbitrary, just because a will which is not, in the end, the expression of irrational desire is not a will at all. In other words, the conception of a will which may be nobody's will is self-contradictory and cannot therefore constitute a rational basis for morality or politics.

Hegel therefore fails, as Hume would have said he must fail, to provide a rational basis for Morality and the State. His dialectical triad of Abstract Right—Morality—Social Ethics can at most claim to be a description of different manifestations of the moral sentiment. It cannot be, as Hegel thought it was, the progressive evolution of a more rational conception of morality, since morality from its very nature is not of a rational character.

Similarly, Hegel's conception of world history as the progressive revelation of the Absolute Idea does not exhibit any rational necessity. It is impossible for a finite mind to deduce the future from the present, and to say that it would be possible to do so if only we knew the Absolute Idea in its entirety is equivalent to the analytic proposition that if the whole of history takes such and such a form, then any selected period of history necessarily takes a certain form. If history has, in fact, developed by a sort of dialectical process with sufficient regularity to justify a generalization, that generalization is an empirical and not a logical principle, for it is without any sort of logical necessity.

The final judgment on Hegel's philosophy must therefore be that, like Kant's philosophy, it fails to refute the Empiricism of Hume. In particular, it fails to establish that synthetic judgments can possess logical necessity. And if it fails to do this it leaves the essential principles of Empiricism inviolate. For Hegel's Coherence Theory of Truth is just an alternative way of stating the empiricist principle that the only basis for a synthetic generalization is a 'fact', but that the generalization so reached is devoid of rational necessity. There is no reason why the empiricist should not accept the Hegelian definition of the truth of such a generalization in terms of its consistency with the less general propositions which are said to describe the 'facts' upon which it is based. Where Hegel claimed to have advanced on the empiricist position was in showing that the ultimate and all-inclusive generalization —the Absolute Idea—is true in an absolute and categorical sense since it is both based upon, and in turn implies, every judgment included in total experience. But this, as previously shown, is simply equivalent to the tautology that if experience as a whole is constituted in a certain way, then every part of experience must be constituted in a certain way. It does not eliminate the ultimate hypothesis that experience is constituted in just that way, nor, therefore, does it constitute any reason why experience *as a whole* should not have been differently constituted.

This conclusion does not, of course, imply that Hegel's philosophy was not a powerful stimulus to fruitful speculation in the historical and social sciences, or that the processes of thought and history which his dialectic claims to express do not have a considerable basis in fact. But it does imply that those illuminating generalizations, which appear to correlate, and in some sense 'explain', the movements of human thought and history, are just the 'natural beliefs' of Hume's Empiricism, and are completely devoid of the rational necessity inherent in analytic thinking. Their application to reality is therefore of a hypothetical and not a categorical character, since it is conditional upon the assumption of their truth. And if the mental processes which result in these generalizations are to be described as 'thought', then it is necessary to draw a sharp distinction between such 'thought' and the very different type of thought to be found in logic and mathematics. The rational necessity inherent in the thinking of logic and mathematics does not characterize the formulation of empirical generalizations, and Hegel's attempt to deduce the latter from an all-comprehensive and self-justifying generalization must be pronounced a failure. In particular, he failed to provide a rational basis for the ultimate principles of morality, or for the doctrine that these principles are most perfectly expressed by the 'will of the state'.

CHAPTER XII

The Utilitarian Theories of Bentham and Mill

JEREMY BENTHAM (1748–1832) and John Stuart Mill (1806–1873) are the outstanding exponents of the theory known as Utilitarianism, which was destined to exercise a profound influence upon both political and economic thought in England during the first three-quarters of the nineteenth century. The theory stands in sharp contrast to the idealism of Hegel in the stress which it lays upon the primacy of the individual and the artificial character of the state.

Bentham was born in London on 15 February, 1748, and was educated at Westminster School and Queen's College, Oxford, which he entered at the age of thirteen. He was called to the Bar in 1769. At Oxford he had acquired a considerable interest in natural science, and he soon realized that his true inclination lay not in the practice of law but in the examination and criticism of its moral basis. He therefore decided to devote his life to working out a scientific system of jurisprudence and legislation. A private income made this possible, and he published a considerable number of books, of which the best known and most important is the *Introduction to the Principles of Morals and Legislation*. In this work Bentham sought to work out a scientific basis for a legal code. The book brought him an international reputation, and his advice on legal codification was sought by several foreign governments. At home, apart from his literary interests, he was engaged for nearly twenty-five years in negotiations for the erection of a 'Panopticon', or model prison in which all convicts could be observed by an unseen inspector; and when this scheme was finally abandoned Bentham claimed, and received, £23,000 by way of compensation from the Government. Other varied activities engaged him in his later years. In 1823 he established the *Westminster Review*, and later put forward schemes for canals through the isthmus of Suez and the isthmus of Panama. He died on 6 June 1832 in his eighty-fifth year.

Mill was born on 20 May 1806, the eldest son of James Mill (1773–1836), historian and philosopher, who ultimately became head of India House, the head office of the East India Company. He was educated by his father, who was a strict disciplinarian, and subjected his son to an arduous training which involved starting the study of Greek at the age of three and Latin, Euclid and algebra at the age of eight. Mill's subsequent studies covered logic, psychology, political economy, and law. His father had intended that he should practise at the Bar, but in 1822 he entered India House, of which he became head in 1856. The company was dissolved in 1858 and its powers transferred to the Government, notwithstanding Mill's eloquent and closely reasoned defence of its record.

Mill subsequently entered Parliament as Member for Westminster in 1865 after a highly unconventional election. In strict accordance with his principles, he refused to canvass, to pay agents to canvass for him, or to promise to attend to the local business of the constituency. Indeed, it was with considerable reluctance that he agreed to address a meeting of electors. Although he never held ministerial office, he made a certain impression in Parliament by his speeches, but he was defeated in the general election of 1868, and thereafter retired to a literary life in a cottage which he had acquired at Avignon.

In spite of his official duties, first in India House and subsequently in Parliament, Mill found time for writing throughout his life, and published a long series of books and articles on a variety of philosophical, political, and economic subjects. His most important philosophical work was his *System of Logic*, published in 1843, in which he sought to establish that induction—the inference from particular instances to general principles—is the logical pattern which all fruitful thinking takes. He subsequently published a treatise on *Political Economy* in 1848, in which he propounded what was at that time the novel suggestion that, although the conditions of production depend on unalterable laws, the distribution of what is produced can with advantage be brought under human control. After that he devoted himself to the writing of three important political dissertations which are of fundamental interest to the political philosopher—

On Liberty (1859), *Representative Government* (1860), and *Utilitarianism* (1861). Mill died on 8 May 1873.

Utilitarianism

The theories of Bentham and Mill mark a return to the individualist principle of which Hobbes and Locke were earlier exponents, and which still remains the dominating tradition of British political theory. It is the principle that the state exists for the sake of the individual, not the individual for the sake of the state, and that the justification of government is to be found in the service which it renders to the individual, whether in satisfying his desires or protecting his rights or realizing his ideals. If, as usually happens, the desires of different individuals differ, then, as Locke realized, it is necessary for government to satisfy one desire rather than another, and the satisfaction of the desire of the majority of individuals is generally assumed, in these circumstances, to be both right and inevitable.

Bentham and Mill both held that the primary human desire is for pleasure or happiness, and that the primary duty of both individuals and governments is to increase pleasure, and to diminish pain, as much as possible. They therefore held that the rightness of an act is measured by its *usefulness* in promoting pleasure. It is for this reason that their theory is called *Utilitarianism*. It differs fundamentally from all forms of Intuitionism, which asserts that acts are intrinsically right or wrong without regard to their consequences. According to Utilitarianism, an act should be approved or condemned according to whether it tends to promote or to diminish pleasure. Only an Intuitionist could consistently assert that it is always wrong to tell a lie. A Utilitarian believes that it is wrong to tell a lie if doing so is likely to diminish pleasure; but that it is right to tell a lie if this is likely to increase pleasure. On the Utilitarian Theory rightness and wrongness are thus definable in terms of the goodness or badness of the consequences of acts; and the goodness or badness of these consequences depends upon whether they are pleasant or painful.

The fundamental premise of Utilitarianism is therefore the proposition that pleasure alone is intrinsically good, i.e. good in itself and not merely as a means to something else which is intrinsically good. But although Utilitarians always accept this proposition in some sense, they do not always make it clear whether they regard it as an analytic or as a synthetic proposition. Of the two Utilitarians whose theories are being discussed in the present chapter, Bentham makes a number of statements which suggest that he understood the proposition analytically and believed that when people call a thing 'good' they really mean that it is 'pleasant', and when they call a thing 'bad' they really mean that it is 'painful'; whereas Mill appears to regard the two epithets as quite distinct in meaning, although synthetically connected.

Bentham's Utilitarianism

Bentham introduces his theory in the following words:

> Nature has placed mankind under the governance of two sovereign masters, *pain* and *pleasure*. It is for them alone to point out what we ought to do, as well as to determine what we shall do. . . . In words a man may pretend to abjure their empire: but in reality he will remain subject to it all the while. The *principle of utility* recognizes this subjection, and assumes it for the foundation of that system, the object of which is to rear the fabric of felicity by the hands of reason and of law.[1]

The principle of utility is more specifically defined as follows:

> By the principle of utility is meant that principle which approves or disapproves of every action whatsoever, according to the tendency which it appears to have to augment or diminish the happiness of the party whose interest is in question.[2]

If Bentham means, as he seems to mean, that all action is determined by desire for pleasure or antipathy towards pain, the majority of modern psychologists would disagree with him. And they would do so for substantially the same reasons as those put forward by Bishop Butler in his celebrated refutation of the doctrine in his *Sermons on Human Nature*. What Bishop

[1] *Principles of Morals and Legislation*, Chap. I, 1.
[2] ibid., I, 2.

Butler pointed out is that action is usually determined not by the desire for pleasure but by the desire for certain conditions, e.g. the satisfaction of hunger, or the achievement of power over others. It may be that the satisfaction of these desires is in fact pleasant, but Butler maintained that the object of a desire is not the same thing as the pleasure which results from attaining it. For example, he said that the object of hunger is not pleasure but food, although the satisfaction of hunger does, in fact, result in pleasure. He would have recognized the existence of a direct desire for pleasure if a man had fasted deliberately in order to make his hunger more acute and thus cause the pleasure resulting from the satisfaction of his hunger to be more intense; but Butler held that the majority of human actions are in fact caused by the desire for certain things or conditions and not by desire for the pleasure which results from attaining these things or conditions.[1]

There is, in short, an important distinction between the desire for pleasure and the desire for things or conditions which cause pleasure when attained; and it is now generally agreed that pleasure is not usually the direct object of desire, although it is a normal concomitant of the satisfaction of desire. But the recognition of this distinction does not mean that Bentham's theory is invalidated at its foundation. For if it is admitted—as most psychologists would admit—that the satisfaction of desire is pleasant, then, even if pleasure is not usually the direct object of action, it is possible to make the pleasure which results from successful action and the pain which results from frustrated action serve equally well as criteria of moral conduct. It is no longer possible to say with Bentham that pleasure and pain always determine what we shall do, but it is still possible to make the pleasure or pain which results from an action the criterion by which the rightness or wrongness of that action is judged.

In any case, Bentham's principle of ethical hedonism—that all action ought to conform to the principle of utility—suggests that some actions do not conform to this principle, and that the essence of moral conduct is to achieve this conformity; and it is this principle of ethical hedonism that is the really fundamental one in his system. Like Hobbes, who defined 'good' as 'the

[1] For a fuller discussion of these points see Professor C. D. Broad's *Five Types of Ethical Theory*, Chap. III.

object of desire' and 'evil' as 'the object of aversion', Bentham defines the basic moral conceptions in terms of non-moral conceptions:

> Of an action that is conformable to the principle of utility one may always say either that it is one that ought to be done, or at least that it is not one that ought not to be done. One may also say that it is right it should be done; at least that it is not wrong it should be done: that it is a right action; at least that it is not a wrong action. When thus interpreted, the words *ought*, and *right* and *wrong*, and others of that stamp, have a meaning: when otherwise, they have none.[1]

In other words, Bentham believes that to say that an action is 'right' means that it conforms to the principle of utility, i.e. augments (or at least does not diminish) the happiness of the party whose interest is in question; while when an action is said to be wrong this means that it does not conform to the principle of utility, i.e. diminishes the happiness of the party whose interest is in question. More shortly, a right action is, roughly speaking, one which increases or does not diminish happiness while a wrong action is one which diminishes happiness. Bentham admits that such an interpretation of the meaning of ethical terms may not appear to be consistent with the common usage of these terms, but he argues that this interpretation is the only possible one if moral terms are to have an objective significance. Only when morality is defined in terms of utility does it amount to more than the 'averment of unfounded sentiments'.[2]

Bentham is here repudiating all claims that moral judgments express *a priori* knowledge and arguing that they are in fact empirical judgments of utility which must be verified by the scientific tests of observation and experiment. Morality, he contends, is a science, and its judgments are therefore subject to the usual criteria of the natural sciences. The contrary assumption that moral judgments are *a priori* judgments leads in practice to all sorts of inconsistent judgments being made without hope of reconciliation, and to all sorts of claims that certain practices are justified in the name of 'natural rights' or 'natural law'. And Bentham thinks that 'natural law' is just a name for irrational prejudice. His object is to replace it by the principle of utility

[1] *Principles of Morals and Legislation*, Chap. I.   [2] ibid., I, 14.

and thus provide an empirical basis for human conduct and its reward or punishment.

In all this Bentham was rebelling against the prejudices and superstitions which he found embedded in the law and morality of his time. Both appeared to him to be irrational in origin; and his contention was that they would remain so until they became applications of the principle of utility. Law, in particular, would remain an incoherent collection of arbitrary conventions until it was subordinated to the ultimate purpose of promoting the greatest happiness of the greatest number.

The Calculus of Pleasures

Bentham realised that it may frequently be difficult to calculate the quantity of pleasure or pain which will result from an act, but he argued that there is no insurmountable difficulty of principle in doing so, whereas there is no rational way whatsoever of ascertaining whether an act or law is right or wrong if 'right' and 'wrong' are not defined in terms of the resulting pleasure or pain. And he thinks that the calculation of the quantity of pleasure or pain resulting from an act is sufficiently accurate to constitute a useful measure of that act's rightness of wrongness provided that account is taken of four respects in which pleasures and pains may vary, namely (i) their intensity; (ii) their duration; (iii) their certainty or uncertainty; and (iv) their propinquity or remoteness. Bentham thinks that in measuring the utility of an act account must also be taken of the fecundity of the pleasure or pain in which it results, i.e. the chance which it has of being followed by sensations of the same kind; and its *purity*, i.e. the chance which it has of *not* being followed by sensations of the opposite kind. But all these characteristics are, Bentham thinks, essentially quantitative. The qualitative distinction sometimes drawn between 'higher' and 'lower' pleasures is, in Bentham's view, quite irrelevant to the calculus of pleasures and the objective theory of morality which he is advancing. As he puts it succinctly, 'Quantity of pleasure being equal, pushpin is as good as poetry.' It is the balance of pleasure or pain resulting from an act which, Bentham thinks, is alone relevant to the determination of its rightness or wrongness.

Bentham does not suggest that an elaborate calculation of consequences must be made before every moral judgment or legislative or judicial operation[1]; the rightness or wrongness of many acts is generally accepted in terms of their known pleasurable or painful consequences. What he thinks is important is that the calculus of pleasures, and not some arbitrary conception of 'moral law', should be appealed to when the rightness or wrongness of an act or law is in dispute.

For the same reason it is not any underlying 'moral' law which gives a binding force to the laws of a community. The latter are upheld by *sanctions*, by which Bentham means inducements to obey the laws or deterrents against disobeying them. And such sanctions must, he naturally thinks, be based on the only two motives for action which he recognizes—pleasure and pain. For the only possible motives which, according to Bentham's psychology, can help to promote respect for these laws is the expectation of pleasure if they are obeyed and the fear of pain if they are disobeyed. Such rewards and punishments Bentham calls sanctions, and he thinks that they may take either a physical or a political or a popular or a religious form according as the anticipated pleasure or pain would result from the operation of natural laws, or from judicial punishment, or from another individual's spontaneous reaction, or from the action of a superior invisible being. In other words, people are less likely to do something if they believe that this will bring them pain from one or other of these sources, and they are more likely to do something if they believe that by so doing they will be rewarded by pleasure from one or other of these sources.

Bentham's Theory of Punishment

A punishment is obviously a familiar example of a sanction as conceived by Bentham, and, like sanctions generally, can be justified only by the principle of utility if the latter is accepted as the basis of morality. In particular, since punishment involves the infliction of pain it can be justified only if it prevents the occurrence of a greater pain. As Bentham expresses the point:

> All punishment in itself is evil. Upon the principle of utility, if it ought at all to be admitted, it ought only to be admitted in as far as it promises to exclude some greater evil.[2]

[1] ibid., IV, 6.   [2] ibid., XIII, 2.

Bentham therefore rejects the theory that punishment ought to be retributive, i.e. that its justification lies in the moral propriety of making the sinner or criminal suffer on account of his sin or crime. In primitive societies this has always been the primary, if not the only, justification of punishment, whether or not it has also been held to have useful consequences in preventing the repetition of crime. The so-called Retributive Theory of Punishment is therefore essentially a moral theory in its contention that a sinner or criminal deserves to suffer, and therefore ought to suffer, on account of his sin or crime. And Bentham's fundamental objection to this theory of punishment is the same as his fundamental objection to conventional morality in general—that it is arbitrary and irrational without either objective basis or internal consistency. Some may believe that a certain crime ought to be punished by flogging; others that it ought to be punished by five years' imprisonment; still others that a sentence of six months' imprisonment would be adequate; and Bentham believes that there is no possible way of justifying any of these arbitrary judgments until the purpose of punishment is defined in terms of utility, and the infliction of punishment therefore determined in accordance with the ultimate object of promoting the greatest happiness of the greatest number. Thus he concludes that the conception of punishment as retributive must be completely abandoned if any rational justification of its infliction is to be given, and that a new conception of punishment as a method of preventing the occurrence of a greater evil, i.e. more pain than is involved in the punishment itself, must be substituted.

Bentham works out the application of this principle in great detail. He lists the various kinds of pleasures and pains which may be experienced[1] and thirty-two kinds of 'circumstances affecting sensibility'[2] which must be taken account of if the effect of punishment is to be accurately estimated. No summary could give an adequate impression of the thoroughness with which Bentham works out this application of his principle of utility.

Assessment of Bentham's Theory

To the political philosopher the question of primary interest is whether, in fact, utility is the only rational basis for conduct.

[1] ibid., V, 1 and 33.   [2] ibid., VI, 45.

Certainly Bentham's argument that the judgments of ordinary morality are subjective and arbitrary is difficult to refute. But if it be admitted that the approbation or disapprobation of an act can be rational only if it is based on an estimate of the probable effects on happiness, the question arises whether such approbation or disapprobation does not depend upon the acceptance of an ultimate moral judgment, not based on the principle of utility, about the goodness or badness of the consequences. It is by no means clear whether Bentham is, in fact, assuming the truth of an ultimate synthetic judgment that 'pleasure is good', or whether he holds that this judgment is analytic, i.e. that by calling a thing 'good' we simply *mean* that it is pleasant. If he held that the judgment is analytic then he was, by implication, reducing morality to the science of happiness, and judgments of approbation and disapprobation to scientific calculations about the probable consequences of actions. But if he held that the judgment is synthetic he was retaining an irreducible element of morality in his analysis of experience, and transferring to the judgments about the goodness and badness of ends all the arbitrary and subjective characteristics which he tried to remove from judgments about the rightness or wrongness of means. In other words, the judgment that a certain act is right may be verified objectively if by calling it 'right' we simply mean that it will increase human happiness; but there can be no genuinely moral sense in which one *ought* to do what is in this sense right unless it be assumed that human happiness is good in a genuinely moral sense. If this assumption is not made there can be no categorical reason why one ought to do anything, but only the hypothetical reason that one ought to do certain things *if* one wishes to promote happiness.

The conclusion to which Bentham's theory points—although he does not himself draw it—is that action can, indeed, only be justified by its consequences; but that these consequences cannot, in the end, themselves be rationally justified. The immediate consequences of an act may, of course, be justified as necessary means to the ultimate consequences which are aimed at. Preparing for war, for example, may be justified as a necessary means (if in certain circumstances it is a necessary means) to the preservation of peace. But there is no method by which, on Bentham's theory, the ultimate ends of action can be justified.

12

They must be chosen, and the choice of ultimate ends is not a rational act.

The conclusion which Bentham could have drawn from these considerations, and which Mill did, perhaps unconsciously, draw,[1] is that since the choice of ultimate ends cannot be rationally justified it cannot be rationally condemned either; that individuals should therefore be left free to choose their ends in so far as this freedom does not restrict the enjoyment of a similar freedom by others. And this, of course, has become the basic assumption of political democracy. If the people desire a society based upon free enterprise, then, according to democratic theory, they ought to get it; but if they desire a society based upon central planning and control, then they ought to get that. And if, as often happens, they disagree about what they desire, then the will of the majority must prevail, as it represents what Locke called the 'greater force'.[2] These are obviously the broad assumptions upon which a democratic society is based, and they all follow from the assumption that the ultimate ends of desire and action cannot be rationally justified and that action can be rational only in the sense that it is likely, in the light of scientific generalizations based upon previous experience, to promote the ends which are in fact desired.

It may be thought that Bentham's theory oversimplifies the ends of action in describing them as simply 'benefit, advantage, pleasure, good, or happiness' (all of which, as he says, 'comes to the same thing').[3] In so far as his theory is a psychological theory —as it is when he says that pleasure and pain alone 'determine what we shall do'[4]—this criticism is justified. For it is a common observation that men desire many things besides pleasure, and that the attainment of some of the things which they desire does not bring them pleasure. But as a philosopher Bentham is concerned not with what men actually desire but with what it would be rational for them to desire, and the underlying assumption of his theory seems to be that it is rational to desire the things which satisfy desire, i.e. result in satisfaction or happiness. In other words, for the common moral distinction between what men desire and what men ought to desire Bentham substitutes the

---

[1] In his defence of individual liberty of thought, speech, and action.
[2] *Of Civil Government*, II, 8.
[3] *Principles*, I, 3.   [4] ibid., I, 1.

distinction between what they desire and what they would desire if they correctly estimated the consequences in terms of pleasure. The difference between his analysis and that of many modern psychologists is that he asserts that pleasure and pain are always the objects of actual, as well as of rational, desire; whereas this seems plainly not to be the case. It may be true that the only rational answer to the question 'Why do you desire to realize X?' is 'Because the realization of X would be pleasant', and that the realization of ends which do not cause pleasure does not satisfy desire; but that does not imply that people are incapable of desiring changes[1] which do not, in point of fact, prove to be pleasant. It does not, therefore, appear that Bentham was justified in saying that pleasure and pain alone 'determine what we shall do', although they may alone determine what it is rational for us to do, i.e. what in Bentham's sense, we 'ought' to do.

Pleasure and pain are the effects of certain conditions or changes, and it appears to be psychologically true that these conditions or changes are frequently the direct objects of desire, and that it is only at the reflective level, when an attempt is made to distinguish rational desires from actual desires, that it may be true to say that the object of every rational desire is pleasure. And Bentham's principle of utility is simply a recognition of the fact that the only objects which it is rational to desire for their own sake are the things which bring happiness, since desire is satisfied only when its fulfilment brings happiness.

These general principles can be illustrated by the following example. Shipwrecked sailors without supplies of fresh water may, as a matter of psychological fact, desire intensely to drink brine; but past experience has shown that to do so would greatly aggravate their thirst, and that the realization of this desire would therefore not bring happiness. It would therefore be irrational for them to drink brine, and if they behave rationally they will not do so. In other words, the *immediate* object of desire may be distinguished from the *ultimate* object of desire, which is to increase pleasure and diminish pain. Action can therefore be defined as 'rational' when it takes the form which, in the light of

---

[1] As Professor Broad has remarked in his discussion of Butler's theory, 'The object of an impulse is never, strictly speaking, a thing or person; it is always to change or to preserve some state of a thing or person.' (*Five Types of Ethical Theory*, p. 67.)

scientific generalizations based on past experience, appears most likely to increase pleasure and reduce pain.

Mill's Account of the Utilitarian Principle

Mill's Utilitarian Theory is less consistent than Bentham's. Bentham recognized that if pleasure and pain alone determine what we ought to do, the source or quality of the pleasure is irrelevant to the determination of the rightness or wrongness of an act—that, as he put it, 'quantity of pleasure being equal, pushpin is as good as poetry'. But Mill rejected this doctrine. To him it appeared that some pleasures are 'higher', and therefore better, than others, even if, as pleasures, they are equal:

> It would be absurd that while, in estimating all other things, quality is considered as well as quantity, the estimation of pleasures should be supposed to depend upon quantity alone.[1]

It is clear from the examples which Mill gives to illustrate this principle that what he calls the 'quality' of a pleasure depends upon its source. This, however, is inconsistent with the principle of utility, which states that the quantity of pleasure in which an act results, and that alone, is the measure of its rightness. It is still more clear that Mill is, in effect, rejecting the principle of utility altogether when he asserts that some states of positive *dissatisfaction* are better than other states of satisfaction:

> It is better to be a human being dissatisfied than a pig satisfied; better to be Socrates dissatisfied than a fool satisfied. And if the fool, or the pig, are of a different opinion, it is because they only know their own side of the question. The other party to the comparison knows both sides.[2]

It is obvious that if in certain circumstances it is better to be dissatisfied than to be satisfied, the principle of utility has been abandoned altogether and some new quality, quite distinct from the pleasantness of the situation, is being accepted as the moral criterion. The fact is that Mill was very conscious of the extent to which Bentham's utilitarian theory appeared to conflict with the austere morality of the Victorian Age, and he was anxious to

[1] *Utilitarianism* (Everyman edition), p. 7.   [2] ibid., p. 9.

effect a compromise which would reconcile them. But in making this attempt he abandoned the principle of utility, and returned in some measure to accept moral dogmas of the sort which Bentham had attempted to eliminate.

Apart from this attempted compromise with the outlook of contemporary morality, Mill's definition of the principle of utility is far from clear in view of the use which he makes of the word 'desirable':

> Pleasure, and freedom from pain, are the only things desirable as ends; and . . . all desirable things (which are as numerous in the utilitarian as in any other scheme) are desirable either for the pleasure inherent in themselves, or as means to the promotion of pleasure and the prevention of pain.[1]

For it is clear, when Mill goes on to offer an alleged proof of this principle, that he is using the word 'desirable' in two distinct senses. Thus he says:

> The only proof capable of being given that an object is visible, is that people actually see it. The only proof that a sound is audible, is that people hear it: and so of the other sources of our experience. In like manner, I apprehend, the sole evidence it is possible to produce that anything is desirable, is that people do actually desire it. . . . No reason can be given why the general happiness is desirable, except that each person, so far as he believes it to be attainable, desires his own happiness.[2]

This argument is vitiated by the ambiguous use of the word 'desirable', which may mean either 'capable of' or 'worthy of' being desired. The fact that people actually see an object proves that it is visible in the sense of 'capable of being seen'; and the fact that people hear a sound proves that it is audible in the sense of 'capable of being heard'. Similarly, the fact—if it be a fact— that people desire happiness proves that happiness is desirable in the sense of 'capable of being desired'. But it does not prove that happiness *ought* to be desired in any genuinely moral sense. The only proposition of practical importance which Mill could have

[1] ibid., p. 6.   [2] ibid., pp. 32–33.

validly inferred from the fact (if it be a fact) that everyone desires his own happiness is that everyone ought (in the *rational* sense of 'ought') to desire the things which bring him happiness; but it does not follow from this that anyone would be acting wrongly, although he would be acting irrationally, if he sought the things which did not bring him happiness.

Having proved, to his satisfaction, that everyone desires happiness, Mill next tries to prove that nobody ultimately desires anything else, although, as he admits, 'it is palpable that they do desire things which, in common language, are decidedly distinguished from happiness. They desire, for example, virtue, and the absence of vice, no less really than pleasure and the absence of pain.'[1] But this consideration does not, in Mill's view, contradict the principle of utility:

> The principle of utility does not mean that any given pleasure, as music, for instance, or any given exemption from pain, as, for example, health, is to be looked upon as means to a collective something termed happiness, and to be desired on that account. They are desired and desirable in and for themselves; besides being means, they are a part of the end. Virtue, according to the utilitarian doctrine, is not naturally and originally part of the end, but it is capable of becoming so; and in those who love it disinterestedly it has become so, and is desired and cherished, not as a means to happiness, but as a part of their happiness.[2]

It is difficult to reconcile the foregoing argument with Mill's earlier statement that 'all desirable things . . . are desirable either for the pleasure inherent in themselves, or as means to the promotion of pleasure and the prevention of pain'.[3] It may be psychologically true that virtue comes to be desired because it promotes happiness, but that does not make virtue part of happiness. And what Mill is primarily concerned to establish is not a psychological theory about what people do desire but a philosophical theory about what it is rational for them to desire or (as he says) about what is desirable, namely the theory that 'pleasure, and freedom from pain, are the only things desirable as ends'.[4] And such a theory implies that, although people may actually desire other things, such as virtue or power or fame, these things are

[1] ibid., p. 33.   [2] ibid., p. 34.   [3] ibid., p. 6.   [4] loc. cit.

desirable only if, and in so far as, they promote happiness. To hold that they are desirable in themselves is to abandon the principle of utility.

The truth is that Mill's application of the principle of utility was less disinterested than Bentham's. To Bentham it was a standard by which the assumptions of conventional morality could be criticized and corrected; but Mill regarded it more as a principle which justified these assumptions and made clear their rational character. It is not therefore surprising that Mill's account of the principle is less consistent than Bentham's. For the principle of utility is, from its very nature, a potential challenge to conventional morality. It repudiates all claims to the *a priori* certainty of moral judgments and assesses their truth by the empirical test of utility. It implies that whether an act is right or wrong never depends upon a 'knowledge' of right or wrong but only upon the tendency of that act to 'augment or diminish the happiness of the party whose interest is in question'.[1] Thus Mill's account of the principle of utility adds nothing of value to Bentham's more consistent exposition; on the contrary, it greatly obscures the meaning and significance of the principle by attempting to reconcile it at all costs with the assumptions of conventional morality.

Mill's Essay 'On Liberty'

It is in Mill's essay *On Liberty* that his most important and consistent contribution to the philosophy of individualism is to be found. For it is here that he draws some of the true implications of the principle of utility. And these implications all follow, in the end, from the consideration that if happiness is the supreme good, and if happiness is found by different people in different ways, then in order to maximize happiness everyone must be left free to realize his desires as fully as possible so long as this freedom does not interfere with the enjoyment of a similar freedom by others. As Mill puts it:

> The object of this Essay is to assert one very simple principle . . . that the sole end for which mankind are warranted, individually or collectively, in interfering with the liberty of action of any of their number, is self-protection.

[1] *Principles of Morals and Legislation*, I, 2.

That the only purpose for which power can be rightfully exercised over any member of a civilized community, against his will, is to prevent harm to others. His own good, either physical or moral, is not a sufficient warrant. He cannot rightfully be compelled to do or forbear because it will be better for him to do so, because it will make him happier, because, in the opinions of others, to do so would be wise, or even right. Those are good reasons for remonstrating with him, or reasoning with him, or persuading him, or entreating him, but not for compelling him, or visiting him with any evil in case he do otherwise. To justify that, the conduct from which it is desired to deter him must be calculated to produce evil to someone else.[1]

A later passage in which the same point is emphasized is also worth quoting:

The only freedom which deserves the name, is that of pursuing our own good in our own way, so long as we do not attempt to deprive others of theirs, or impede their efforts to obtain it. . . . Mankind are greater gainers by suffering each other to live as seems good to themselves, than by compelling each to live as seems good to the rest.[2]

These passages set forth the essential features of Mill's defence of individual liberty, and show that he bases this doctrine on the utilitarian principle that happiness is the measure of goodness, and that action must therefore be justified or condemned by its tendency to increase or diminish the happiness of individuals. And he emphasizes that interference with individual liberty may result not only from the action of a tyrannical minority but also from the action of a government expressing the will of the majority. The 'tyranny of the majority' may, he thinks, be just as inimical to individual liberty as the tyranny exercised by a minority government maintaining itself by brute force, if the majority employ their weight of numbers to suppress the freedom of the individual. As he argues in a well known passage:

If all mankind minus one were of one opinion, and only one person were of the contrary opinion, mankind would be no more justified in silencing that one person, than he, if he

[1] *Essay on Liberty*, Chap. I.   [2] loc. cit.

had the power, would be justified in silencing mankind. Were an opinion a personal possession of no value except to the owner; if to be obstructed in the enjoyment of it were simply a private injury, it would make some difference whether the injury was inflicted only on a few persons or on many. But the peculiar evil of silencing the expression of an opinion is, that it is robbing the human race; posterity as well as the existing generation; those who dissent from the opinion, still more than those who hold it. If the opinion is right, they are deprived of the opportunity of exchanging error for truth: if wrong, they lose, what is almost as great a benefit, the clearer perception and livelier impression of truth, produced by its collision with error.[1]

Mill later sums up the case for toleration in two succinct sentences: 'All silencing of discussion is an assumption of infallibility.'[2] and 'The usefulness of an opinion is itself matter of opinion.'[3] In short, however much the opinion and will of the majority must be followed because of their greater influence, it must never be forgotten that the majority is a majority of *individuals*, and that for the majority to suppress the opinions of the minority is to challenge the very foundation upon which majority rule is itself ultimately based.

It is clear that in these passages Mill is defining the basic assumptions upon which modern democracy is based. For the essence of such democracy is not the uncompromising application of the will of the majority but the insistence that this will must be determined by the free expression of the wills of individuals, and must tolerate and recognize minority wills which diverge from the general consensus of desire. It is for this reason that democracies sometimes tolerate the expression and propagation of opinions which, if generally accepted, might destroy democracy itself. In Britain, for example, Fascists and Communists have generally been accorded the same freedom of speech and political association as the parties which accept the democratic principle of toleration; and any special discrimination which has been exercised against them—such as the 18B Regulation during the Second World War and the more recent restrictions on the employment of Communists in the Civil Service—has been

---

[1] ibid., Chap. II.　　　　[2] loc. cit.　　　　[3] loc. cit.

regarded with considerable misgiving by many who were not affected by it. It might, of course, be argued that a democracy has no obligation to tolerate those who are themselves intolerant of criticism and opposition, but democratic opinion in Britain at least has generally preferred to accord them the normal measure of toleration in the belief that the opinions and desires of individuals constitute the only standard by which the form and purpose of government ought to be determined.

Mill's plea for toleration was based on the belief that no one is infallible, and that all opinions—at least on matters of morals—are liable to error. He did not, like Hume, raise the more fundamental question whether opinions on moral matters are subject to the criterion of truth and falsity at all. His language[1] suggests that he believed that moral judgments are objectively true or false, but that men's minds are incapable of judging with certainty whether they are true or false. But Hume would, of course, have said that such judgments do not describe an objective act or object but a subjective feeling; that they describe what people feel about certain acts or objects, and not how those acts or objects are characterized. If accepted, this analysis would clearly strengthen Mill's defence of individual liberty, for it would imply that the ultimate motives of action are desires; and that there is no rational ground for suppressing one desire in favour of another. On this analysis the problem which reason can help to solve is that of facilitating the maximum gratification of the maximum number of desires; and that is just an alternative way of describing the utilitarian ideal of the 'greatest happiness of the greatest number'.

Utilitarianism and Democracy

Thus Bentham's theory of Utilitarianism and Mill's theory of Liberty together define the essential principles upon which liberal democracy is based. For the latter is a form of government

[1] E.g. in the passage from the *Essay on Liberty*, Chap. II, already quoted, where Mill says: 'If the opinion is right, they are deprived of the opportunity of exchanging error for truth: if wrong, they lose, what is almost as great a benefit, the clearer perception and livelier impression of truth, produced by its collision with error.' The implication of this passage is that opinions are either right or wrong, and that there are ways in which the wrong, i.e. false, opinions may be recognized and corrected.

under which policy is ultimately determined by the free expression of the individual's will. It is the antithesis of forms of government in which the will of the individual is held to be less real or less true than the will of a group of individuals, whether or not they are held to constitute an organic whole. On the democratic analysis the individual man or woman is the fundamental unit, and the expression of the individual's will is the ultimate force which, when combined with the expression of the wills of others, must determine policy.

Such an analysis clearly implies, although the implication is not always recognized, that there is no impersonal standard of morality to which the action of men or governments ought to conform. Moral standards are created by groups of individuals, and while in practice it is necessary to determine policy in accordance with what Locke called the 'greater force' of the majority, the freedom of self-expression permitted to individuals or minorities who disagree with the majority is an implicit recognition that the will of the majority prevails only because it is the will of a majority, and not because it is in any objective sense 'right'. If the will of the majority were, in an objective sense, right or true, there would be no justification for tolerating opinions and movements constituting a potential challenge to it.

These are the general principles embodied in the theories of Bentham and Mill, although neither philosopher fully appreciated their significance. The real meaning of Bentham's principle of utility is that there is no independent criterion of morality, that what brings happiness to an individual is right—in so far as it does not diminish the happiness of other individuals more—and that rightness and wrongness can be defined in terms of individual desire and happiness. This, in turn, implies that there is no way of proving, on *a priori* grounds, that some forms of satisfaction are good and that others are bad; they are all good in so far as they promote happiness and do not diminish it; and the desire of the individual is therefore the ultimate criterion of morality and the ultimate justification of government. The problem of government is not, according to the Utilitarian Theory, to determine what ought to be desired—for the latter is a confused and misleading expression without objective significance—but to determine how the maximum number of desires can be most fully satisfied; and the complex machinery of government can be justified, in the end, only by its efficiency in realizing this general aim.

Mill's plea for liberty of speech, thought and action is, as already observed, a direct implication of the utilitarian principle. For if the satisfaction of individual desires is the criterion of virtue and the justification of government, it follows that anything which diminishes such satisfaction must be condemned except where it is necessary to promote the maximum satisfaction on the whole. If the satisfaction of individual desire is prevented for any other reason, the individualist basis of government is being abandoned and the way opened for government based upon force, exercised either arbitrarily or in the name of some alleged moral principle. To the utilitarian all such attempts to found government on moral law are attempts to base it on a foundation which cannot be rationally justified and are bound to conflict with the rational aim of maximising happiness, except where the moral law is itself an expression of the principle of utility.

CHAPTER XIII

Marxism, Communism, and Socialism

HEINRICH KARL MARX (1818–1883) was born at Treves in Rhenish Prussia, the son of a Jewish lawyer. He was educated at the local High Grammar School, and at the Universities of Bonn and Berlin. It was at Berlin that he became closely associated with the young Hegelians and began to work out his adaptation of the Hegelian dialectic to a materialist theory of human society. Marx had originally hoped to teach at the University of Bonn, but his extreme political views made him unacceptable there, and he joined a radical newspaper, the *Rheinishe Zeitung*, becoming one of its editors in 1842. It was, however, suppressed in 1843. He then went to Paris, where he met his future friend and collaborator, Friedrich Engels (1820–1895). Engels was the son of a rich cotton spinner, who owned a factory near Manchester, and he was thus able to make a close study of the English industrial system. His observations led him to conclusions very similar to those of Marx, and the two collaborated closely after their first meeting in 1844.

Marx's writings were soon viewed with disfavour by the authorities in Paris, and he went to Brussels, where Engels joined him. Both participated actively in the socialist working class movement and collaborated in the writing of the *Manifesto of the Communist Party*, which was published early in 1848. It had hardly appeared when the revolution of that year broke out in France. Marx hoped and expected that this would be followed by a revolution in Germany, and he went with Engels to Cologne. There they founded a new daily paper to encourage revolutionary measures, and when the King of Prussia dissolved the National Assembly later in the year Marx and his associates advocated the non-payment of taxes and armed resistance to the King. Marx was subsequently acquitted at a trial for high treason, but was expelled from Germany in 1849. After a short stay in France he went to England, where he remained for the rest of his life.

Marx was a voluminous writer, and it is impracticable in a single chapter to do justice to all his works. But a general conception of his theory can be derived from his two most famous publications. One is the *Manifesto of the Communist Party*, originally published in February 1848, and reissued in Britain in 1948 on the occasion of its centenary with a new appreciation by the late Professor H. J. Laski. Its importance was rightly emphasized by Professor Laski in the following words:

> It is admitted by every serious student of society to be one of the outstanding political documents of all time; in the influence it has exerted it compares with the American Declaration of Independence of 1776, and the French Declaration of Rights of 1789. Its character is unique, not only because of the power with which it is written, but also because of the immense scope it covers in its intense brevity. It is a philosophy of history, a critical analysis of socialist doctrines and a passionate call to revolutionary action.[1]

The other book to which I shall refer is the famous *Capital*,[2] which develops in detail the economic theory briefly referred to in the *Manifesto*. The first volume of the *Capital* was published in 1867: the other two, which Marx had not completed when he died, were published posthumously.

Dialectical Materialism

As observed in Chapter XI, the philosophy of Marx was largely inspired by Hegel's dialectical idealism. Marx agreed with Hegel that reality is a dialectical process, but differed in holding that this process is of a material, and not a logical, character. Hence Marx's philosophy is often referred to as dialectical materialism. It is called materialism because Marx held that the dialectical process is a process, not of thought, but of the material reality which thought reflects. Hegel was an idealist because he believed that thought is the fundamental

[1] *Manifesto of the Communist Party*, p. 31. (Allen and Unwin: 1948.)
[2] Vol. I is conveniently available in two volumes of the Everyman Library, translated by Eden and Cedar Paul, and with an introduction by Professor G. D. H. Cole.

reality, that there is no 'external' reality to which thought corresponds, and that the criterion of truth must therefore be found in the coherence of thoughts and not in their correspondence to 'things'. Marx was a materialist in the sense that he repudiated this doctrine of the primacy of thought and believed that the nature of thought is determined by the material reality of which it is the reflection. By calling this reality 'material' he did not mean that it is 'physical' as distinct from 'mental'. His material reality embodies the whole universe of so-called 'physical' and 'mental' processes, and the object of calling it material is to emphasize that it is that to which thought must correspond if it is to be valid. Thus Marx's theory is not a theory of physical determinism in the narrow sense, but a theory according to which the physical and mental interact in accordance with laws which must be empirically discovered.

The use of the word 'dialectical' to describe Marx's materialism suggests that the evolution of the material process is necessary, just as, according to Hegel, the dialectical evolution of thought is necessary. And some of Marx's interpreters have taken this view. Thus Professor Sabine says that 'the question is whether dialectic, either idealist or materialist, can avoid Hume's proof that all necessity is merely conditional, and all value merely a relation to human propensities'.[1] But there are two objections to this interpretation of Marx's theory. In the first place, as observed in Chapter XI, Hegel failed to show that synthetic thinking can ever possess logical necessity, or therefore that dialectical thinking, which is synthetic thinking, can be logically necessary. Secondly, even if synthetic thinking were logically necessary it would not follow that a material process—which is not a logical process at all—could possess the essentially logical characteristic of necessity. If Marx is a materialist he cannot consistently attribute necessity to the material process which, on his theory, constitutes reality. As a material process it is a process whose laws—if it conforms to laws—must be wholly empirical and devoid of any logical necessity. And if the word 'dialectical' is used to describe the progress of its evolution it must be recognized that this does not imply that there is any necessity in the evolution so described.

So interpreted, Marx's theory is not a challenge to Hume's Empiricism but an expression of it. Like Hume, Marx is saying

[1] *History of Political Theory*, p. 698.

that no judgment claiming to be about the real world—no scientific or moral or religious judgment—has any logical necessity, and that the truth of such judgments depends on their correspondence to observable parts of the material process. For Marx, as for Hume, necessity can characterize only analytic judgments and from these nothing can be deduced about the characteristics of the real world. Marx, however, has little interest in analytic judgments—except the fundamental one that reality is a material process—for such judgments do not, in his view, contribute anything to the shaping of history or the understanding of its laws. And his object, as he once expressed it, was not to interpret the world (i.e. in the *a priori* sense) but to change it.[1] Thus for Marx it is science, and science alone, which can extend man's understanding of the real world. Other alleged sources of knowledge, such as religion and philosophy, are of no importance except in so far as they influence action, and provide data for scientific generalizations about action. Thus the religious belief in the existence of a Divine Being is, on Marx's view, without foundation or significance except in so far as it has a practical effect on the actions and reactions of those who accept it, or unless there is some scientific evidence for its truth.[2] Similarly, moral convictions are without objective validity because there is no scientific way of demonstrating their truth. There is no evidence by which the belief that 'X is right' may be verified or refuted: the fact that A believes that 'X is right' is not evidence that X is right but only that A believes that X is right. Thus all that the scientist can do in the field of morality is to discover what moral beliefs different people or groups of people hold and to ascertain whether there are general laws describing the causes and consequences of these beliefs. But these general laws, like all scientific laws, will be purely empirical and devoid of any rational necessity.

The implications of Marx's theory for philosophy are similar. He would, I think, have been in full agreement with modern Logical Positivists in denying the 'possibility of metaphysics'. That is to say, he would have denied that metaphysical generaliza-

---

[1] *Theses on Feuerbach*, XI.
[2] As some modern mathematicians and astronomers have suggested, e.g. Sir Edmund Whittaker in his *Space and Spirit*. But Marx held that there was no such evidence.

tions about the universe claiming *a priori*, as distinct from scientific, validity can ever have objective significance. For such generalizations are synthetic propositions, and synthetic propositions can never be *a priori*. They can be justified only by experience, and there is no experience which can confirm or refute a metaphysical proposition. If a proposition can be confirmed or refuted by experience it must be a scientific, not a metaphysical, proposition. On the other hand, Marx would probably have raised no objection to the positivist's conception of philosophy as the study of the logical relationship of propositions, since these relationships are independent of actual experience and apply to experience only in a hypothetical sense.

If the foregoing interpretation of Marx's 'materialism' is correct the word 'dialectical', when applied to his theory, must simply mean 'causal' in the purely empirical sense. The purpose of using the word 'dialectical' is to emphasize that the causal process is one of *interaction* between what are usually referred to as the 'material' and 'mental' spheres, so that material conditions modify mental conditions, and mental conditions in turn react on material conditions. But on the materialist hypothesis all such action and reaction is, of course, purely empirical. There is no *a priori* necessity in it, and it is for the scientist—the social scientist—to discover the empirical laws to which social evolution conforms. The main difficulty which confronts him in doing so is the obvious one that he himself participates in the social process which he is trying to describe, and may therefore find it difficult to take the detached view which is essential if his description is to be accurate.

Thus the fundamental difference between the theories of Hegel and Marx is that on Hegel's theory reality is a logical system while on Marx's theory it is a causal system, i.e. a system which develops in accordance with laws of a purely empirical character. To Hegel dialectical logic is the key to truth while to Marx the scientific method is the only one by which knowledge of the real world can be established. Thus Marx's theory is, strictly speaking, not a philosophical but a scientific theory. Its only philosophical implication is that philosophy (except in the purely analytic sense) is impossible, and that science provides the key, and the only key, to the understanding of both nature and man—including the various moral and philosophical systems in which man has from time to time believed. The validity of Marx's theory must therefore be judged by the criteria of science and, in particular, by its success in describing the facts of social and political evolution. It attempts to do so by the hypothesis that these facts are determined by economic relationships, and consideration must now be given to the basic principles of Marx's economic theory.

Marx's Economic Theory

Marx's economic theory is a development of the 'Labour Theory of Value' which was originally formulated by Locke and popularized by the economic writers of the early nineteenth century. Locke expressed the basic principle of the theory as follows:

> Whatsoever, then, he [a man] removes out of the state that Nature hath provided and left it in, he hath mixed his labour with it, and joined to it something that is his own, and thereby makes it his property. It being by him removed from the common state Nature placed it in, it hath by this labour something annexed to it that excludes the common right of other men. For this 'labour' being the unquestionable property of the labourer, no man but he can have a right to what that is once joined to, at least where there is enough, and as good left in common for others.[1]

In short, by working on the raw materials of nature a man adds something to them which is unquestionably his own, and thus makes the finished product his personal property. It is also, Locke thinks, this labour which creates the greater part of the product's value:

> If we will rightly estimate things as they come to our use, and cast up the several expenses about them—what in them is purely owing to Nature and what to labour—we shall find that in most of them ninety-nine hundredths are wholly to be put on the account of labour.[2]

This was the principle which was accepted and developed by the early nineteenth century economists, who saw in a system of

---

[1] *Of Civil Government* (Everyman edition), p. 130.
[2] ibid., p. 136.

private enterprise, free from government interference and control, the most effective way of ensuring that every man received the proper return for his labour. The main qualification which they introduced arose from reflection on the facts of exchange and from the observation that the prices at which goods are actually exchanged are determined by factors other than the labour which has contributed to the production. Of these additional factors the most obvious are demand and monopoly. The price at which something can be purchased may be greatly increased both by an increased demand and by a monopoly of supply, but there are advantages in distinguishing that part of the price due to the labour expended in producing the article in question. Adam Smith called this part of the price the *natural value*, Macculloch called it the *real cost*, and Marx called it the *exchange value*, although he recognized that it is not the value at which goods usually exchange in existing societies.

In spite of his pretensions, however, Marx's economic theory is not purely scientific. A purely scientific economic theory would attempt to discover how economic value is determined and influenced. And an examination of this sort would show that several factors besides the amount of labour expended in producing a manufactured article contribute to the determination of the price at which it is exchanged. But Marx, like many other economists, had a moral as well as a scientific object in view. He was anxious to show not only how price is determined, but also how it ought to be determined, and his view, briefly stated, is that goods ought to be exchanged at their 'exchange value'. For only if this is done will the labourer receive a fair return for his labour, and each labourer own the wealth to which his labour entitles him. He may not, of course, retain the actual goods which his own work has produced, but he should, if he exchanges them, obtain an equivalent value of other goods in their place. In thus arguing Marx is, of course, developing, in the light of the facts of exchange, the fundamental principle of Locke's theory—that the labourer creates value by working on his raw material, and that he has a right to the possession of the value so created. Marx is simply adding that, in a more advanced society where manufactured goods are exchanged, the labourer who sells the product of his labour should obtain in exchange something upon which an equivalent quantity of labour has been expended.

The Labour Theory of Value is, therefore, in part scientific and in part moral. It is in part moral because it does not merely state how price is determined in existing society but also how it would be determined in an ideal society; and this distinction rests upon the moral assumption that certain conditions would be ideal and that actual conditions may fall short of this ideal. Marx believed that in ideal conditions a man would receive, in exchange for the product of his labour, something on which an equivalent quantity of labour had been expended.

The early nineteenth century economists believed that this fair exchange of goods would be ensured by a system of *laisser-faire*, i.e. a system of completely free enterprise in which industry would be free from all forms of government restriction and private monopoly. In such circumstances they believed that the demand for goods would have the result that every man would obtain in return for the goods which he produced an equivalent value of goods produced by others. Marx believed that, on the contrary, a system of free enterprise would have just the opposite result. And he thought that this would be due to two distinct, but related, factors, namely (i) the private ownership of *capital* (i.e. the means of social production), and (ii) the practice of buying and selling labour power for the creation of new capital. These two factors, Marx thought, would lead to a growing inequality of wealth which would in turn lead to class war between the bourgeoisie and the proletariat, whom Engels defined as follows in a footnote to the *Manifesto of the Communist Party*:

> By bourgeoisie is meant the class of modern capitalists, owners of the means of social production and employers of wage labour. By proletariat, the class of modern wage labourers who, having no means of production of their own, are reduced to selling their labour power in order to live.

These definitions incidentally make it clear that by 'capital' Marx denotes 'the means of social production', i.e. the material equipment, such as land, factories, and machinery which are necessary to produce goods for which there is a social demand. He does not mean 'property' in the sense of personal possessions. Indeed, he specifically denies that Communists desire to abolish 'the right of personally acquiring property as the fruit of a man's labour'.[1] It is not property in this sense which Marx wishes to abolish but 'capital, i.e. that kind of property which exploits wage labour, and which cannot increase except upon conditions of begetting a new supply of wage labour for fresh exploitation'.[2] Thus a man's garden is not by itself capital, but it becomes capital if he employs a gardener at a fixed wage to work it, and sells the produce at a profit to himself.

Marx thinks that the existence of capital prevents the labourer from securing the just reward for his labour because the owner of the capital, merely in virtue of that ownership, receives some of the value which the labourer has created. This is because under the capitalist system labour has itself an exchange value for the capitalist, who pays for it by wages, the level of these wages being determined by the cost of the food, shelter, clothing, etc. which the labourer and his family require in order to live.

Now Marx contends that under the capitalist system the labour-time necessary to provide the needs of the labourer may be, and usually is, less than the time which the labourer has to work in order to earn the wages with which to buy these necessities. If this is so the labourer must be working for only part of his day in producing the equivalent of his wages; during the remainder he must be producing what Marx calls *surplus value*, and this goes into his employer's pocket. Surplus value may be shortly defined as 'the value produced by the labourer over and above the cost of his keep', and is roughly identical with what is commonly called *profit*. Such profit is, of course, usually shared by a number of capitalists, such as bankers and landlords, in addition to the owner or owners of the factory where the goods are being manufactured. But in all cases it constitutes, in Marx's view, a return to people who do not actually contribute to the work of producing the goods, which is the real process of creating value.

From these considerations Marx concludes that the capitalist and the labourer have opposite interests in industry. The capitalist's interest is to increase his profit by reducing wages or lengthening hours or intensifying the speed of work so that he gets a better return for the wages which he pays. The labourer's

---

[1] *Manifesto of the Communist Party*, p. 143 (Edition of 1948: Allen and Unwin).
[2] ibid.

interest, on the other hand, is to secure higher wages or reduced hours or lower productivity, so that his wages produce less surplus value. This opposition of interests will, Marx believes, result sooner or later in a revolutionary attack by the proletariat upon the capitalist class, followed by the seizure of their capital, and the establishment of a proletarian dictatorship which 'sweeps away by force the old conditions of production'.[1]

But it is not, in Marx's view, merely the opposing interests of capitalist and worker which make probable the transfer of power to the proletariat; the change is also determined by the fact that the worker's position becomes progressively worse owing to the acquisitive and competitive character of the capitalist system. Thus the capitalist keeps part of his profits to expand production by the purchase of new machinery, and this is liable to result in over-production leading to economic slumps and unemployment. Again, the competition between capitalists necessitates the cutting of costs either by reducing wages or by intensive mechanization or by the merging of several companies into combines. And these latter measures are likely to create redundancy among the workers. Thus Marx believes that the capitalist system, if not controlled in the interest of the workers, will lead to a progressive worsening of their condition which will provoke them to seize power and organize the system of production in accordance with their interests.

It is here that the dialectical contradiction, which Marx believes to be inherent in the capitalist system, becomes manifest. For it is, according to Marx's analysis, a system which prevents the majority of its members—the proletariat—from receiving the due reward for their labours, and, once this becomes apparent to them, they will, in Marx's view, inevitably condemn what they believe to be the injustice of their situation, and take the necessary steps to eradicate that injustice by placing capital, i.e. the means of social production, under the control of their own representatives. Thus the evolution and ultimate collapse of the capitalist system is determined, in part, by a moral reaction to its economic consequences, and cannot be accounted for wholly in terms of economic factors, although the moral reaction is itself due to changed economic conditions.

This analysis shows why Marx does not mean by 'dialectical

[1] *Manifesto of the Communist Party*, p. 153.

materialism' a system in which moral beliefs are the passive reflection of economic facts. On the contrary, he means that economic and moral factors interact so that, while the inequalities of wealth caused by the operation of the capitalist system lead to its moral condemnation, the latter in turn leads to the radical transformation of that system. There is, however, no logical or *a priori* necessity in these interactions; their necessity is *de facto* and empirical, and is of exactly the same kind as the necessity of the generalizations of the natural sciences. The laws of social evolution are, in fact, themselves scientific generalizations, although those who participate in that evolution may be able to formulate these laws only in retrospect.

The Socialist Revolution

Marx was not wholly consistent in working out this theory. He frequently implies, particularly in the *Manifesto*, that revolution in the form of civil insurrection is bound to be the culmination of the conflict between the bourgeoisie and the proletariat, and that this will therefore sooner or later be the fate of every capitalist community. But this conclusion does not follow from his theory of dialectical materialism, for there is nothing in that theory which implies that the conflict must be resolved in the same way in every community. It may be true that, if the capitalist class is uncompromising in defending its privileges without regard to the interests of the proletariat, a violent revolution is likely. But it is not obvious that economic justice cannot be achieved by constitutional and peaceful means in a democratic community if the capitalist class yields to the pressure exercised by the proletariat through the ballot box. Marx himself seems to recognize this when he writes:

> The first step in the revolution by the working class is to raise the proletariat to the position of ruling class to win the battle of democracy.[1]

> The proletariat will use its political supremacy to wrest, by degrees, all capital from the bourgeoisie, to centralize all instruments of production in the hands of the state, i.e. of the proletariat organized as the ruling class; and to increase the total of productive forces as rapidly as possible.[2]

[1] ibid., p. 151.　　　　　　[2] ibid., p. 151-2.

It is obvious that these aims have already been partly achieved in Britain by a constitutionally elected Socialist Government, and further steps in the same direction may well be taken in the future if the majority of the electorate so desire. Indeed, it is interesting to note the extent to which the specific objectives of Communist policy as laid down in the *Manifesto* have already been achieved in Britain and other democratic countries, and the extent to which they would now be endorsed even by non-Socialist parties. Marx listed these objectives as follows:[1]

1 Abolition of property in land and application of all rents of land to public purposes.
2 A heavy progressive or graduated income tax.
3 Abolition of all right of inheritance.
4 Confiscation of the property of all emigrants and rebels.
5 Centralization of credit in the hands of the state, by means of a national bank with state capital and an exclusive monopoly.
6 Centralization of the means of communication and transport in the hands of the state.
7 Extension of factories and instruments of production owned by the state; the bringing into cultivation of waste lands, and the improvement of the soil generally in accordance with a common plan.
8 Equal obligation of all to work. Establishment of industrial armies, especially for agriculture.
9 Combination of agriculture with manufacturing industries; gradual abolition of all the distinction between town and country by a more equable distribution of the population over the country.
10 Free education for all children in public schools. Abolition of children's factory labour in its present form. Combination of education with industrial production, etc.

However revolutionary these objectives may have appeared in the middle of the nineteenth century, many of them have already been achieved, in part at least, by the ordinary processes of Parliamentary democracy. Indeed, the essence of the Marxist revolution is not that it should be violent but that it should be revolutionary—revolutionary in the change which it brings about

[1] ibid., p. 152 f.

in the control of the means of social production. In capitalist society these means are owned by a privileged minority and (Marx believes) controlled to the disadvantage of the vast majority. The primary object of the social revolution, which he both desires and anticipates, is to place the means of social production under the control of the state, which he defines as the 'proletariat organized as the ruling class', with a view to ensuring that they are used in the interest of the proletariat. He describes the change succinctly as follows:

> In bourgeois society, living labour is but a means to increase accumulated labour. In communist society, accumulated labour is but a means to widen, to enrich, to promote the existence of the labourer.[1]

In other words, Marx believes that in bourgeois society the surplus value created by the labourer goes into the pockets of the bourgeoisie, while in Communist society any value created by the labourer beyond what is returned to him as wages will be used, under the direction of society, to widen and enrich his life in various ways. He believes that the injustices of the capitalist system will be prevented only when the means of social production and the distribution of wealth are controlled by the state itself. And during the first stage of the revolution he means by 'the state' simply 'the proletariat organized as the ruling class'.[2] At this stage, therefore, all that the application of his theory involves is the substitution of government by the organized proletariat for government by the organized bourgeoisie.

The Classless Society

But the stage of proletarian dictatorship is only transitional, and will, Marx believes, be followed by a classless society in which 'all production has been concentrated in the hands of a vast association of the whole nation'.[3] When this happens 'the public power will lose its political character'.[4] Marx elaborates this point in a passage which is worth quoting at length:

> Political power, properly so called, is merely the organized power of one class for oppressing another. If the proletariat during its contest with the bourgeoisie is compelled, by the

[1] ibid., p. 144.   [2] ibid., p. 152.   [3] ibid., p. 153.   [4] loc. cit.

force of circumstances, to organize itself as a class; if, by means of a revolution, it makes itself the ruling class, and, as such, sweeps away by force the old conditions of production, then it will, along with these conditions, have swept away the conditions for the existence of class antagonisms and of classes generally, and will thereby have abolished its own supremacy as a class.

In place of the old bourgeois society, with its classes and class antagonisms, we shall have an association in which the free development of each is the condition for the free development of all.[1]

This final stage has sometimes been described as one of 'anarchy', meaning not a condition of lawlessness but one in which a central government has become unnecessary. And some of Marx's followers undoubtedly understood it in this sense. But it is doubtful whether Marx himself thought that it would ever be possible to dispense with a central government. On the contrary, there are passages in the *Capital* which strongly suggest that in his opinion there will always be important functions for a central government, even if it ultimately loses its 'political' character. One of the most important of these functions he describes as follows:

> Only when production will be under the conscious and prearranged control of society, will society establish a direct relation between the quantity of social labour time employed in the production of definite articles and the demand of society for them.[2]

Under the capitalist system there is, in Marx's view, no such relationship between labour and social demand since the economic inequalities arising from the private ownership of capital, and the lack of any central planning of the use of capital, alike contribute to the perpetuation of an economic anarchy in which the idle demands of the rich may command labour more easily than the urgent needs of the poor simply because of the money which can be made available to pay for them.

It seems clear, then, that Marx anticipates a continuing need

[1] loc. cit.   [2] *Capital*, III, tr by E. Unterman, p. 221.

for a central government to draw up a list of what would now be called 'social priorities' and to ensure that the resources of the community, both material and human, are effectively utilized to satisfy these needs. And he appears to believe that there will be general agreement about these social priorities and the measures necessary to satisfy them once the old conditions of production, i.e. the capitalist system, have been destroyed. Once this has happened 'the public power will lose its political character'[1] and a genuinely democratic basis for Communism will become possible. Opposition to Communism depends, Marx thinks, upon the continuance of the capitalist system, and will disappear as soon as that system has been abolished by the dictatorship of the proletariat. Indeed Marx believes that true democracy is impossible so long as capitalism survives, since capitalism is essentially a system of exploitation and inequality. Democratic equality will, he thinks, be achieved only when the economic organization of the community is centrally planned and controlled.

In countries, such as Russia, where Communist governments are already in control, this central planning and control of the economy is a conspicuous feature, but it is associated with an equally rigid control of speech and publication and political association which many would regard as a denial of the most fundamental of all democratic liberties. It seems probable that Marx would have defended these restrictions on the ground that existing Communist states are still at the stage of dictatorship, and that it would be premature to dispense with this form of government until all vestiges of the capitalist system and the bourgeois mentality have been eliminated, and all danger of attack by other bourgeois countries has disappeared. When, but only when, these conditions are satisfied, will there emerge the 'association in which the free development of each is the condition for the free development of all' and in which everyone freely accepts and supports the ideal of planned production for the satisfaction of social needs.

The Planned Society

If the emotional prejudices associated with the word 'Communism' can be put aside, there is much in Marx's theory which is likely to attract those who recognize the inadequacy of *laisser-*

[1] *Manifesto*, p. 153.

faire and the need for some central planning of production for satisfying the needs of the individual in an equitable manner. And they are likely to attach most weight not to Marx's theory of surplus value—which is generally recognized by economists to be based on an inadequate analysis of value—but to his theory that production is a co-operative process, that value is determined not only by the labour of those who work on the raw materials of nature but also by the extent to which the finished product satisfies the demand of the consumer, and that value is therefore partly determined by social relationships and is not an intrinsic quality of a manufactured article. And if these principles are true of a complex industrial community it follows that the Labour Theory of Value is inadequate to determine the just rewards of labour in such a community. In the simple society contemplated by Locke, where men supplied their own needs by working on the raw materials of nature, it appeared reasonable to say that a man had a right to the product of his labour; but in a complex industrial community, where several people generally co-operate in the production of manufactured goods, and manufacture them for the use of others, this simple definition of a just reward is quite inadequate, and a definition in terms of the social value of a man's labour must be substituted. But there is, of course, plenty of room for disagreement about what is socially valuable, since this conception cannot be defined in terms of individual desire, but only in terms of some general conception of how society ought to be constituted.

But who is to say how society ought to be constituted? And who is to specify the manner in which the free play of economic forces is to be restricted? The great theoretical attraction of the individualist theory of *laisser-faire* is that it does not raise these difficult and controversial questions but defines a thing's value in terms of what people will pay for it, and a worker's value in terms of what he can earn in a free and uncontrolled economy. Yet there is unanimous, or almost unanimous, agreement that some departure from *laisser-faire* is necessary in a modern industrial society, and this departure is justified on one or other of two grounds.

In the first place, it may be justified on the utilitarian ground that the majority of people will get more of what they want in a controlled than in a free economy. This is in principle the same argument as Hobbes used to justify government generally—that the individual will, in general and in the long run, realize more of his desires under government than without government. It is just an application of Hobbes's argument to the specifically economic field for the purpose of justifying a measure of economic government.

Secondly, control of the economy may be justified on the moral ground that a free economy has consequences, e.g. great disparities of wealth, which are morally evil.

Marx makes no attempt to base his argument on utilitarian grounds, and it is the second principle which is the real ground for his condemnation of the capitalist system and of his plea for the substitution of a system in which 'the labour power of all the different individuals is consciously applied as one single social labour power'.[1] Without the assumption that economic inequality is morally bad Marx would have no ground for condemning the capitalist system as morally bad. And without moral assumptions about the sort of society which ought to be fashioned by the 'single social labour power' he would obviously have no moral ground for justifying the measures necessary to realize such a social order.

The Moral Assumptions of Marxism

Thus moral assumptions are essential to Marx's theory on both its critical and constructive sides, yet as a materialist philosopher and a social scientist he cannot consistently make such assumptions. In making them he is himself becoming part of the material process which he is claiming to describe, and he is failing to distinguish between the process and its description. His task, as a social scientist, is to analyse and describe the process of social evolution and to formulate the laws in accordance with which that evolution appears to proceed; and the resulting description of the way in which society does evolve can never, by itself, be a valid basis for the inference that society ought to evolve in that way, and that people ought to promote that type of evolution.

The fact is that Marx, like Hegel, failed to adhere consistently to his own theory. Marx, as it has been said, was not a Marxist. He did not recognize that his own theories were subject to the

[1] *Capital*, I, p. 50. Quoted by Lord Lindsay in *Karl Marx's Capital*.

relativity to which, on his materialist premises, all empirical generalizations are necessarily subject. He did not realize that his condemnation of the capitalist system was, on his own materialist premises, determined by the special features of that system during his lifetime. And, like many subsequent social scientists, he failed to recognize that, once idealism has been abandoned, there can be no rational way of justifying the ultimate ends of action. All that science can show is how certain ends can, in practice, be most quickly and efficiently attained; it cannot show that these ends, whether desired or not, *ought* to be desired; for science is exclusively interested in what is, not in what ought to be. It can show men how to do things, but not why they ought to do them.

Thus if Marx had remained true to his materialist outlook he would not have written as though there were a moral obligation to promote the realization of a Communist society.[1] He would have been content to predict the probability of such a culmination, and, if he personally desired it, he might have utilized his scientific analysis to draw men's attention to the features of existing society which he believed would inspire them to revolutionize its character. And this, in effect, is what he actually did. His economic analysis of the capitalist system underestimates the importance of several factors, such as monopoly and demand, which affect price, and places primary emphasis on the factor of surplus value, and on the contention that in a capitalist society the worker is deprived of the just reward for his efforts. And there is no doubt that this emphasis has exercised an immense influence in politics which has extended far beyond the boundaries of official Communism. Indeed, much of Marx's analysis has become implicit in the outlook of liberal democracies. For example, the need for government control of the capitalist system in the interest of wage-earners has been generally accepted, and this has been largely due to the political pressure exercised by the wage-earners themselves in the belief that they have not been receiving a fair return for their labour.

---

[1] As Lord Lindsay has said: 'In spite of Marx's disclaimer of morality, no one can read *Capital* without being aware of the vehemence of moral passion which inspires it. His description of capitalism is full of moral indignation. His fundamental inspiration is a passion for justice.' (*Karl Marx's Capital*, p. 114.)

The Logical Basis of Marxism

If the moralizing and propaganda in Marx's writings are discounted as inconsistent with his primary thesis, two distinct but interconnected questions must be considered: (i) Is Marx justified in his materialist assumption that the only possible knowledge about the real world, and the only possible ground for rational action in the real world, is scientific knowledge? (ii) If the preceding question is answered in the affirmative, does Marx provide a reasonably accurate and adequate scientific theory of social evolution?

The first of these questions is, of course, the fundamental question of all philosophy—that of the nature and scope of human knowledge. And the answer to it closely depends on the answer to the second, for if Marx's scientific theory of social evolution appears to say all that can be said about human society with any pretence to objective truth, that will by itself be a weighty consideration in support of his materialist assumption that 'man's ideas, views, and conceptions, in one word, man's consciousness, changes with every change in the conditions of his material existence, in his social relations and in his social life',[1] and that moral and philosophical theories, far from having objective significance and providing rational guidance, are merely the causal by-products of an irrational process.

Marx himself does not appear to have appreciated these implications of a materialist philosophy. To him the ideal of human equality is obviously not just one possible ideal but the *right* ideal, to which all the strivings of mankind ought to be directed. And systems, such as the capitalist system, which prevent the attainment of equality ought, in his view, to be ruthlessly destroyed. Yet the fact that Marx and the vast majority of human beings recoil from the moral nihilism which a materialist philosophy necessarily involves does not by itself imply that rational belief about the real world can be attained by other methods than those of science. And the continuing difficulty of reaching any general agreement on the large issues of morality and metaphysics is by itself a standing challenge to all who reject the materialist view of the subjective nature of these controversies.

In considering the narrower question of the adequacy of Marx's

[1] *Manifesto of the Communist Party*, p. 150.

economic theory, a distinction must be drawn between the validity and the influence of his principles. There can be no doubt that their influence has been immense. The theory that the capitalist system necessarily involves the exploitation of the real producers of value and the denial to them of an equitable return for the value which they produce has been one of the primary inspirations of Communist and Socialist movements everywhere. But it is a distinct question whether these movements and their consequences have in practice confirmed Marx's predictions regarding the overthrow of the capitalist state and the ultimate evolution of a Communist society. If his predictions are understood to imply that every capitalist society will sooner or later suffer a violent revolution culminating in a proletarian dictatorship, they cannot be said to have been so far fulfilled except in Russia, China and some of the smaller states. But if the essence of Marx's theory is held to be that class distinctions, based upon economic inequality, will gradually disappear and all production be 'concentrated in the hands of a vast association of the whole nation',[1] there is considerable evidence that a general movement of this character is taking place—admittedly in different ways—in the various capitalist societies. For the extreme disparities of wealth which formerly existed are, in general, being progressively reduced by taxation, and business enterprise is being gradually brought under stricter control by government. While Marx appears to have thought that such changes could be brought about only by a bloody revolution, it is consistent with his own materialist principles to say that this was a reasonable expectation in the light of the economic and political situation in Britain in the middle of the nineteenth century, but that in the light of subsequent developments—and particularly the record of concessions obtained from capitalists through parliamentary procedure—it is no longer reasonable to predict that violence would be necessary to achieve the Communist State. In other words, different material conditions may cause the bourgeoisie of different countries to react in different ways to the pressure of the proletariat, so that, while in some countries revolutionary action may be necessary to bring about the centralized control of industry, in others political pressure may be fully adequate.

[1] ibid., p. 153.

If Marx's 'revolution' is interpreted in this wider sense it cannot be denied that the history of modern democracies provides considerable evidence of the tendency for private enterprise to be replaced by public control. In Britain, for example, the coal, gas and electricity industries, and a considerable section of the inland transport industry, have, since 1945, been placed in the ownership and under the control of the 'state'. Whether Marx would have regarded the Boards, Commissions and Authorities which have been appointed to control these industries as satisfactory for the purpose in view may well be doubted, but at least the theoretical object of nationalizing industries appears to be fundamentally the same as that of the revolution which Marx exhorted the 'workers of the world' to carry out, namely the planned control of industry for the purpose of ensuring that the economic resources of the community are fully exploited and effectively utilized for satisfying, on an equitable basis, the real needs of the people.

Communism and Socialism

There is, however, an important difference between the two principal methods of achieving a planned society which proves, on analysis, to be the main factor distinguishing Communism from Socialism. The difference is that in a Socialist society the social ideals to which the central planning is directed are subject to the criticism and endorsement of a free electorate. In a Communist society, on the other hand, freedom of thought and association is denied and adverse criticism of the policy of the central government is condemned and punished. In such circumstances there can be no assurance that the aims of the government have a democratic foundation, and the claim that they represent the true 'will of the people' is pure presumption and is exposed to all the objections which can be made to an Organic Theory of the State. To a democrat, indeed, the claim of a government to represent the 'will of the people' must appear wholly unjustified in the absence of democratic machinery through which that will can be freely expressed. The fact is that Socialism—or at least the present British variety—seeks to reconcile the fundamental ideals of Marx with the democratic machinery based upon the individualist assumptions of the utilitarian tradition. In other words, it is attempting to create a society based upon social

14

justice and the satisfaction of needs, while leaving to the people's judgment the ultimate decision whether, and how far, such a policy is to be carried out. The Communist believes that the free judgment of the people cannot be trusted to endorse such ideals until they have been realized—that until they have been realized those who benefit from economic inequality and privilege will oppose these ideals, and may oppose them with a substantial measure of success. But to this criticism the Socialist may well reply that this is a smaller risk than the risk of sacrificing democracy for ever by denying the basic liberties of thought and political association.

Marxism, Communism and Socialism

The three terms 'Marxism', 'Communism' and 'Socialism' have different meanings and are often confused. Marxism is a theory, partly philosophical but primarily scientific. It makes a general philosophical assumption, and thereafter proceeds to formulate the scientific, i.e. empirical, laws to which social evolution appears to conform. The philosophical assumption of Marxism is the assumption that the universe is a process of which the only possible knowledge is empirical or scientific knowledge. Apart from this fundamental proposition—which is treated as an analytic proposition—Marxism consists of a series of scientific propositions, of which the most important is that 'man's ideas, views and conceptions, in one word, man's consciousness, changes with every change in the conditions of his material existence, in his social relations and in his social life'[1] or, more briefly, that 'intellectual production changes its character in proportion as material production is changed'.[2] These are empirical generalizations, for which Marx claims no *a priori* certainty. He simply claims that dispassionate observation confirms their truth, and that the way to understand men's ideas, i.e. their beliefs (particularly on political, moral and religious questions), is not to seek for some *a priori* necessity which they do not possess but to discover, by scientific enquiry, their empirical relationship to the material environment of those who profess them. And he believes that observation shows that these relationships are of a constant character, so that laws may be formulated specifying the sort of ideas which will result from a

[1] ibid., p. 150. [2] loc. cit.

given type of material environment. There is, according to Marx, no other sense in which these beliefs can be 'understood'.

Marxism may therefore be briefly defined as the theory that (a) the only possible knowledge about the universe is empirical knowledge, and (b) scientific investigation shows that the evolution of society is determined by the interaction between men's material conditions and their ideas in accordance with certain empirical laws which may be discovered by scientific investigation.

While Marxism is thus a philosophical and scientific theory about the nature of social evolution, 'Communism' and 'Socialism' are words which are usually employed to designate certain political policies, i.e. programmes of action devised in order to achieve certain ends. The relationship between these policies and Marxism is that they aim, in varying degrees, at achieving the ends which Marxism is believed to justify. The difference, in so far as there is a difference, between Communists and Socialists is that Socialists accept the principle of achieving their ends through the machinery of a free democracy while Communists accept this only in so far as it is inevitable, and are ready to resort to unconstitutional means to attain their ends when such methods appear likely to be more successful. But both policies are mainly shaped by the Marxist ideal of changing existing society into one in which 'the labour power of all the individuals is consciously applied as one single social labour power',[1] i.e. in which the means of social production are placed under central control with a view to ensuring that these means are used for the maximum satisfaction of what are assumed to be the 'social needs' of the community. Both policies are directly opposed to the policy of free enterprise or *laisser-faire*, which they believe is bound to cause injustice and poverty.

But although these seem to be the ends of both Socialism and Communism, there is no ground for the belief that Marxism *justifies* these ends in a moral sense, i.e. shows that they ought to be pursued. All that Marxism as a scientific theory can say is that men do, or will, or must seek these ends because of the motives which determine their action. But to say that is quite different from saying that men *ought* to pursue such ends. A scientific proposition can never be the sole ground for a moral proposition, and according to Marxism moral propositions are in any case

[1] *Capital*, I, p. 50.

simply empirical propositions describing the reactions of men to their environment. They do not therefore provide a justification, but only an explanation, of men's actions. They show—in a purely empirical sense—why men *do* act in a certain way; for on an empirical theory the word *ought* must be defined in terms of empirical concepts, i.e. propositions containing the word 'ought' must be expressed in terms of propositions which are empirically verifiable.

Thus if Communism is based on certain moral ideals these ideals must be found elsewhere than in Marxism. The real relationship between Communism and Marxism seems, indeed, to be that Communists assume that there is a moral obligation to promote the ends towards which Marxism asserts that society is in any case advancing. But Marxism itself provides no justification for this assumption.

Socialists, as already observed, aim at the same general ideals as Communists, but accept the necessity of achieving those ideals through the machinery of a free democracy. In other words, they accept the individualist and utilitarian theory that the object of government is to promote the good of the individual, and that the individual is the best judge of what his good is. And they assume, by implication, that at least the majority of individuals in any society will, sooner or later, come to support freely the Socialist ideal of a planned society. Communists reject this assumption on the ground that until the ideals of Communism have been achieved the judgment of individuals will be perverted by the economic inequalities which surround them, and progress towards these ideals will therefore be impeded.

The Influence of Marxism

It is clear from the foregoing discussion that the practical influence of Marx's theory has been the exact opposite of its logical implications. His materialist philosophy and scientific generalizations should have encouraged the dispassionate scientific analysis of practical problems and the rejection of all dogmatic claims that certain ideals are objectively right and that others are objectively wrong. But the practical influence of Marxism has been very different. Far from encouraging the dispassionate scientific analysis of practical problems, it has inspired the violent condemnation of certain features of existing society and a fanatical determination to destroy these features and replace them by a new order. These two opposing tendencies are not least in evidence in Marx's own writings, where the clear enunciation of the materialist principle is followed by violent condemnation of the capitalist system. The truth is that in advocating the scientific study of society Marx forgot that his own emotional reactions to industrial conditions in the middle of the nineteenth century had no logical connection with his science, apart from being yet another illustration of the causal relationship between material conditions and human consciousness.

CHAPTER XIV

Political Philosophy in Contemporary Politics

IT IS obvious that in a country with a democratic constitution the differences of principle which divide political parties may be greatly diminished in practice by the democratic sanction which necessarily controls the application of those principles. Neither the parties of the Right nor of the Left can, as a rule, hope to apply their ideal policies without some modification and compromise in deference to public opinion. The Party of the Right usually has to move towards the Left and the Party of the Left usually has to move towards the Right when transforming ideals into practical policies. Such compromises are necessary because a democratic constitution as such can hope to survive only if the government in power avoids measures which appear radically unjust to those who oppose its policy and abstains from action which would be strongly resisted by a large section of the electorate. Thus a fundamental distinction must be drawn between the philosophies of, say, Conservatism and Socialism on the one hand and the extent to which these philosophies have been applied when Conservatives and Socialists respectively have been in power in the British Parliament.

Rationalism and Empiricism in Politics

A further distinction of great importance must be drawn before the place of political philosophy in contemporary politics can be accurately defined. For the reasons set forth in Chapter I, the fundamental distinction in political philosophy is necessarily between rationalist and empiricist theories, and that must be the division of truly philosophical significance behind the controversies of the present time. It is, of course, necessary to bear in mind the popular conception of a political philosophy as a series of moral assumptions or hypotheses justifying certain political policies and ideals. But that conception, as already shown, ignores the fundamental philosophical issue whether these moral assumptions can be rationally justified, or are simply empirical hypotheses which can provide only a hypothetical justification of a political creed.

Both because the theoretical difference between Conservatism and Socialism is obscured in practice by the force of public opinion, and because there are varying shades of opinion even among the official leaders of the Conservative and Socialist Parties, it is difficult to define their differences in terms of one or other of the fundamental philosophical alternatives just noted. But it is clear from the discussion in Chapter X that Conservatism is, in general, based upon empirical arguments of the sort put forward by Hume and Burke and that the difficulty of defining Conservative principles in precise and universal terms arises from the fact that these principles tend to vary in accordance with changing circumstances. The only principle sufficiently general to apply to all forms of practical Conservatism seems to be that of Utilitarianism. Conservative policy in all its manifestations does appear to be directed to the promotion of the greatest happiness of the greatest number and to vary in accordance with what seems, at a given time, to be the most effective way of achieving that utilitarian ideal.[1] Socialist policy, on the other hand, has always tended to assume a more rigid and doctrinaire character by insisting on the universal and unconditional validity of certain principles, such as social equality, or the state control of major industries and services. It is, for example, obvious that the Socialist Governments in Britain since the end of the second world war have tended to hold that such principles are inherently right and justifiable, and to regard as a secondary consideration whether, in fact, their

---

[1] Cf. R. A. Butler: 'We regard the State as a trustee for the interests of the community and a balancing force between different interests.' (*Fundamental Issues*, p. 7. Published by the Conservative Political Centre, 1946.)

Cf. also Quintin Hogg (now Lord Hailsham): 'The whole essence of the type of democracy in which they [Conservatives] put their trust is that the public good is attained by the interplay of rival forces, of which they recognize themselves to be but one. The whole basis of modern Conservatism is the rejection of the absolutist claims of the modern Socialist state.' (*The Case for Conservatism*, p. 13. Penguin Books, 1947.)

application will increase the happiness of all. Such an attitude clearly implies the validity of a rationalist morality and cannot be justified on empiricist assumptions.

Socialism and Communism

A rationalist philosophy has, of course, frequently been cited as the justification of a totalitarian government in which the right to criticize the moral principles implied by its policy is denied. That the British Socialist Party, despite the rationalist implications of its principles, has been able to take its place in the traditional two-party system of the British constitution, and has found it possible to work within the framework of Parliamentary democracy, is explained by the influence of the individualist and democratic tradition of political thought in Britain. While Socialists have, as a rule, no doubt about the moral rightness of the principles which they advocate, one of these principles is the principle of democratic consent, and they would therefore regard it as morally wrong to compel acceptance of other principles, such as the state control of industry, without the sanction of the electorate. On the other hand, just because they believe that these principles are the expression of objective and universal moral laws, they are confident that their truth will gradually become apparent to the great majority of people.

Thus Socialism of the type at present supported in British politics differs from Communism in its acceptance of democratic and Parliamentary methods for realising the aims laid down in the *Communist Manifesto*. Marx thought that these aims could be achieved only by revolutionary action and a dictatorship of the proletariat. While one variety of Socialism called Syndicalism, which has attracted considerable support on the Continent, resembles Communism in its policy of placing industry under the control of trade unions (which, in practice, if not in theory, comes very near to the dictatorship of the proletariat), Socialist parties have in general sought to achieve their aims through Parliamentary democracy. The Communist party has, of course, also been ready to avail itself of democratic machinery, but only so long as it has been too weak to use more forceful measures. Thus the fundamental difference between Socialists and Communists is that Socialists believe that a Communist society, or at least the greater part of it, can be achieved without the sacrifice of political democracy,[1] while Communists believe that this is quite impossible.

Another suggested difference between Socialists and Communists is that Socialists regard the state ownership and control of the means of production, distribution and exchange as a permanent feature of a just society, whereas Communists consider that the state ownership and control of industry is only a passing phase which is essential for the political re-education of the individual, and that when this task has been accomplished the state as a central organization will 'wither away' and give place, in Marx's own words, to 'an association in which the free development of each is the condition for the free development of all'.[2]

What exactly Marx meant by this 'withering away' of the state has been the subject of much controversy. The key to Marx's meaning probably lies in his statement that 'political power, properly so called, is merely the organized power of one class for oppressing another'. For the state is a political organization, and the need for it will therefore disappear when, following the elimination of class distinctions, political power no longer serves a purpose. This does not, however, mean that there will be no need for some central organization of the processes of production. It simply means that this organization will no longer serve a political purpose but will, instead, be a purely administrative arrangement for achieving the true will of every member of the classless society. Thus the 'withering away' of the state does not mean the disappearance of all central organization but only the elimination of the political forces by which that organization is directed in the capitalist state, and in consequence of which it fails to achieve a proper relation between 'the quantity of social labour time employed in the production of definite articles and the demand of society for them'.[3] In Marx's view Socialists must for this reason fail to achieve true social justice so long as they work within a system of Parliamentary democracy, for he believes that such a system is bound to perpetuate classes and class distinctions.

---

[1] i.e. democracy in the 'liberal' sense. Communists regard 'liberal' democracy as a travesty of true democracy, for the reasons given in Chapter XIII.
[2] *Manifesto of the Communist Party*, p. 153.
[3] *Capital*, Book III, p. 221.

Thus the refusal of democratic Socialists to adopt the means which Marx prescribes will, in his view, prevent them from achieving the ends which they profess to seek.

In Britain, the attempt to achieve Socialism without the sacrifice of political liberty is natural in view of the traditional individualism of the British outlook and the extent to which this has been given theoretical expression by political philosophers such as Hobbes, Locke, Hume, Bentham and Mill. Each of these thinkers argued that the purpose of the state is to promote and protect the rights or interests of the individual, and they assumed that there is no justification for discriminating between one individual and another. Bentham, in particular, held that the maximum happiness of each must constitute the maximum happiness of all, and argued that this must be the ultimate object of a rational politics. And when the application of the economic principle of *laisser-faire* resulted in gross inequalities of wealth and happiness, the Benthamite ideal was redefined in Socialist terms as 'social equality' and 'fair shares for all'.

The general form taken by British Socialism is, in short, the result of the individualist's emphasis on the happiness of the individual and the Marxist claim that an uncontrolled economy prevents the attainment of that happiness. Socialists adhere to the individualist ideal while accepting much of the Marxist prescription for the attainment of that ideal. Communists differ in holding that the maximising of individual happiness can be achieved only by the temporary sacrifice of individual liberty in the political sphere—i.e. the liberties of free speech, a free press and free political association. And this difference is ultimately an expression of the Marxist theory that a society is an organism, and that individuals may misconstrue the real interests of society as a whole. Communist policy therefore assumes, by implication, an Organic Theory of the State, and cannot be consistently supported by those who reject that theory. For the individualist the Marxist ideal of social equality must stand or fall by the judgment passed on it by the individual members of a community, and if it is supported it will be supported either because it is believed to be a moral ideal or simply because it is desired.

If we discount the Communist theory of an ultimate anarchy, which has so far shown no sign of emerging in actual Communist states, the essential difference between Socialist and Communist Parties lies not in their objectives but in the methods by which they seek to attain these objectives and the reasons by which they seek to justify them. For both the primary objective may be briefly defined as 'social equality', i.e. the removal, or at least the drastic reduction, of the inequalities arising from inherited wealth and private ownership of the means of production, distribution and exchange.[1] But while democratic Socialists believe that this objective will ultimately be supported by the vast majority of people on grounds either of interest or morality, Communists believe that its attainment will be effectively prevented so long as those who benefit from social inequality are free to exercise their political and economic powers in defence of the existing system. Hence, Communists argue, the socially privileged must be deprived of these powers by force if social inequality is to be eliminated. And this, in practice, means that freedom of speech, publication and political association must be withdrawn until the social revolution has been accomplished and the 'bourgeois mentality' effectively destroyed.

Conservatism and Socialism in Britain

The common foundation underlying the differences of policy between the major parties now operating in British politics can be illustrated by reference to the respective attitudes of the Conservative and Labour Parties to the major issues of contemporary politics. Both accept the principle of the 'Welfare State', even if Conservatives believe that it could and should be run more economically. Both agree that it is necessary to control industry, even if Socialists believe in carrying such control considerably further than Conservatives. Both accept the desirability of some redistribution of wealth, although they may take different views of the extent to which, and the way in which, this redistribution should be carried out. Both support the United Nations Organization and the North Atlantic Treaty Organization for the purpose of preventing war, and accept the consequent obligation to create and maintain an agreed level of armed strength. In short, the differences between the policies of the Conservative and

[1] Cf. *Manifesto of the Communist Party*, p. 143: 'The theory of Communists may be summed up in the single sentence: Abolition of private property [i.e. capital].'

Labour Parties in Britain are differences of degree rather than of kind in the proposals advanced for the abolition of privilege and the promotion of equality.

Similar differences existed between the Conservative and Liberal Parties before the Labour Party took its place as one of the two major parties in 1922. It is true that Liberals—as their name indeed indicates—tended to regard Mill's essay *On Liberty* as the classic expression of their individualist philosophy, and their long and uncompromising support of the economic principle of Free Trade was a notable illustration of this attitude; but in the sphere of social reform the Liberal Government which held office between 1906 and the outbreak of the first world war carried through many measures of a 'collectivist' character which involved interference with the liberty of some individuals in the interest of others. On the other hand, while Conservatives have, on the whole, been less disposed to profess specific principles, they were the first to accept and introduce the principle of Government control of industrial conditions in the interest of the workers,[1] and in their advocacy of tariff reform they also rejected the principle of *laisser-faire*.

For the reasons mentioned earlier in this chapter, these differences of practical policy are not necessarily identical with the differences of theoretical principle professed by the parties in question. The theoretical differences may in practice be substantially qualified, and thus obscured, by considerations of expediency. It is therefore necessary to look beneath the superficial differences of party policy if the more fundamental differences of philosophical principle are to be accurately defined. And at this level there is a fundamental difference underlying the policies of the Conservative and Socialist Parties of contemporary Britain. The impossibility of defining Conservative policy in precise terms, and, still more, in terms that do not change from time to time, shows that it must ultimately be justified by an Empiricist Theory of Morality. It is not consistent with the 'eternal and immutable' principles of the rationalist. The moral ends of politics are, for the Conservative, determined by the generally prevailing view of what those ends should be, and the generally prevailing view is recognized to be subject to modification and development under changing circumstances. Such was the view

[1] In the Factory Acts.

of both Hume and Burke, and its illustration in the history of the Conservative Party is obvious.

It is equally obvious that the theoretical ideals of British Socialism are based upon the assumption that moral principles are *a priori*. The nationalization of essential industries and services, the redistribution of wealth, and the abolition of privilege are advocated not on the ground that they are generally desired but on the ground that they are intrinsically good, and because, even if they involve some sacrifice of happiness, good ends ought to be pursued. A just society is, to the Socialist, more important than a prosperous or a happy one—if it cannot be both at the same time.[1] The nationalization of essential industries and services is advocated not primarily because nationalization is counted on to improve efficiency or to reduce prices or to result in some other material benefit but because it is held to be morally wrong that essential industries and services should be under private control and thus possible sources of private profit. No doubt the Socialist believes that the just society will, on the whole and in the end, also be the happiest, but if this were not so he would say that it was more important to make society just than to make it happy.

While Socialism—at least of the British variety—thus differs from Communism in basing its policy upon moral principles, these principles have, as already observed, been largely borrowed from the *Manifesto of the Communist Party*. The general ideal of 'social equality' is a Marxist ideal, and Socialists have accepted it as a moral ideal, although it cannot be so regarded by a consistent Marxist. Yet although Marx was in theory a materialist, he defended the ideal of social equality with all the fervour of a moralist, and much of what he advocated has, as shown in Chapter XIII, been readily incorporated in the creed of modern Socialism.

Thus the difference between the Conservative and Socialist Parties in modern Britain corresponds to the philosophical difference between the Empiricist and Rationalist Theories of

---

[1] Cf. Douglas Jay, *The Socialist Case* (1947), p. 28: 'The State choosing collectively between the welfare of different sets of people must employ some other criterion than a calculus of desires or happiness. And the only possible criterion available for the collective choice is the direct judgment that this or that state of society, as a whole, is the better.'

Morality. Conservatism is in principle a more flexible, variable and adaptable political creed. Socialism is inclined to be rigid, uncompromising, and authoritarian. But these tendencies are greatly obscured in practice by the necessity imposed on both parties of working within the framework of parliamentary democracy.

Democratic and Authoritarian Types of Government

It is in communities where the machinery of parliamentary democracy does not operate that the political implications of a Rationalist Theory of Morality are most clearly manifest, for these implications are not then obscured or modified by considerations of expediency or compromise. During the present century these conditions for the uncompromising application of a rationalist morality have been provided by two opposing systems of government—Fascism and Communism. Although in some ways sharply opposed, these systems both exemplify the authoritarian principle of government and thus stand in sharp opposition to all forms of democracy. And although Marxism, as a materialist philosophy, cannot consistently admit the possibility of *a priori* moral principles, Communists in practice accord to their ideals the unquestioning and uncritical respect due to moral principles of unconditional validity.

The difference between democratic and authoritarian government can be defined in different ways. It is the difference between government by consent and government by authority; between utilitarian and moral government; between the conception of the state as a useful mechanism and the conception of it as an end in itself; between acceptance of the individual's will and judgment as the ultimate directive of action and acceptance of the 'general will' of the state as the definition of the 'real' will of the individual. And in practice the difference is that between a state in which the ultimate sanction for government is recognized to be the will of the majority and that in which a minority of individuals claim the right to govern the majority and succeed in getting the majority to admit that claim.

The philosophical basis of authoritarian government is the Organic Theory of the State (or of Society), with its implication that there is a 'general will' defining the moral standard to which individuals ought to conform. Even the Marxist adaptation of the Organic Theory preserves this essential principle by asserting that the forces which determine social evolution represent the interests of classes and that the interests of classes define the true interests of individual members of these classes, even if individuals sometimes take a different view of what their interest is. According to all such theories, the claim of the few to exercise authority over the many rests upon the fact that the individual human being is an organic constituent of a more comprehensive social unit (whether a state or a class), and that neither his real desires nor his real duties can be determined except in terms of his place and function in that more comprehensive unit. Moreover, it is held that the correct determination of that place and function must be entrusted to experts, since the individual as such may misunderstand what his 'real' desires or duties are. But to supporters of an individualist philosophy the insuperable objection to a theory of this sort is the impossibility of determining, except in a purely arbitrary way, who the alleged experts are, and therefore what the true interest and duty of any given individual is. In the subordinate function of selecting the most effective means for the realization of specified ends, the democrat readily admits the place of experts; but he insists that their function is essentially advisory, and that, when their advice has been given, one individual has as much right as another to decide what is to be done, although, to avoid deadlock, the view of the majority is accepted. This view follows logically from the Empiricist Theory of Morality.

The Authoritarian Theory of Government is at present illustrated almost exclusively by Communist states. Before the second world war it was also illustrated by the Fascist Governments of Germany and Italy; and some features of Fascism are still found in Spain and other countries. The Marxist holds that, whatever the superficial resemblance between Communist and Fascist states, the political philosophies upon which they are based are fundamentally different in that the authoritarian features of a Communist dictatorship are only means—though necessary means—to the achievement of true democracy, whereas the authoritarian features of a Fascist state are necessary and permanent elements in a system where the state is revered as the highest expression of the human spirit, and thus the essential foundation of the good society.[1] The Fascist state is therefore generally admitted to exemplify the authoritarian principle of government, while Communists claim that the dictatorship of the proletariat is a transitional stage in the evolution of society. But to supporters of democracy this theoretical distinction has yet to be justified, since there is so far no sign that the authoritarian governments of Communist states will 'wither away'. On the contrary, everything that has so far taken place in these states suggests that, as time goes on, the power of their governments will become more absolute and unchallenged, and the character of government in a Communist state will thus become indistinguishable from the form which it takes in a Fascist state, however different the ostensible objects of the different systems may be.

The Causes of War

These alternative forms of government have important consequences for the conduct of international relations. If all the world's states were democratic, there is no reason to doubt that the democratic method of solving disputes by negotiation and compromise would be extended to the international sphere. For all the indications are that the large majority of individuals in all nations are opposed to war, and would refuse to sanction resort to war except in self-defence, and it therefore seems unlikely that the occasion for self-defence would ever arise if all nations had democratic governments. The danger of war arises from the existence of authoritarian states in which the decision to make war lies in the hands of a few individuals who can count on the

[1] Cf. Rocco, 'The Political Doctrine of Fascism' in *International Conciliation*, No. 223, p. 21: 'Fascism therefore not only rejects the dogma of popular sovereignty and substitutes for it that of state sovereignty, but it also proclaims that the great mass of citizens is not a suitable advocate of social interests for the reason that the capacity to ignore individual private interests in favour of the higher demands of society and of history is a very rare gift and the privilege of the chosen few.'

Cf. also Mussolini's definition of Fascism in the *Enciclopedia Italiana*, Vol. XIV (translated by Jane Soames in the *Political Quarterly*, 1933): 'Fascism is a religious conception in which man is seen in immanent relation to a higher law, an objective Will, that transcends the particular individual and raises him to conscious membership in a spiritual society.'

rest of the community to implement their decision without question or hesitation. It was this consideration which made Germany and Italy standing threats to peace before the outbreak of the second world war; and it is this consideration which, in the opinion of many people, makes Soviet Russia and Communist China and their satellites constitute a standing menace to peace today, however much their rulers may claim to be seeking peace, and however alien to Marxist philosophy the resort to international war may appear to be. If, as in the democracies, the individual citizen had the final decision to make, all the empirical evidence points to the probability that he would refuse to sanction war as a means of settling international disputes, and if the citizens of all countries possessed this power and exercised it in this way it follows that governments would be compelled to settle their disputes by peaceful methods.

The widespread fear of war at the present time is explained quite simply by the consideration that a large proportion of the world's population lives under Communist governments, which regard the democratic states with fear and suspicion, while the democratic states regard the Communist states in the same way. To the Communist states the democracies are bourgeois societies depending upon an economic and social system which can only survive if resort is periodically made to war; while to the democracies the Communist states appear as totalitarian systems under the complete control of absolute dictators whose actions are unpredictable and who are bound, sooner or later, to be corrupted by the absolute power which they possess.

There is no obvious way by which this deadlock of suspicion and distrust can be brought to an end. It resembles the 'state of nature' as conceived by Hobbes, with the opposing groups of states living, like Hobbes's individuals, in a condition of continuous tension, whence the lives of their peoples tend to be 'poor, nasty, brutish, and short'.[1] Hobbes would have said that this situation can be brought to an end only if the rival states voluntarily lay down their 'right to do all things' and transfer this right to an international sovereign body capable of maintaining the peace; and he would have said that this is likely to occur only if the rival powers come to the conclusion that it is in their interest to make this surrender of national sovereignty. There

[1] *Leviathan*, Chap. XIII.

has, however, been abundant evidence in recent years that sovereign states are most reluctant to make any real surrender of their sovereign powers, even when they are not divided by the mutual suspicions which characterize the relations of the democratic and Communist states. It therefore seems unlikely that the present tension will be removed by the creation of a single international sovereign power. On the other hand, both sides may stop short of precipitating war from fear of the incalculable consequences which it is likely to have.

Among the democracies themselves the problem of maintaining peace without the transfer of sovereignty to an international organization is simpler. For their policies are all subject to popular consent, and the available evidence suggests that it would be difficult for any government to obtain such consent for aggressive purposes.[1] The vast majority of the citizens of all democracies desire peace and, after the experience of two world wars, are unconvinced that there is any purpose, except resistance to aggression, for which it would be either justifiable or advantageous to fight. Moreover, their experience of the functioning of democratic machinery at home inevitably suggests to them that it can and ought to be employed in the international field as well, and that agreement by compromise is better than resort to force as a solution of international disputes. Thus the maintenance of peace and the gradual creation of recognized machinery for the solution of international problems appears to be perfectly possible, so far as the democratic states are concerned, without a formal surrender of their sovereign powers.

The fact is that the relationship of the democratic states bears a much closer resemblance to Locke's conception of the 'state of nature' than to Hobbes's. The fear, suspicion, and tension which characterized the state of nature as conceived by Hobbes are familiar features of the so-called 'cold war' which has now existed for some years between the democratic and Communist states, and Hobbes's conclusions seem to be in many ways directly applicable to their relationship. But the democracies need not be antagonistic and mutually hostile. In general, like the majority of individuals in Locke's state of nature, they recognize

---

[1] This generalization is not contradicted by the periodical use of armed force to coerce subject peoples, e.g. in Malaya or Kenya, since such campaigns are essentially police activities on a large scale.

the advantage of observing a moral code, although in their case it is, of course, a code defining the rights and duties of nations instead of the rights and duties of individuals. There is, in short, a desire among the democracies to co-operate with one another in a peaceful and mutually advantageous manner; and the purpose of expressing this desire through the medium of international agreements and organizations is the same as the purpose which, according to Locke, made it desirable to establish civil government, namely the 'inconveniences' which result when men are 'judges in their own case'.[1] It is obvious that there may be corresponding 'inconveniences' in international relationships if states insist upon being 'judges in their own case', and an important advantage to all nations in setting up some form of government on an international basis.

National Sovereignty and International Relations

It has, of course, been made abundantly clear during the past few years that sovereign states are still reluctant to make a formal surrender of their sovereignty. The 'veto' which any one of the five Great Powers may exercise on action approved by the recognized voting procedure of the United Nations and the resistance shown—not least by Britain—to all proposals to accord the Council of Europe powers which might encroach upon national sovereignty are notable illustrations of this reluctance. But, again, this opposition to a surrender of sovereignty corresponds exactly to Locke's account of the basis of civil government. What the democratic states oppose is not membership of international organizations but the surrender of that power—as expressed in their control over their armed forces—without which they would not be able to withdraw from the international organization if it ceased to serve the purposes for which it was established. As Locke said of civil government: 'There remains still in the people a supreme power to remove or alter the legislative, when they find the legislative act contrary to the trust reposed in them.'[2] The democratic states wish to retain that power to 'remove or alter' the international organizations in which they participate if these organizations 'act contrary to the trust reposed in them'; and the power to do this would not exist if these states had surrendered

[1] *On Civil Government*, Book II, para. 13.
[2] ibid., para. 149.

the essence of their sovereign power—their control over their armed forces—to an international body.[1]

But the maintenance of sovereign power by individual states is, as already observed, no necessary obstacle to the maintenance of peace. Not power by itself but its object is what may menace peace. If power is sought and maintained for domination and conquest it is bound to be a standing menace to peace. But if those purposes would never be sanctioned by a democratic community, sovereign power in the hands of a democracy can be no menace to its neighbours. And, of course, the measure of power maintained by the democracies during the past thirty years might have fallen almost to the level of token forces but for the menace of totalitarian aggression by such authoritarian states as Germany, Italy, and the Soviet Union.

Sovereign power, in short, is by itself a neutral factor in international relations. It can be used to foment war, or it can be used to support international machinery for the peaceful settlement of international disputes and the organizing of collective resistance to aggression. If the latter are the objects of the democratic states their retention of sovereign power will not menace peace and will help to ensure that the international organizations which are set up fulfil, and do not disappoint, the purposes for which they were established.

Although the fear and suspicion which are shown by the democratic and Communist states towards each other constitute a serious menace to peace, the danger may well be less than it would be if a Fascist government controlled a powerful country. For Communists at least profess to seek peace, and it has still to be shown that they are prepared to resort to international war—as distinct from revolutionary propaganda and action—in the furtherance of their aims. On the other hand, the Fascist conception of government is derived directly from the philosophy of Hegel, and accepts war as a desirable and necessary measure for bringing about higher and more valuable forms of social life, and ensuring that the nation which is most fitted to dominate the

---

[1] Some surrender of sovereignty is involved in membership of the North Atlantic Treaty Organization and the European Defence Community; but this, of course, has been brought about by the common fear of Soviet aggression and not by a failure to co-operate with other democracies on a basis of full national sovereignty.

world does so. According to this theory, any opposition to war by individuals must be ruthlessly suppressed, and no restriction on the 'will of the state' must be tolerated in its dealings with other states. As observed in the chapters on Rousseau and Hegel, there is no obvious reason why a universal state should not gradually emerge from these conflicts, but neither Rousseau nor Hegel appeared to think this possible.

For the time being, however, the dominating feature of world politics is the contrast and opposition between the democratic and Communist states, and this contrast is ultimately based upon the fundamental philosophical alternatives which have been defined above. The question at issue is the question whether the individual or the state is the primary entity, and whether the actions of government are therefore to be justified by reference to the will of the individual or by reference to the will of the state. It is true that Marxism subordinates the individual to society rather than to the state, and regards the state as a temporary and transient device of exploitation. But in its subordination of the individual to social forces which he cannot, and, in his own interest, should not, attempt to resist, Marxism exhibits the essential characteristics of an Organic Theory.

CHAPTER XV

The Justification of Government

IF A SHORT and simple phrase is required to describe the essential purpose of political philosophy as commonly understood, the justification of government would seem to meet the need. For it is clear from the foregoing analysis of a number of important and representative political philosophies that this is, in fact, their primary objective. Politics itself may be defined as the organization and regulation of compulsory human relations in a community or, more briefly, as the organization of government; while political philosophy, as commonly understood, is an attempt to define the moral principles prescribing what the methods and aims of government ought to be. But this, for the reasons given in Chapter I, is a somewhat superficial conception of political philosophy, for it ignores the underlying question whether these moral principles are *a priori* propositions of universal validity or whether they are empirical generalizations which can only justify hypothetical conclusions about what the methods and aims of government ought to be.

It is quite clear that many of the most important political philosophers have assumed that the moral principles which justify government are either self-evident or capable of rational demonstration and therefore constitute a categorical basis for its justification. But such philosophers—of whom Plato and Locke are typical examples—have not, in general, considered the fundamental question whether propositions which are admittedly synthetic can be rationally justified. Kant and Hegel and their followers are the only political philosophers who have recognized the real significance of this question and have attempted to provide a rational justification of synthetic moral propositions. Hegel's solution, as was shown in Chapter XI, was to argue that the good will is the rational will, that the rational will is the will of the state, and that the nature of this rational will can be dialectically deduced from the notion of will as such.

The fallacies in Hegel's argument were explained at length in Chapter XI and need not be reconsidered here. If the reasons there given for rejecting his conclusions are valid some form of Empiricism must necessarily be accepted, and this implies that the series of moral propositions which have often been accepted as adequate political philosophies are, in fact, simply empirical generalizations which can have no universal application or validity and may vary from place to place and from time to time. In short, Empiricism implies that the only justification which can be given for government is a hypothetical one and that there is no possible way of providing a categorical justification at any stage. The justification must take the form put forward by either Hobbes or Hume, namely that if certain ends are desired, or are held to be 'good', and if certain methods are the most effective for achieving those ends, then those methods ought to be adopted. But the conclusion that those methods ought to be adopted is a hypothetical one depending on the validity of the two hypothetical propositions from which it is deduced; and the word 'ought' does not possess the categorical significance which is usually attached to it.

Implications of Empiricism

The most important implication of Empiricism is that there is no rational way of resolving ultimate differences regarding political ideals since the assertion that X (e.g. the general happiness) is such an ideal is, according to Empiricism, necessarily a synthetic proposition and thus devoid of rational necessity. It does not, of course, follow from this that there is no rational way of resolving many of the less ultimate differences which actually arise. It may often be possible to show that the opposing aims of two political organizations are logically inconsistent with some more general aim which is accepted by both. It might, for example, be possible to resolve the differences between the Conservative and Socialist Parties regarding the extent to which industry should be controlled by government if both adhered consistently to a more general aim, such as reducing the cost of living. For then it would be possible, in theory at least, to resolve the differences by showing that a specific form of government control either does, or does not, tend in practice to reduce the cost of living. It is, in general, possible that many disagreements could be resolved by the rational process of drawing the logical implications of assumptions held in common by the parties to the dispute. But, unless Hegel's theory of reasoning is accepted, there is no ground for assuming that this process, however far it is carried, will lead to universal agreement on ultimate moral principles and, therefore, no ground for assuming that differences about such principles can ultimately be eliminated.

If Empiricism is accepted it therefore follows that there is no rational assurance that disagreement about political principles and ideals can be resolved. This in turn implies that there is no justification for the common assumption that the incompatible views of totalitarian and democratic communities about the rights of the individual cannot both be true. Empiricism implies that, in the only sense in which such doctrines can be true, both may be true and that an ultimate and irresolvable difference may therefore exist.

If this conclusion is accepted, it follows that there is no *rational* way of eliminating ultimate differences of moral principle, and that in practice such conflicts must be resolved by one of three alternative methods, namely force, compromise, or toleration. In other words, if the different principles accepted by different states result in the adoption of policies which ultimately bring these states into conflict, then this conflict can be resolved only if one of these states succeeds in dominating the other; or if one meets the other half-way by some measure of compromise; or, finally, if they avoid conflict by 'agreeing to differ' in a spirit of mutual toleration. In any case, the acceptance of the Empiricist Theory, far from promoting conflict, might help to prevent it by showing that such a conflict would simply be a conflict of opposing forces and not, as is frequently assumed, a conflict between 'right' and 'might'.

Implications of Rationalism

On the other hand, a Rationalist Theory of the kind defended by Hegel implies that in the will of the state there is an absolute standard of morality with which no compromise ought to be permitted. And this in turn implies that between the wills of two states there may be a conflict which ought to be resolved by a trial of strength. No doubt Hegel's theory also implies that states may fall short of perfection, and that their wills may not therefore be wholly good. But, as was shown in Chapter XI, he provides no criterion for showing how good states may be distinguished from bad ones; and the practical effect of his theory, when accepted, has been to strengthen the assumption that 'the state can do no wrong'. Hence when the wills of different states are in conflict the acceptance of the Hegelian theory tends to encourage the adoption of a rigid and uncompromising attitude and a resort to war. And to Hegel war was far from being an unqualified evil. As he put it: 'War has the higher significance that by its agency the ethical health of peoples is preserved in their indifference to the stabilization of finite institutions; just as the blowing of the winds preserves the sea from the foulness which would be the result of a prolonged calm, so also corruption in nations would be the product of prolonged, let alone "perpetual" peace.'[1] In other words, the conflict of states shows that none has achieved the ultimate good in its 'finite institutions', and war has the salutary consequence of promoting moral progress by preventing the perpetuation of existing imperfections.

Hegel's political theory has undoubtedly exercised its influence in this direction, although a proper understanding of it should have encouraged a more modest view of the powers of finite intelligence. But where Hegelianism has been influential, its insistence on the limitations of human judgment has been largely ignored, and the conception of the general will eagerly seized upon as providing an absolute standard of moral value. This conception has been welcomed in the belief that it provides a universal and objective criterion of morality, and the problem of determining when a will is truly 'general' has been conveniently ignored.

Hume's Empiricism

The alternative analysis offered by Empiricism is not faced with the difficulty of establishing an absolute standard of morality. On the other hand, it need not, and as expounded by Hume does not, deny the reality of moral experience. As was shown in Chapter X, Hume took special care, particularly in the later exposition of his theory in the *Enquiry*, to emphasize that the 'pleasing

[1] *Philosophy of Right* (tr. by T. M. Knox), p. 210.

16

sentiment of approbation' in which moral approval consists is 'pleasant' in quite a specific sense of that word, since it may enjoin the performance of acts which are far from 'pleasant' in the ordinary sense. Thus Hume was able to account in purely empirical terms for the distinction commonly drawn between duty and inclination; and it is by no means obvious that such an analysis of moral experience is inadequate, even though it implies that the laws of morality are simply empirical generalizations about the moral feelings of individuals or groups of individuals.

If moral laws can be reduced in this way to empirical generalizations about the occurrence of the feelings of approbation and disapprobation, the question arises whether there is any general 'law' which describes the circumstances which normally evoke these feelings. As was shown in Chapter X, Hume believed that these feelings generally express a natural human tendency to feel pleased at what tends to promote happiness (whether in oneself or in others) and to feel displeased at what tends to diminish happiness (whether in oneself or in others). But this, again, is a purely empirical generalization, and Hume does not think that it is universally true. From instinct, habit, or tradition men sometimes approve acts which do not tend to promote the general happiness; and although Hume believed that if such men could be convinced by empirical evidence that such acts did not in fact promote the general happiness they would usually cease to approve them, he recognized that this, also, was a purely empirical generalization, and that there is no reason why men must approve acts which tend to promote the general happiness. As he said in a striking passage:

> 'Tis not contrary to reason to prefer the destruction of the whole world to the scratching of my finger. 'Tis not contrary to reason for me to choose my total ruin, to prevent the least uneasiness of an Indian or person wholly unknown to me. 'Tis as little contrary to reason to prefer even my own acknowledged lesser good to my greater, and have a more ardent affection for the former than the latter.[1]

There is, in other words, no *reason* to explain why the vast majority of people would never entertain these preferences. The explanation is the purely empirical one that such preferences are

[1] *Treatise of Human Nature*, II, iii, 3.

determined not by reason but by feeling (or 'sentiment', as Hume says), and that the feelings implanted in human nature are such that the vast majority of people cannot help preferring a scratch on the finger to the destruction of the world, or the 'uneasiness of an Indian' to personal ruin, or a greater to a smaller personal good. In the same way, Hume believed that the vast majority of people cannot help approving acts which are shown to be useful, or disapproving acts which are shown to be the contrary of useful. He recognized that in practice the feelings of approval and disapproval are largely determined by habit and convention, but he believed that the application of the principle of utility can do much to influence those feelings, and to ensure that acts which, under changed circumstances, cease to have the utilitarian value which they formerly possessed are no longer approved. For he held that few, if any, people would approve an act which they believed to be contrary to the principle of utility.

These considerations show where the ultimate difference between the Rationalist and Empiricist Moral Theories lies. The Rationalist Theory implies that virtue is its own reward and its own justification. The Empiricist Theory implies that moral judgments, as synthetic propositions, could conceivably have been other than they are, and offers an empirical explanation why they are what in fact they are. The explanation offered by Hume is that moral judgments are what they are because experience has shown that certain habits of conduct tend to promote the general happiness and because such conduct is the sort of conduct which usually evokes the feelings of moral approval. But this association between the feeling of moral approval and the utilitarian tendencies of an act is empirical and contingent, and does not imply that the feeling of moral approval can never be excited by acts which have no utilitarian tendency, or that there is any *a priori* sense in which it 'ought' to be excited by acts which do have a utilitarian tendency.

One important consideration which supports the Empiricist Theory is that it can account so simply for the varying and often inconsistent moral judgments which are actually made. Such inconsistencies are particularly striking when the moral codes of different communities or different epochs are compared, but they may be found within a single community as well. In contemporary Britain, for example, different people take opposing views about the morality of gambling, divorce, and blood sports, and express these views in contradictory moral judgments. Such disagreements are easily explained by the Empiricist Theory, which asserts that they are based upon the different moral feelings aroused in different persons by contemplation of the same activity. The Rationalist Theory, on the other hand, implies that such activities are either good or bad quite independently of the feelings which they excite, and it must therefore provide some criterion for determining which of two contradictory moral judgments is true and which is false. And this, of course, is just what Rationalist Theories from the time of Plato onwards have failed to do, and what, in Hume's opinion, they could not conceivably succeed in doing.

The fact is that any moral theory which claims to be adequate must offer some explanation of the undeniable facts of moral controversy. People do frequently disagree about what is right and what is wrong, and the Rationalist Theory, which asserts that conflicting moral judgments are logically inconsistent, must obviously show how to distinguish between those which are true and those which are false. On the other hand, the Empiricist Theory is not faced with this problem, if it regards these incompatible moral judgments as judgments describing the different feelings excited in different persons by contemplation of the same act or situation. The Empiricist Theory may, of course, indicate a method by which such differences may be eliminated if it can show that moral approval is generally excited by the contemplation of acts which tend to promote the general happiness, for it may then be possible to distinguish, in the light of well established empirical generalizations, between acts which really have this tendency and those which are falsely believed to have it.

Meaning of 'Justification'

It follows from the foregoing considerations that the sort of 'justification' which can be offered for government takes a fundamentally different form according to whether a Rationalist or Empiricist Theory of Morality is adopted. The Rationalist Theory implies that there are moral principles of an *a priori* character which constitute an objective and unconditional justification of certain forms of government. The Empiricist Theory implies that moral principles are necessarily of a synthetic and empirical character, and that the justification of government which they provide is therefore conditional on the truth of these principles in the particular context to which they are applied. For, since these principles are synthetic propositions, they are devoid of rational necessity, and it is for experience to say whether, in a given context, they are, in fact, true. For example, the moral principle—generally accepted in some form by democratic peoples—that a human being has certain absolute rights which any government ought to respect is, if true, an important criterion for determining whether a certain form of government is, or is not, justified. But the Empiricist Theory of Morality implies that this principle is without rational necessity, and may not, therefore, be universally true. And if in some contexts it is not true, it will be possible to justify forms of government which do not observe it. In terms of Hume's particular application of Empiricism, a form of government which does not recognize the principle of individual rights can be justified in so far as the denial of that principle does not arouse the sentiment of moral disapproval.

But Empiricism need not, of course, take the form which was defended by Hume. It may, as in the theories of Machiavelli, Hobbes and Bentham be combined with a Naturalistic Theory of Morality. Such a theory asserts that the basic moral concepts of *good*, *bad*, *right*, and *wrong* can be defined in terms of non-moral concepts such as *pleasant*, *painful*, *expedient* and *inexpedient*. It asserts, in other words, that moral terms are synonymous with non-moral terms, and that there is nothing specific or peculiar in what is commonly described as moral experience.

This naturalistic interpretation of morality does not, however, affect the issue of primary interest to the philosopher. Whether or not moral experience is unique and irreducible is a question for the psychologist to determine; and however he answers that question the issue which concerns the philosopher is whether moral or quasi-moral propositions are *a priori* or empirical. For, if they are empirical, they are without rational necessity, and cannot afford more than a hypothetical justification for action. Whether or not 'the good' means simply 'the desired', the proposition 'X is good' cannot constitute more than a hypothetical justification for seeking X if it is an empirical proposition, for the justification will then be based on the hypothesis '*if* X is good'.

Only if the proposition 'X is good' is *a priori*, and thus necessarily true, will the justification for seeking X be categorical and unconditional.

Justification, in short, means moral justification, and, like morality itself, has a meaning whether or not moral concepts can be defined in terms of non-moral concepts. Government is said to be justified if its methods are 'right' and its ends are 'good', whether or not 'right' and 'good' can be defined in non-moral terms. The question of philosophical importance is whether a categorical or only a hypothetical justification of government can be given, and this, as already shown, depends on whether moral propositions—however interpreted—are *a priori* or empirical. The justification of government can be an unconditional and categorical justification only if moral propositions are *a priori* in character. If these propositions are synthetic and empirical their truth in any given context cannot be assumed. Only experience can show whether they are true in a given context. What sort of experience is relevant to their truth depends, of course, on the nature of the moral experience which such propositions describe. If Hume was right in holding that moral experience consists in the feelings of approval and disapproval which certain acts, characters or situations arouse, then a moral proposition will be true or false according to whether it accurately describes the moral feelings which are aroused in a given situation. And Hume's theory therefore implies that the justification of government must depend on the moral feelings which it arouses, and that a specific form of government may be justified in the opinion of one individual or community and not in the opinion of another.

Hume thought that his theory was quite consistent with the fact that the members of a given community are, as a rule, in general agreement about the form of government which they approve, for he thought it only natural that the combined influence of tradition, habit and self-interest should tend to evoke in them the sentiments of approval and disapproval towards the same things. Where this general measure of agreement does not exist, he would have said that conditions are ripe for revolution, and that the latter is very likely to occur unless one of the opposing factions is of negligible strength and can be effectively suppressed.

It may be said in criticism of the Empiricist Theory that it bases the justification of government on moral principles which can be defined in the light of experience but which can never be justified by the necessity of reason; and that some form of Rationalist Theory must therefore be preferred in view of the final and categorical nature of the justification which it claims to give. But to this the empiricist may reply that none of the attempts made by rationalists from Plato onwards have succeeded in demonstrating the rational necessity of moral propositions, or of resolving the existing conflict between the moral principles of different races, nations and individuals, except where they have shown that some of the accepted principles are logically inconsistent; and of course empiricists are equally entitled to say that logically inconsistent principles cannot all be true. In short, the empiricist can argue that the rationalist has not, in practice, been any more successful than the empiricist in finding ultimate and self-evident moral premises which are universally accepted, and that his failure to do so at once illustrates and justifies the empiricist's contention that such premises are, from their very nature, empirical in character and without rational necessity.

Justification of Different Forms of Government

The essential distinction between authoritarian and democratic forms of government is the distinction between government by those who claim authority through superior knowledge and government by those who claim authority through popular support, and this distinction is, in the end, an expression of the distinction between the Rationalist and Empiricist Theories of Morality. For a Rationalist Theory of Morality implies that government ought to be authoritarian, and an Empiricist Theory implies that it ought to be democratic in these senses. A Rationalist Theory implies that government ought to be authoritarian because it implies that there are moral laws which are necessarily and universally true, and that anyone who apprehends those laws clearly and applies them consistently enjoys an authority which others ought to respect and obey. This was the form of government which Plato defended just because he believed that only a minority of people were capable of apprehending the *a priori* truths of morality. On the other hand, according to the Empiricist Theory of Morality moral laws are empirical generalizations, and no such generalizations are necessarily universal. No one, therefore, can claim that his moral judgments are universally applicable and authoritative; for a different and apparently incompatible judgment made by someone else may be equally true in the only sense in which such judgments can be true.

The democratic practice of permitting the free expression of individual opinions, while accepting the opinion of the majority as the ultimate directive of policy, is an implicit recognition of these principles of Empiricism. It would, of course, be untrue to say that all supporters of democracy are aware of the underlying philosophical principle, but it is true to say that the Empiricist Theory of Morality implies that a moral judgment cannot be rejected as false on the ground that it is *prima facie* inconsistent with one which is accepted as true. Two logically inconsistent judgments cannot, of course, both be true, but on the Empiricist Theory one man's judgment that X is good and another man's judgment that X is not good may both be true in the sense that the contemplation of X excites the feeling of moral approval in the one and excites the feeling of moral disapproval in the other, i.e. the two judgments are not really inconsistent. Thus the Empiricist Theory of Morality supplies the ultimate justification for the moral toleration which is the essential feature of the democratic way of life.

Which of the various moral judgments actually made is accepted as 'authoritative' depends, in a democracy, upon which receives the widest support. In other words, the judgment of the majority is accepted, in practice, as authoritative; but this does not imply that the judgment of a minority is not an equally true and valid moral judgment, and does not therefore justify the suppression of a minority opinion on the ground that it is false. The authority of a democratic government is therefore quite different in character from that of an authoritarian government, which derives its authority from conformity to the *a priori* moral laws by which alone it can be justified. The authority of a democratic government originates in the support of the majority and is therefore based not on an assumed *a priori* right but on power—on the recognition that, as Locke put it, 'it is necessary the body [community] should move that way whither the greater force carries it'.[1] On the other hand, it may also be possible to justify the authority of a democratic government on grounds of utility

[1] *Of Civil Government*, Book II, para. 96.

if it is true that the realization of the will of the majority promotes the greatest happiness of the greatest number.[1]

Political Theory and Political Practice

A distinction was drawn at the beginning of this chapter between the exercise of government and its justification. The distinction is important, although the two aspects of government are closely related. The exercise of government always involves in some measure the control of the many by the few, and such control necessarily depends on the consent of the many. Such consent may be, and often is, wholly irrational, being based mainly upon habit and tradition. But questions have always been asked by some about the rational justification of the institutions and practices supported by these irrational forces, and it is to these questions that the political philosopher attempts to give an answer. Even if the answer is—as it must be for an empiricist—that government can be justified only by non-rational considerations, that is itself a rational proposition of the first importance, and there will remain for reason the important function of discovering and prescribing the most effective means by which the non-rational ends of government may be achieved. If, on the other hand, the answer is—as the rationalist believes—that there are rational norms by which government must be justified or condemned, there will be rational grounds for prescribing the ends of government as well as the means employed to realise them.

The broad alternatives in political theory which have been distinguished in the preceding chapters are therefore based upon the Rationalist and Empiricist Theories of Morality respectively, and these alternative Theories of Morality are in turn based upon Rationalist and Empiricist Theories of Logic. It would, of course, be untrue to say that these alternatives have always been defined

---

[1] As was shown in Chapter X, Hume himself thought that government by a cultured minority was more likely to promote the greatest happiness. But support for such a form of government is not inconsistent with democratic liberty if the government receives the spontaneous support of the majority of citizens. This situation is, in fact, illustrated by all modern representative democracies where it is generally recognized by the people as a whole that the detailed business of government must necessarily be conducted by a minority of statesmen and their advisers, and that 'public opinion' can offer useful guidance only on the most general issues.

and distinguished in political theory; but they are the logical alternatives between which a choice must be made. The justification of government is a moral justification, and the form which it takes therefore depends upon the form and logical status of moral propositions. If, as Plato, Aquinas, and Kant would all have said, moral propositions possess the rational necessity of mathematical propositions, a categorical justification of government can be given; but if such propositions are synthetic and empirical a hypothetical justification is all that can be looked for. A categorical justification is the logical foundation of government by authority, while a hypothetical justification is the only possible justification of those forms of government which recognize the right to freedom of opinion and accept the need to govern within the limits of general consent. Which form of justification is valid depends, in the end, on whether moral propositions are *a priori* or empirical. And, since such propositions are in any case synthetic, the issue ultimately turns on whether synthetic propositions can be *a priori*.

The ultimate question is therefore Kant's famous question: Are synthetic *a priori* propositions possible? And the answer to that question must itself be an *a priori* proposition, for no empirical facts could be relevant to its truth. As an *a priori* proposition it will be true if it could not conceivably be otherwise, and false if it could not conceivably be so, i.e. is self-contradictory. And it is on this ground that the empiricist ultimately takes his stand. He contends that the conception of a synthetic *a priori* proposition is self-contradictory, and the assertion that a synthetic proposition can be *a priori* therefore necessarily false. To the empiricist the synthetic, in virtue of its very meaning, excludes the necessary, and the necessary excludes the synthetic. For him a synthetic proposition *means* a proposition which can be denied without self-contradiction, and of which the truth can therefore be established only by experience. If these contentions are valid, the ultimate premise of rationalism must be rejected as self-contradictory, and Empiricism accepted as the true account of the nature of thought. And from this it will follow that the justification of government must be hypothetical in character, and conditioned by whatever moral assumptions are made about its proper aims and methods.

But even if this conclusion has to be accepted, it does not imply that reason has not a function of great importance in the practical life. Even if moral generalizations are without rational necessity, they may exhibit patterns of empirical uniformity which can be studied scientifically and made the basis for the rational control of social forces. It may even be found, as Utilitarians contend, that the promotion of the general happiness is the ultimate object of all moral approval; and, if that be so, a principle will exist by which conflicting moral judgments may be reconciled in a rational manner. In short, it does not follow that, if moral judgments lack rational necessity, they are likewise devoid of empirical consistency.

Indeed, the empiricist maintains that it is only when the inherent limitations of reason are recognized that it becomes possible to control action in a rational manner. It is only when reason, in Hume's words, is recognized to be the 'slave of the passions' that the rational control of action issuing from the 'passions' becomes possible. Otherwise, in the view of the empiricist, reason is likely to be perverted to the futile task of seeking some *a priori* justification of the ends of action, when its only possible function in the practical life is that of deducing the conditions and consequences of attaining specified ends, and thus perhaps modifying action by changing its anticipated results.

For the empiricist, therefore, the function of reason in the practical life is essentially utilitarian. It cannot, from its very nature, determine or prescribe the choice of ends. It can only specify, in the light of causal generalizations based on past experience, what means are likely to be most effective for the attainment of the ends desired, and what the attainment of these ends is likely to involve. The problems of politics, to the empiricist, are therefore scientific problems, and the true functions of the rational statesman those of a social scientist. The ends which he promotes must be discovered by a scientific study of human desires, and the means which he adopts by a scientific study of the conditions under which those desires can be most fully satisfied. For the rationalist, on the other hand, reason has directive as well as instrumental functions, and can prescribe the ends which ought to be pursued as well as determine the means by which specified ends may be attained. To him the problems of politics are moral as well as scientific problems, for he recognizes an *a priori* distinction between what is and what ought to be, between desires and duties; and he holds that the ideal statesman is one who is aware of this distinction, and who seeks to realise, as far as may be, the pattern of the ideal state.

INDEX

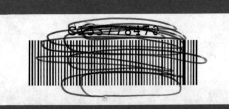

From Harvey River

From Harvey River

A Memoir of my Mother
and her Island

LORNA GOODISON

Atlantic Books
London

First published in Canada in 2007 as *From Harvey River: A Memoir of My Mother and Her People* by McClelland & Stewart, Ltd, Toronto, Ontario.

First published in hardback in Great Britain in 2009 by Atlantic Books, an imprint of Grove Atlantic Ltd.

10 9 8 7 6 5 4 3 2 1

A CIP catalogue record for this book is available from the British Library.

ISBN: 978 1 84354 995 6

Printed and bound in the UK by CPI Mackays, Chatham ME5 8TD

Atlantic Books
An imprint of Grove Atlantic Ltd
Ormond House
26-27 Boswell Street
London WC1N 3JZ

www.atlantic-books.co.uk

To Doris and Marcus

Family Tree

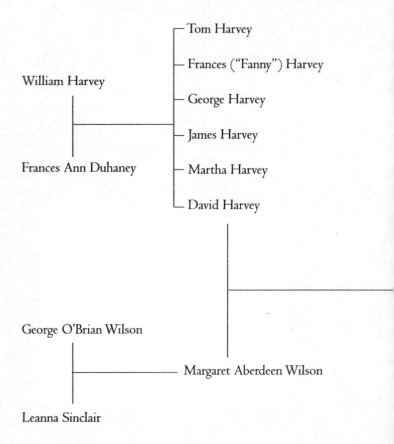

William Harvey

Frances Ann Duhaney

- Tom Harvey
- Frances ("Fanny") Harvey
- George Harvey
- James Harvey
- Martha Harvey
- David Harvey

George O'Brian Wilson

Leanna Sinclair

Margaret Aberdeen Wilson

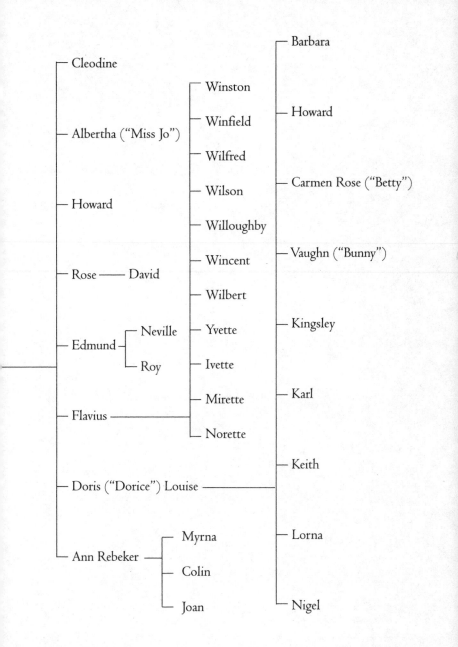

Prologue

hroughout her life my mother lived in two places at once: Kingston, Jamaica, where she raised a family of nine children, and Harvey River, in the parish of Hanover, where she was born and grew up. Harvey River had been settled by her grandfather William Harvey, who gave his name to the river, and the river in turn gave its name to the village. I do not think that there was ever a day in my childhood when the river or the village was not mentioned in our house. Over the years Harvey River came to function as an enchanted place in my imagination, an Eden from which we fell to the city of Kingston. But over time I have come to see that my parents' story is really a story about rising up to a new life. As a child I constantly asked my mother about her life before, as she put it, "things changed." I listened carefully to her stories, and repeated them to myself. I also took to asking urgent questions of my father. I have an image of me standing outside the bathroom door calling in to him over the noise of the shower, "So what was your mother's name, and what was her mother's name?" But my father's people do not live long, and he died when I was fifteen years old. So I never did get to ask him all my questions. After my mother Doris's death nearly thirty-five years later, I began to "dream" her, as Jamaicans say, and in those dreams I continued to ask her questions about her life before and after she came to Kingston. And then there was this one very vivid visitation when I dreamt that I went to see her in her new residence, a really palatial and splendid sewing room with high stained-glass windows, where she was now in charge of sewing gorgeous garments for top-ranking angels. She said they were paying her a lot for her sewing in this place, and that all her friends came to talk angelic big-woman business with her there as she sewed. She said she could not tell me more as she did not want me to stay with her too long, because the living should not mix-up too much with the dead. But as I was leaving the celestial workroom, she handed me a book. This is that book.

part one

*T*he baby was plump and pretty as a ripe ox-heart tomato. Her mother, Margaret Wilson Harvey, gently squeezed the soft cheeks to open the tiny mouth and rubbed her little finger, which had been dipped in sugar, back and forth, over and under the small tongue to anoint the child with the gift of sweet speech. "Her name is Doris," she said to her husband, David.

In later years, my mother preferred to spell her name Dorice, although in actual fact she was christened Doris. But she was registered under a different name altogether – Clarabelle. This came about because of a disagreement between her parents as to what they should call their seventh child. Her father, David, was a romantic and a dreamer, a man who loved music and books, and an avid reader of lesser known nineteenth-century authors. He had read a story in which the heroine was called Clarabelle, and he found it to be a lovely and fitting name. He told his wife, Margaret, that that was to be the baby girl's name. Well, Margaret had her heart set on Doris, because it was the name of a school friend of hers, a real person, not some made-up somebody who lived in a book. Doris Louise, that was what the child would be called. They argued over it and after a while it became clear that Margaret was not going to let David best her this time. He had given their other children names like

Cleodine, Albertha, Edmund, and Flavius. Lofty-sounding names which were rapidly hacked down to size by the blunt tongues of Hanover people. Cleo, Berta, Eddie, and Flavy. That was what remained of those names when Hanover people were finished with them. Margaret had managed to name her first-born son Howard, and her father had named Rose. Simple names for real people.

There was nobody who could be as stubborn and hard-headed as Margaret when she set her mind to something. She was determined that her baby was not going to be called Clarabelle. "Sound like a blasted cow name," she said. David gave up arguing with his wife about the business of naming the pretty-faced, chubby little girl, especially after Margaret reminded him graphically of who exactly had endured the necessary hard and bloody labour to bring the child into the world. He dutifully accompanied her to church and christened the baby Doris, on the last Sunday in June 1910. Then the next day he rode into the town of Lucea and registered the child as Clarabelle Louise Harvey, and he never told anyone about this deed for fifteen years. As a matter of fact, he is not known to have ever told anyone about it, because the family only found this out when my mother tried to sit for her first Jamaica Local Exams, for which she needed her birth certificate. When she went to the Registrar of Births and Deaths, they told her that there was no Doris Louise Harvey on record, but that there *was* a Clarabelle Louise Harvey born to David and Margaret Harvey, née Wilson, of Harvey River, Hanover. She burst into tears when she heard what her legal name was. "Clarabelle go to hell" her brothers chanted when the terrible truth was revealed. Not one to take teasing lightly, she told them to go to hell their damn selves.

Eventually her name was converted by deed poll to Doris.

Thereafter, she signed her name Dorice, as if to distance herself from the whole Clarabelle/Doris business. Besides, Dorice, pronounced "Do-*reese*," conjured up images of a woman who was not ordinary; and to be ordinary, according to my mother's oldest sister, Cleodine, was just about the worst thing that a member of the Harvey family could be.

~

Cleodine was definitely not ordinary. She held the distinction of being the first child to be born alive to her parents, David and Margaret Harvey. She emerged into the world on January 6, 1896, as a tall, slender baby with a curious yellowish-alabaster complexion. The child Cleodine immediately opened her mouth and bellowed so loudly that the midwife nearly dropped her. Before her, not one of the five children conceived by Margaret had emerged from her body alive. Every one had turned back, manifesting themselves only as wrenching cramps, clotted blood, and deep disappointment.

This time around, her husband, David, had watched and prayed anxiously as Margaret's belly grew big with their sixth conception. Would this baby be the one to make it? Would it be the one to beat the curse of Margaret's seemingly inhospitable womb? The doctor had ordered her to bed the day it was confirmed that she was again pregnant, and once this happened, her mother, Leanna, had announced that she intended to mount upon her grey mule and gallop over to Harvey River each morning to take care of her daughter. Leanna forced her to lie still for most of the nine months, forbidding her to go outside, even to use the pit latrine. Instead she made her use a large porcelain chamber pot which she herself emptied. She bathed her daughter like a baby each morning and combed her long hair into two plaits, pinning them across her head in a coronet. She prepared nourishing invalid food and fed her steamed egg custards and cornmeal porridge boiled for hours into creaminess and sweetened with rich cow's milk. She made her thyme-fragrant pumpkin soup and fresh carrot juice, because Margaret's cravings were all for golden-coloured foods, which she ate sitting up in her big four-poster mahogany marriage bed. Another reason for feeding her these soft foods was that Margaret had become afraid that any abrupt, jarring movement might dislodge the foetus. She chewed upon these soft foods slowly and gently, and later, to occupy herself she sat propped up in bed quietly stitching and embroidering every imaginable type of garment, except for baby clothes.

After Leanna departed each evening to return to the arms of her husband, John Bogle, David sat by Margaret's bedside and filled her in on what was happening in the village. He read to her from the newspapers or the Bible, and then he retired to the adjoining bedroom to sleep alone. Margaret and he had both agreed that nothing, not even their much-enjoyed conjugal lovemaking, should endanger the safe delivery of this child. David, who was an extremely private and modest man, had to bear with his mother-in-law, Leanna, saying the same thing to him each evening before she left: "Remember Mas D, no funny business tonight." And David, who believed that all such matters were truly private, would flush and say to his mother-in-law: "Don't worry about me and my wife's business."

For every one of those turned-back births, Margaret had prepared elaborate layettes. David had even bought an ornate, Spanish-style christening gown in Cuba the first time that she had become pregnant, a gown which they had given away in despair after they lost child after child. This time she was determined that she would prepare nothing for this baby just in case. Just in case fate had decided to insult her once again, she was preparing to insult fate first. See, she would say to fate, I never expected any baby to be born alive, because I never even prepared any baby clothes. Not a small sheer poplin chemise or a soft white birdseye diaper. Not one woollen bootie did she knit or crochet, not one bootie the length of her index finger. No beribboned bonnet big enough to cover a head the size of a grapefruit; nothing. She had given away all the clothes she had made for her lost babies. Then one year later she found out she was pregnant again, but this time she was prepared for the worst. She would take to bed and chew gently, yes, but not one garment would she make in case she lost this baby too. Not one garment would she make, but every time she had such a thought, the foetus would deal her a swift kick from inside the womb. It was as if the baby Cleodine wanted to step out and occupy her place in the world immediately, because hers had been nearly a breech birth. However, the midwife succeeded in persuading her to come in headfirst, and she crowned promptly at 6 a.m., then shouldered her way out, announcing her presence with a commanding bawl.

"Oh my God, look Missus Queen," was what Margaret said when she saw her first-born, because the baby bore an amazing resemblance to Queen Victoria. When the news went out through the village that a baby girl had broken Margaret and David Harvey's bad-luck-with-children cycle, the Harvey relatives came calling. Many of the women arrived bearing beautiful garments they had sewn in secret because everyone in the village knew of Margaret's attempt to disarm fate by refusing to prepare for this baby. They brought exquisitely embroidered baby dresses, dozens of gleaming white birdseye napkins already washed clean in the Harvey River and dried near the field of lilies. They brought knitted woollen caps and booties, mostly in white and yellow, not pink or blue, because nobody wanted to go so far as to predict the sex of the baby that the whole village all but fell down and worshipped. Born to rule, the little girl Cleodine was hailed as a "Duppy Conqueror," a mortal who triumphs over the baddest of ghosts, because she had cleared all the killing spirits out of her mother's way.

First-born children set the pace; they are the engine of the sibling train, the source of authority, inspiration, and energy for all the brothers and sisters who follow. The first child in a family must be raised to be bold, ambitious, strong and confident, the example for all the other children coming behind. Or so Margaret and David, like many parents of that time, believed – that the first child in a family was undoubtedly the most important one.

For the first year of her life, Cleodine's long narrow feet did not touch the ground because someone was always holding her aloft, showing her off to admiring strangers. Look she was born with two teeth, look she had nearly a full mouth of teeth before she was eight months old, look she is obviously bright, very bright. Look at her eyes, amber brown like a tiger's eyes, and those extraordinary fingers, like those of a piano player. The child often waved them like the conductor of an orchestra.

Maeve, Queen Maeve, was what Margaret's father, George O'Brian Wilson, had wanted to call his first female grandchild by his favourite child, Margaret. Queen Maeve the powerful mythical Celtic queen. But David said no, and put his foot down. He would name his first child, he and he alone. Yes, she would be named after a queen, for she was a queen and he toyed with the idea of calling her Victoria. But secretly he was hoping that the child would grow out of her resemblance to Queen Victoria, who, let's face it, was not a pretty woman.

Cleopatra, Queen of Egypt. A beautiful woman, powerful enough to mesmerize King Solomon. That would be the child's name. When he told Margaret that the baby's name was Cleopatra, he lowered his voice and said, "Cleopatra, we can call her Cleo; my Cleo, Cleo mine." Margaret looked at him and said, "Cleo Mine or Cleo Thine?" And they liked the sound of that and called the baby Cleodine, who proceeded to grow up and rule over everybody in Harvey River as long as she lived there.

Two years after the triumphant entry of Cleodine into the world of Harvey River, Margaret gave birth to another baby girl. In what would become an act of prescience, they named the girl Albertha. Having produced a healthy and intelligent child in the form of Cleodine, Margaret was a little more re-laxed about giving birth the second time around. She did not take to her bed as she had done when she was carrying Cleodine, but she was completely convinced that if she was going to bring this baby to full term she would have to behave as seriously as possible for the duration of this pregnancy. If, in her mind, hard-chewing had posed a danger to the safe delivery of Cleodine, then she decided that mirth, laughter, frivolity, these things would surely serve to place harm in her way. Again, she had not made any clothes for this baby, but this time it was not because she was trying to pre-empt fate, this time she had no need to prepare baby clothes because Cleodine had been showered with so many beautiful garments by the overjoyed people of Harvey River that this second baby would always be able to wear her big sister's gorgeous outgrown dresses.

Everybody called Albertha "Miss Jo" from the day that she was born. Perhaps they called the small girl "Miss Jo" because there was an absence of anything jovial about her grave, unsmiling little presence. The baby seemed to have absorbed her mother's fear of joy as a dangerous force while she was in the womb, the same fear that caused some Jamaicans to quote proverbs like "Chicken merry, Hawk near" to people who seemed overly happy. The truth was that Margaret and David had been hoping for a boy. Nothing would have made them happier than the birth of a male Harvey, so while there was some rejoicing at the safe delivery of this second child, alas, Miss Jo was not destined to be a star like Cleodine, who, when taken into her mother's room to view her sister, immediately said: "I big, you little." Albertha grew into a fair-skinned, always inclined-to-stoutness girl of medium height. Her outstanding features were her broad, high cheekbones, and her dark eyes, which could have been described as lovely if they did not perpetually seem so sad. From very early in her life she displayed certain prudish tendencies which made it quite clear that she did not enjoy the rude and rustic ways of country folk. She was pious and chaste and she never laughed at the smutty jokes involving the sex life of animals in which country children took delight. The rude, suggestive words of Jamaican folk songs did not cause her to giggle, like they did other small children.

> Gal inna school a study fi teacher
> bwoy outside a study fi breed her
> Rookumbine inna you santampee, rookumbine . . .

No, such songs did not cause her any amusement whatsoever. Her presence was a check on any loud-laughing, rude-joke-telling gathering. She was forever declaring that such and such a person was "too out of order," forever complaining to her parents that one or the other of her siblings had transgressed in some way. All dancing, except maybe a stately waltz, was nothing but coarse slackness to her. She passed her time mostly reading and doing elaborate embroidery, for which she developed a great talent. This was the one area in which she grew to outstrip her older sister, a fact that greatly angered the competitive Cleodine, but which caused Miss Jo to ply her needle the more to scatter lazy daisies and raise up padded petals of roses across the surface of tray cloths and doilies, even as she looked with sadness and disapproval upon any coarseness and impropriety.

~

After Margaret had given birth to two daughters, she yearned deeply for a son, so when Howard was born, he was like a messenger sent from beyond to assure her that, yes, she was a complete woman. He looked just like a cherub, an angel baby. She breast-fed him until he could walk and talk. She rose at least seven times at night to check on the rise and fall of his breath as he lay asleep in his cot. Whenever he had a cold she would put her mouth to his tiny nostrils to draw the mucus down to clear his breathing; and in the rainy season, she warmed his clothes in her bosom before she dressed him. She did not go so far as to mark his limbs with the symbolic "no trespassing" hieroglyphics, like many mothers in the village who would draw ancient African symbols with laundry blue on the backs and bellies of their babies. This was done to warn away sucking spirits. Neither did she resort to pasting sickly-smelling asafetida around the tender, vulnerable fontanelle or "mole" as Jamaicans call it, throbbing at the top of his head, in the hope that its acrid, medicinal smell would keep away ghosts and envious spirits. David, a staunch Anglican and the son of an English father, would not have had it. He did not hold with what his father called barbaric practices. Margaret, in any case, was not going to leave her son's care and protection to any random spirit guardians. She preferred to watch him herself. However, she did surreptitiously sweep his tiny feet with a soft broom when her husband was not looking. This was to prevent him from becoming a "baffan," or fool.

She never allowed any strangers to hold Howard. She rarely ever took him out in public until he was about three years old, because she didn't want people to "overlook" him, that is, to look at him too much with longing, envious eyes. She did not cut his luxuriant mass of black curls which cascaded down past his shoulders until he could speak clearly. And so, for the first few years of his life, he did indeed look like a beautiful, sexless angel. Margaret dressed him in sailor suits made from appropriate sharkskin. "You are a sailor like your grandfather," she would say as she transformed him into a nautical cherub, and her husband would say, "I don't want my son to take after your father." But even as Margaret dressed the boy in sailor suits, she harboured a deep fear that he would die from drowning. She had run through all the possible harm that could befall a child living in that village, and had identified the river as the thing that posed the most danger. "There was no child born in Harvey River at that time who could not swim," my mother would say. Everyone in the village used the river. They washed their clothes there, pounding them clean on the grey shale rocks. Everyone drew drinking water from the river, which ran clean and clear, coursing down always fresh from its secret source somewhere in the interior of the Dolphin Head Mountains. They all swam in it too. Mothers would take small babies there for the ritual bathing and sopping and stretching of their limbs; they would release the babies into the river where they would instinctively kick their arms and legs.

All the children of Harvey River could swim, all except for Howard. Margaret had decided that the child should not bathe in the river, for that was where she would lose him, although no one in the village had ever drowned in it. Only once, a man from the nearby village of Chambers Pen had been stumbling home one night, drunk on john crow batty white rum, and while weaving a rummish path home in the dark turned right instead of left and fell in the river. "All the crayfish and janga must be drunk now," said the people of the village. David's father, William Harvey, had joked, "That man had only a little blood in his rum stream." William was especially proud of his joke because one of his ancestors, born in 1578 and also named William Harvey, had discovered the circulation of blood and had been physician to James I and Charles I.

For a time, David humoured Margaret's fear of the boy drowning. But when one day he came upon her bathing Howard in a wooden washtub, he grew angry and yanked the boy – who was tall for his age – out of the tub, took him down to the river, and taught him how to swim. After that there was no stopping Howard and the river. But every time he scampered away half-naked and gleeful, Margaret would worry until he returned damp and glowing like one of the Water Babies in Charles Kingsley's story. And those babies had all drowned.

The boy grew into the most handsome of young men. He became a sweet boy, a boonoonoonoos boy, a face man, eye-candy man, pretty-like-money, nice-like-a-pound-of-rice man. Lord, women loved him. Older women looked at him greedily, as if he were some sweet confection that they could eat slowly and then lick their fingers long afterwards. Young girls just openly offered themselves to him. "Here I am, handsome Howard, pick me, choose me." They fought to get to sit beside him at school and in church, to have him sweep those long lashes up and down the contours of their trembling bodies, to call them by name. "Yes, it's you Cybil, you I talking to." "Me, you mean . . . Howard, me? Oh yes, oh joy!" They befriended his sisters in order to get a chance to visit the Harvey household and be near to him, to drink from the same teacups from which his lips had sipped, to peep into his room and see the bed that he slept in. He could have had any woman in the district. That is why he never married, he just had too many beautiful women to choose from. Why then did he follow a Jezebel clear to Lucea, there to meet his death?

⌒

"My Irish Rose" is what George O'Brian Wilson had said when he first saw his fourth grandchild. He also called her his Rose of Tralee and his Dark Rose, and the baby just smiled. David and Margaret agreed she just had to be called Rose because nobody had ever seen a more beautiful baby. Unlike Queen Victoria Cleodine, the unsmiling Miss Jo, and the almost-too-handsome Howard, Rose was perfectly beautiful inside and out. This baby was born smiling, causing her mother to wonder why, why was this baby smiling already, what was she smiling about? Perhaps she was smiling because everybody who ever laid eyes on her, loved her.

People liked being near the beautiful baby who hardly ever cried and who cooed like a little Barbary dove at the sight of sunbeams streaming in through the front window. More than ever the people of Harvey River began to find excuses to visit David and Margaret's house, because somehow being in the presence of this child just made everyone feel better. First of all, no one could help noticing that even more than other babies she had an especially sweet body scent, as if she had been birthed in the bed of lilies that grew behind the Harvey house. Her flawless brown skin had a pinkish glow to it, and her soft black hair curled on her head like petals. She was born with an unusually sweet disposition, which could be credited to the fact that Margaret was never happier in her life than in the years after Howard was born.

Margaret had not entertained any strange no-hard-chewing, no staid no-smiling superstition when she carried Rose. The moment she had conceived Howard, she somehow knew that she was going to get her wish for a son. And she had made herself six blue dresses which she wore throughout the duration of her pregnancy. That was the only "strange" thing that she did. After the birth of Howard, she treated the rest of her pregnancies normally, as she went on to deliver up a new baby every two years.

"Three rinse waters, they must go through three separate rinse waters so they will be completely clean." Margaret, who was pregnant with Edmund at the time, had suspected that the girl who came to do the washing was only rinsing the family's white clothes twice, for they were looking a little dingy. So after she had walked the girl back to the river to perform the third rinsing, Margaret returned to the house, where she had left Rose napping on a blanket on the floor, to find the child missing. They searched under every bed, every chair, table, and wardrobe, under every bush in the yard, but there was no sign of Rose, and a great wailing came up from the Harvey house.

Just at that exact moment, David's half-brother, called Tata Edward, was taking his daily constitutional in the midday sun, when he spotted the village crazy woman walking swiftly away from Harvey River with a small child held tightly in her arms. "My little girl, my little girl, look how she favour me, look how she favour me, I am taking her with me to Panama" was what she kept saying as Tata Edward dealt her a swift blow with his walking stick, causing her to let go of his beautiful niece. Being an excellent cricketer, he then swiftly flung himself sideways onto the grass and caught Rose before she fell to the ground. The poor woman, whom the villagers called Colun, had gone insane waiting for her lover to send for her to join him in Panama. Like everyone else, she had fallen in love with Rose, and for two years she had been peeping at the child through the hibiscus hedges surrounding the Harvey house. When she had made up her mind to steal Rose, she had spent days making a house of leaves and branches for the two of them to live in in the bushes outside Harvey River. The child just kept smiling while all the commotion was going on around her.

"Look how this damn blasted woman, who fool enough so make man mad her, come take way my child! Is me tell her to fret herself till her head start run over that idiot who fool her and gone a Panama? Why she come pitch pon my house and my child?" Margaret cried and cursed the poor woman and thanked God and Tata Edward. David prayed aloud from Psalm 91. "He that dwelleth in the secret place of the most High, shall abide in the shadow of the Almighty. I will say of the Lord He is my refuge and fortress: my God in him will I trust. Surely he shall deliver thee from the snare of the fowler, and from the noisesome pestilence. He shall cover thee with his feathers, and under his wings shall thou trust; his truth shall be thy shield and buckler, thou shall not be afraid of the terror by night; nor of the arrow that flieth by day." And the district constable came and arrested the poor woman for the "crime" of being insane while the two-year-old Rose – who, for her part, seemed to have been born with some sweet secret – just kept smiling all the time.

As she grew, Rose's ability to keep a secret endeared her to her siblings and, later, to her school friends. If someone said, "Rose, I going tell you something and you mustn't tell anybody you hear?" the pretty little girl would just smile, shake her head, and use her thumb and forefinger to screw her lips shut. And her sibling or school friend might say, "swear to God." And Rose would just say, "not telling." And you could be sure that no matter what, Rose would never, ever reveal a secret or disclose anything told to her in confidence.

~

Because her belly had been more pointed than round, Margaret was happy to hear that everyone predicted her fifth baby would be a boy. There were only three things that caused her any discomfort during her pregnancy. First, she felt irritable all the time as opposed to just some of the time, and she found it disconcerting that she had suddenly lost her appetite for dry white Lucea yam, which was her favourite food. But the strangest thing of all was that she, who did not believe in ever going too far from her house, inexplicably developed a case of wanderlust and began to visit friends and neighbours in surrounding villages. Everyone in Harvey River began to remark on this. "Guess who mi buck up walking out a while ago? No, Mrs. Harvey! I never see her outta road yet, and make matters worse she big, big, soon have baby!" "David," Margaret would say, "I feel to go and visit my mother." "You sure, Meg? You are a lady that hardly ever leave your house. I can send to call your mother, she will ride come." "No, I want to go."

And so it went, all during her pregnancy stay-at-home Margaret became walkbout-Margaret, until the minute that Edmund was born, when she lost all interest in ever leaving the house. The baby Edmund was born in the middle of the night. "This baby born quick quick," said the midwife. "Him just slip out and slide right past me, like him want go walkbout already." Because he weighed just under six pounds, they had to pin him by his chemise to a pillow so Margaret could hold him to feed him properly. "Aye, he looks like a leprechaun, like one of the little people," said George O'Brian Wilson when he came to see his latest grandson. "Mind he doesn't get up in the night and make mischief on ye all." David and Margaret had had a good laugh when George Wilson said that. The little baby Edmund, who was also born with a short temper, howled.

It seems that all Edmund ever wanted to do was to leave Harvey River. As soon as he could talk, he would say, "Too dark." Then he would say, "Too damn dark." "What is too dark?" they would ask him, and he would say, "Here."

As he grew he also developed a dislike for bush. "Too much bush," he'd say, and everyone would say, "So what you expect, you live in the country." That did not stop Edmund from disliking his birthplace. All that bush. Everywhere he looked all he could see was bush, and under every bush the duppy of some godforsaken slave. The boy's heart did not sing out with joy as he beheld dawn rising pink and slow, moving like the folds of a woman's nightdress up over the Dolphin Head Mountains. His spirit did not rise and canter like a young horse over the verdant green pastures each day, because he hated all the macca, the thorns set there in the green grass to pierce his bare feet. The wicked cow-itch weed that itched you till your skin would bleed. The nasty white chiggoes that bored into your feet and laid sickening mock-pearl parasite eggs. Grass lice, ticks, cow, goat, and horse shit, flies and mosquitoes.

"Jamaica is a blessed country, there are no fierce animals or poisonous snakes here, and Harvey River is like the Garden of Eden." David was always saying that. Edmund used to kiss his teeth when he heard it. Yes, but what about all those blasted insects, what about the thick darkness? He particularly hated the peenie wallies, fireflies, damn stupid little flies with that weak on and off light coming out of their backsides. He craved real lights. Street lights. He had heard that in Montego Bay and Kingston the streets were lit by tall gas lights. "Moon pan stick" country people called those lights.

And then there was the darkness of the people. Country people, always telling each other "mawning Miss this or Mas that." Who the hell wanted any mawning from them, thought Edmund. And the worst part was, if he did not answer them they would run and report him to his parents, who would chastise him for not having good manners. Good manners be damned. When he was thirteen years old he had actually asked his father one day where good manners ever got any black man and had his father ever noticed that backra and backra pickney, who were famous for not having good manners, always seemed to reach very far. David had been appalled by that statement, and called Edmund a savage.

Edmund could not understand how he was so unlucky as to have been born in the country. From the first time that his father took him to Kingston when he was ten years old, he knew that the city was the place for him. There the streets had names, King Street and East and West Queen Street and Port Royal Street and Rum Lane. Not "outta road," like in the country.

Town had milk shops where he could go and order as much liver and light (light being what Jamaicans called the lungs of the cow or goat) for breakfast as he wanted. Eat, belch, pay his money, and walk out like a big man. Also rum bars where a man could order his rum by the QQ (a quarter quart), by the flask or the tot, put a question to the barmaid, who was probably called Fattie, and take her home to his room that he had rented. His room where he could turn his own key and come in at any hour of the day or night he pleased because he was his own man. Town, where cars drive up and down day and night. Cars and buses and trucks and tramcars ran all the time. Not like this back-a-bush place with only donkey, mule, and horse. Who the hell said country nice? Not Edmund.

He considered it God's make mistake why he was born in Harvey River. He was Moses among the bulrushes. If only Pharaoh's daughter would just appear and carry him to town. As a child he would run outside to stare at any motor vehicle that managed to fight its way up to the village. He fashioned a steering wheel from an old pot cover and "drove" wherever he went, going "brrrum, brrruum" in imitation of the noise of motor vehicle engines, and he made hissing, screeching sounds whenever he stopped, like the boiling over hissing brakes of trucks.

David rode a horse and Margaret had a pretty, dainty-stepping donkey, but nobody who lived in the village owned a motor car. Edmund had been taken to Montego Bay as a child and had seen the taxi men driving tourists around. Even as a boy, he had been struck by the elite corps of smartly dressed men in starched white shirts and black pants, who all spoke "Yankee" and smoked cigarettes and had the prettiest women, because girls just loved a man who drove a car. Later, he would hear that tourist women – mostly rich Americans and English-women – would sometimes fall in love with a taxi man.

While Howard was being taught to become a saddler by his grandfather George Wilson, and his younger brother Flavius had expressed a desire to be apprenticed to the tailor in the next village, Edmund was expected to help his father with the cultivation of the coffee, cocoa, and yams, and if ever there was a man who hated agriculture that would be Edmund. As he explained to Flavius, who was a born farmer, what the hell would he, Edmund, be digging, digging in the ground for? The only thing he ever wanted to dig for was gold. Gold to make ring and chain and decorate his teeth and give as earring and brooch to women as presents. As far as he knew there was no gold to be found in Jamaica. He would much rather buy rice and bread from a shop than eat yam. As a matter of fact he refused to eat yams once he left Harvey River.

~

"Why the baby looking at me so?" said everyone who ever held my uncle Flavius in their arms when he was an infant. "Hey boy, if you see me again you will know me?" is what the children at the village school would ask him when he began to attend classes there at age seven. David and Margaret used to wonder when and if their sixth child ever slept because it seemed that no matter what hour of the night they checked on the children in their beds, the light of the Home Sweet Home lamp would reveal Flavius to be awake, alert, and staring hard into the darkness. Soon after he learned to walk, he armed himself with an old cooking spoon for a shovel and took to digging in the ground around the Harvey house. Then one day Flavius stopped staring so hard into people's faces and took to walking with his head held down, a habit which greatly upset his parents. "Hold your head up, what do you have to be ashamed of, why you holding down your head so?" said his father, who had named him after a Roman nobleman in one of the books he had read. But Flavius was not ashamed; he was searching for something. Sometimes in his digs he found coins, and once somebody's gold ring which must have been very old because the gold was so thin it was almost translucent. Another time he found a pewter spoon and the head of a china doll. He kept his "treasures" in a pile beneath the house, and he always said that when he built his own house in Harvey River, he intended to transfer his things there because, unlike his brother Edmund, Flavius had no desire to leave Harvey River. He was sure that whatever he was searching for was to be found right there in the parish of Hanover – and that included a wife. But before he identified a prospective helpmate and mother for their children – he intended to have a large family – he decided that he should be sent to learn tailoring, for he was not one to put all his eggs in one basket. Everybody said the boy had a good hand for planting, and in his time he reaped quite a few prize yams. Flavius reasoned that while the yams were growing, he could just as well be stitching somebody's wedding suit. And as only madmen walked around without trousers, the men of Hanover would always need the services of a tailor. So he was sent off to learn how to "build" suits and trousers from tailor May of Grange, Westmoreland, whose father and grandfather before him had all been fine tailors. After being apprenticed to tailor May for a year, Flavius came back to Harvey River and began to sew for the men in the area. He grew to be quite proud of the fact that almost any man, even a struggling, ordinary-looking man from the country, could be mistaken for an important person when he put on one of Flavius's well-constructed suits. When he finally proposed to a young woman named Arabella with whom he had gone to school in Chambers Pen, a petite girl with large soulful eyes and a still spirit, Flavius had his ducks all in a row.

Ann Rebeker Harvey was the last child or "washbelly" born to David and Margaret. The late pregnancy had come as a complete surprise to Margaret, who had naturally assumed that her child-bearing days were over after she gave birth to my mother, Doris, at age forty. Margaret was stunned when she discovered that she was going to be a mother for the eighth time, for frankly, she was tired of the whole giving birth business. The sickness, the bigness, the breast-feeding, the constant careful watching over the child till it was old enough to walk and talk. The never feeling tidy, the constant mother's perfume smell of baby powder and puke outweighed the heartstopping beautiful moments, the sheer joy and pure delight that babies bring. She therefore elected to go through her last pregnancy with a fatalistic, what-is-to-be-must-be, woman-must-have-out-her-lot, we-are-the-vessels-of-the-world kind of attitude.

Ann emerged into the world one June morning, looking like a chubby Hindu goddess made from milk chocolate. Her round little "head-cup," as Jamaican people call the skull, was covered by a cap of shiny blue-black hair, and instead of letting out a loud cry when the midwife gave her a welcome-to-the-world slap, the first sound that the baby Ann made was a cross between a laugh and a shout. She promptly proceeded to charm everyone around her when she opened her wide, heavily fringed dark eyes and proceeded to wink! Everyone instantly fell under her spell, everyone except her exhausted mother. Her siblings, even Cleodine, always treated her as if she was a pretty doll who was born to amuse and delight them, and they all vied to take care of her, which suited Margaret just fine.

"One of you come and take this baby little, make me get to sleep, she is one fiery little thing, just want to laugh and play day and night. I'm a old woman I can't manage her." Her brothers and sisters were happy to oblige and from early on she developed into a very sociable being. Ann walked and talked before any of her siblings, and from the time she was small she was able to keep a roomful of people in stitches by doing her solemn wink and pulling ridiculous faces.

As soon as she could talk in sentences, she began to do funny, wicked imitations of everyone in the village, including the local Anglican minister. Her brothers and sisters would often put her to stand on a chair in the dining room of the Harvey house and say, "Go on Ann, preach like parson now," and the little girl would say, "Peeeple of Hawvy Rivah, heed the wohords of the a-passil Pawll . . ." catching the minister's affected preaching voice exactly. It was the same minister who had told her father, David, when he went to call upon him to welcome him to the parish, "Oh, I already met your half-brother Edward, whose mother was from England. Surely he is the king of the Harveys." "King to you," David had replied, "but not to me."

This same minister loved to preach from Ephesians 6:5, about how masters should be kind to their slaves and slaves were to be obedient to their masters. David had finally told the Englishman one morning after church that he would appreciate it if he stopped quoting from that passage in the Bible because slavery was fully abolished in Jamaica in 1838, and as the natives had it to say, "Massa day done!"

People soon began to beg the little girl Ann to do her imitations, especially the one of the village mendicant, who always came by the Harvey house at the same time every day saying the same thing. "Morning mi massa, morning mi missus, beggin' you something to help poor me one." The "poor me one" was a bird whose low plaintive cry sounded to the ears of the Jamaicans as "Poor me one," and this man had adopted its name to aid him in his solicitation of alms. Everybody had forgotten his real name anyway, so they all called him "Poor me one."

But the man was not poor. He was a miser, and some people said that when he died they would probably find crocus bags of gold hidden under his banana trash mattress. The small child Ann had waited for him one morning, and as he drew up to the gate to sound his alms-begging request, the young girl borrowed the man's own voice and pre-empted him, calling out, "Morning mi kind massa, morning mi kind missus, beggin' you something to help poor me one." He never stopped at their gate ever again.

Unlike her siblings, Ann – the baby of the family, eighth child of David and Margaret, Ann with the blue-black hair, who grew to look like a girl in a Gauguin painting – did not fear her mother, Margaret. All the Harvey children humbled themselves under their mother's stern, often unsmiling gaze, and they tried to respect her oft-quoted edict, "No child of mine will ever rule me." No child, except Ann. It wasn't so much that the girl wanted to rule her mother, it was just that she was born free. The girl looked like a Gypsy. It was amazing how all the mixing of bloods produced people who looked like Indians and Gypsies. People who, if they were flowers, would be birds of paradise and Cataleya orchids. Ann, the last child of David and Margaret Harvey, looked like a bird of paradise. She radiated a kind of energy that was hard on her mother. "David, tell her that she cannot back-answer me."

"Just allow her, she is a good child, don't break her spirit."

"What, and make her rule me in my own house?"

People would call out to her, "Come here Ann Rebeker and give me a joke." And the child would do just that. It seemed as if she had been put on the earth to bring joy and happiness to everyone except Margaret.

"Show off bring disgrace, and high seat kill Miss Thomas' puss," she'd say.

"Lord, Margaret, just allow the child to prosper."

Where did this girl get this joy? This uncontainable, bubbling-over merriment that made her laugh and joke and giggle so much?

Unlike Margaret's other children, Ann never, ever appeared to be afraid of her. Once, when Margaret had quoted the Biblical injunction to her about honouring one's mother and father, the girl had reminded her that the same passage also said that parents should not provoke their children to wrath.

ow Harvey River became Harvey River. For all we know, the village of Harvey River used to have another name, but when my mother's paternal grandfather and his brother founded it in 1840, the old name was lost forever. The Harvey River was the source of life to everyone in the village. It was named by David's father, William Harvey, and his brother John, two of five brothers named Harvey who had come from England, sometime during the early half of the nineteenth century. They were related to one Thomas Harvey, a Quaker who had come to Jamaica in 1837, along with Joseph Sturge, the two men later writing a powerful and moving account of slavery in the British West Indies. The other Harvey brothers split up and went to live in different parishes in Jamaica after their arrival; only William and John stayed together. One version is that the two took up jobs as bookkeepers on the San Flebyn sugar estate, but one day soon after their arrival they witnessed something that made them decide to abandon all ideas about joining the plantocracy.

The estate overseer had hired two new Africans fresh off the boat in Lucea Harbour. Although slavery was officially abolished in 1838, some Africans were now being brought to Jamaica, along with East Indians and Chinese, to work as indentured labourers on sugar plantations where production was severely affected by the loss of slave labour.

Among the new Africans was a set of twins from Liberia, the great-grandchildren of fighting Maroons who had been transported there from Jamaica after the Maroon War in 1795. These fierce fighters had been banished to Nova Scotia in Canada, and had later settled in Liberia. The twin boys had grown up hearing many tales of Jamaica and of the courage of their ancestors, runaway Africans who refused to accept the yoke of slavery. The twins even claimed to be related to the supreme warrior woman, Nanny of the Maroons. Grandy Nanny, as I have heard some Maroons call her, had led her people in a protracted guerrilla war against the British until they were forced to make peace with her, on her terms.

These two young men had chosen to travel to Jamaica from Liberia on a one-year contract as indentured labourers, mainly to see for themselves the green and mountainous land to which their foreparents always longed to return. Maroon Country, where places had sinister and coded names like "Me No Send, You No Come."

They stood like twin panthers on the docks at Lucea, with such a fierce, mesmerizing presence that the overseer of the San Flebyn estate, one Grant Elbridge, felt compelled to hire them as a matching pair. He did this partly with his own amusement in mind, for he and his wife often indulged in elaborate sex games with the Africans on the property. One week after he hired them, Elbridge announced that the twins had to be whipped, abolition of slavery or not, for who the hell were these goddamned twin savages to disobey and disrespect him? The night before, when he had summoned them to his overseer's quarters, and he and his wife had indicated to them that they wanted them to take off their clothes, the two, acting as one, had spit in his face and stalked out into the dark night.

So Elbridge ordered the twins to take off their shirts again, this time in the middle of the cane field, and the twins obeyed at once. They tore off their shirts and bared their chests to him before the other labourers who now worked under conditions that were hardly better than before their emancipation. The huge, dark eyes of the twins locked onto Elbridge.

The Harvey brothers, who had been ordered by Elbridge to leave their bookkeeping and come down into the cane piece to watch him in his words "tan the hide off these heathen savages," stood close to each other and watched sick to their stomachs as the long, thick strip of cowhide lashed across the backs of the Maroons, raising raw, bloody welts. But they became truly terrified when they saw that it was Elbridge who bawled and bellowed in pain. The whip dropped from his hand and coiled loosely like a harmless yellow snake when he fell, face down, in the cane field. The Maroon twins seemed to have mastered the "bounce back" techniques of Nanny, who was able to make bullets ricochet off her body back at the British soldiers. Just as the bullets had bounced off Nanny's body into the flesh of the soldiers, so too did the twins redirect Elbridge's chastisement onto him. As Elbridge screamed and writhed in pain, the Harveys watched as the Liberian twins walked out of the cane piece and turned their faces in the direction of the Cockpit Country, knowing that no one would ever find them once they disappeared into Maroon territory. After witnessing this, the Harveys resigned their jobs as bookkeeping clerks on the San Flebyn estate and decided to find some land to make a life for themselves.

In the spirit of true conquistadors, William and John Harvey had come across a small clearing up in the Hanover Hills on a Sunday as they combed the area outside the estate in search of a place to settle themselves. It was not far from a place named Jericho and the entire area was cool and scented by pimento or "allspice" bushes. They did not know it then, but in the years to come, almost all the world's allspice would come from the island of Jamaica.

Tall bamboo trees bowed and bumped their feathery heads together to create flexible, swaying arches, and here and there solid dark blocks of shale jutted up from the ground in strange Stonehenge-like formations. On close examination, they saw that the rocks had bits of seashells embedded in them, so it is fair to say that at some point that area must have been under the sea. The clearing was verdant green and watered by a strong, coursing river. They had reached it by following one of the paths leading away from the estate. These paths had been created by the feet of men and women fleeing from the beatings and torture that was their only payment for making absentee landlords some of the richest men in the world. "Rich as a West Indian Planter" was a common saying when sugar was king during the eighteenth and nineteenth centuries.

Some of those paths led to small food plots often set on stony hillsides, which amazingly had been cultivated by the enslaved Africans to feed themselves. At the end of fourteen-hour working days cultivating cane, and on Sundays, their one day off, they had planted vegetables like pumpkins, okras, dasheens, plantains, and yams, the food of their native Africa. For some reason, the soil of the parish of Hanover produced the best yams known to the palate. The moon-white Lucea yam was surely the monarch of all yams, my mother always said. Every time she cooked and served Lucea yam, she would tell us the same story that Jamaica's first prime minister, Sir Alexander Bustamante, who was himself a native of Hanover and a man who claimed to have been descended from Arawak

Indians, would say that "Lucea yam is such a perfect food that it can be eaten alone, with no fish nor meat." She too subscribed to the belief that the Lucea yam needed nothing, no accompanying "salt ting," as the Africans referred to pickled pig or beef parts, dried, salted codfish, shad, and mackerel which was imported by estate owners as protein for their diet.

The clearing, which was later to become the village of Harvey River, was near the hillside plots farmed by some of the formerly enslaved Africans, many of whom now worked as hired labourers on nearby estates. The two Harvey brothers decided to "settle" the land, and, giddy at the prospect of imitating men like Christopher Columbus, Walter Raleigh, and Francis Drake, they named the river after themselves. They had spent the night sleeping on its banks, having come upon the place towards evening.

"Do you think this river has a name?" said William.

"Aye, it has one now," said John.

They had bathed in it, and caught fat river mullets and quick dark eels which they roasted on stones. Then they had fallen asleep to the sound of the rush of the waters they now called by their name.

The Harvey brothers built their first small house of wattles and daub. Later they built a larger house of mahogany, cedar, and stone. Then William had sent for his wife, Lily, and his six children whom he had left behind in London when he and his brother had come to Jamaica. Nobody knows where their money came from, but they were able to acquire considerable property in the area, and to live independently for the rest of their days.

In time the village grew. Grocery shops were established, there were at least two rum bars, a church, and a school. But no matter who came to live there, the Harveys were considered to be the first family of the village. And when the government built a bridge over a section of the Harvey River and tried to name it after some minor colonial flunky, William Harvey himself went and took down the government's sign and erected a sign of his own saying Harvey Bridge.

He was a tall, big-boned man
the earth shuddered under his steps
but the caught-quiet at his centre
pulled peace to him like a magnet.

Whenever she spoke of her paternal grandfather, my mother would say that he was one of the biggest, tallest, quietest men that anybody had ever met. Actually, because she had a love for imagery, she would say something like, "When he walked, the ground would shake, but he was silent as a lamb, a giant of a man with a still spirit." True or not, there was something remarkable about the character of William Harvey, who was one of the few Englishmen in his time to legally marry a black Jamaican woman. By all accounts he was a very moral man who would not have countenanced living in sin with Frances Duhaney. He took her as his legal wife in the Lucea Parish Church, and none of his English neighbours attended the wedding. Some of them even cautioned him that black women were only fit to be concubines. William's response to that particular piece of advice was that any woman who was good enough to share his bed was good enough for him to marry.

He married her after his English wife died and left him with six children. He went on to have six more children with Frances Duhaney — Tom, Frances, George, James, Martha, and my grandfather David — and from all accounts he cared for them all, from the blond, blue-eyed Edward born from his first wife to the dark, Indian-looking David and all the others of varying skin shades in between. He gave each of them equal amounts of land, which he surveyed himself, and he encouraged them to read and to love the books he had brought with him from England. He was known on occasion to chase outsiders from Harvey River, and if, as I suspect, those outsiders were dark-skinned like his own wife, then I'm not sure what that says about the very moral character of William Harvey except that he was deeply complicated and flawed like most people.

William had chosen Frances Ann Duhaney as his future wife when he went one day to the village of Jericho to purchase a pig and some chickens from her father. My great-grandfather seemed to have been a man of clear and unequivocal feelings. According to my mother, he identified my great-grandmother as his second wife from the first time that he laid eyes upon her.

Frances Ann Duhaney, called "Nana" as a sign of respect after her marriage, was a fine-featured woman with jet-black skin. Her surname, Duhaney, probably meant that her African grandfather had been owned by the Duhaney family, proprietors of the Point Estate at the eastern end of Hanover. The original form of their name was de Henin, from the descendants of Phillip de Henin of the Netherlands.

William Harvey had spotted the beautiful young girl moving efficiently about her father's yard. In the hour or two that it took William to buy the pig and some chickens from Mr. Duhaney, he noticed how lightly the young girl moved, how effortlessly she performed her tasks, feeding the chickens, sweeping up the yard, building a fire, disappearing and reappearing in no time bearing a pail of water drawn from the river, peeling yams and dasheens and feeding the peels to the pigs. Her face was so serene throughout, her high smooth forehead never breaking a sweat. It seemed to him that she hummed a low and compelling tune all the time, like a worker bee. Her lips were a shade darker than the rest of her face, as though she had been suckled on the juice of some sweet, energizing black berry. He had asked her father for her hand in marriage.

Soon the young girl was moving swiftly, silently, and efficiently about the Harvey house on bare feet. She rarely wore shoes inside her house. It was as if she needed her soles to always be in touch with the powerful work energy issuing up from the Hanover ground through the floorboards, the same energy that enabled labourers to perform the ferocious, back-breaking tasks involved in the production of sugar cane; an endless cycle of digging, planting, weeding, cutting, grinding, and boiling under the ninety-six-degrees-in-the-shade sun, and the cut of the whip. Nana Frances pulled that same work energy up through the soles of her feet, and that allowed her to work tirelessly. William always said that it was not just her beauty, but her silence, devotion, loyalty, and capacity for hard work that drew him to her.

Nana Frances would get up early every morning, after only a few hours' sleep, to make big country breakfasts or "morning dinners" of roasted yams and breadfruit, bammies made from grated cassava, fried plantains, fried eggs, stewed liver, kidneys, and light, and escoveitched fish, washed down with quarts of coffee and chocolate tea. William was a big man who liked his food. She knew that, and she liked to cook for him and his trenchermen children. She would wash huge hampers of laundry in the river, beating the clothes clean on the river stones, washing linen as white as the proverbial Fullers soap. She kept the big wooden house clean, staining what seemed like acres of mahogany floors with red oxide and burnishing them with a club-shaped coconut brush. She dusted and polished the heavy mahogany furniture with cedar oil, she cleaned the ornate silver cutlery with ashes taken from the belly of the iron stove, and she used the pulp of sour Seville oranges to shine the copper and brass utensils. Crouched on her hands and knees, she moved across the floors, her small calloused hands beating out a Johnny Cooper rhythm: Joh-nny Coo-per, Joh-nny Coo-per . . . that was the scansion and sound of the coconut brush beating out its domestic rhythm on the planks of the wooden floor. She starched and ironed clothes with small triangular-faced irons made by the local blacksmith, irons that were heated on wood or coal fires. She was forever bending over some source of heat or water, to iron, cook, set steaming plates of food before the big-boned Harvey men, proud of her reputation as a hard worker. She seemed to like it when people said, "She can work you see!" But she never encouraged her own daughters to work like that. She always told them, "I work enough for everybody already, you go and study your book." So when her son David married Margaret Wilson, Nana Frances advised the new bride to hire a maid to help her with her housework. Above all, she cautioned, "Don't go and wash clothes in the river. Get somebody to do that for you. Don't make these people think you are ordinary."

Her eldest son, Tom, took Nana's admonitions against ordinariness very seriously. He had been sent to Rusea's High School in Lucea, but growing bored with the dry curriculum that was imported without modification from English public schools, he took to skipping school and going to listen to the cases being tried in the Lucea courthouse. In time he persuaded his younger brother David to cut school and join him. At home they began to study the law books that their father had brought with him from England, and after a while they both knew enough law to be able to give effective legal advice to the poor and defenceless of Hanover. David's talents lay more with civil cases. He was a gifted writer who wrote many letters on behalf of people unable to do so. He had a way of choosing appropriate phrases, for selecting the right words to express the plight of some poor, wronged person. Tom's talents lay more with criminal cases which he would "try" the night before the actual case, using his brothers and sisters as the accused, as witnesses, and as members of the jury.

"Go to my son Tom and my son David, they will tell you what to tell the judge." Nana, proud that her sons were not ordinary, was forever recommending her sons' village lawyer practice to any wronged person. Their reputation, no doubt helped by their mother's tireless word-of-mouth promotion, grew to the point where the local judges issued an order banning them from practising within a five-mile radius of the courthouse. So Tom and David set up office under a Lignum Vitae tree with its masses of lavender blossoms, exactly five miles from the Lucea courthouse. Dressed like most men of their time, in dark trousers and white shirts and wearing felt hats, they stationed themselves under the spreading branches of the national tree of Jamaica while poor people, many of them walking barefoot, came to them for help. Many is the time David Harvey gave his own clean shirt laundered by his mother, Nana Frances, to some poor man to enable him to stand with dignity before a hard-eyed judge. My mother's father and her uncle instructed hundreds of people how to defend themselves against the British colonial laws that valued the smallest piece of property over the life of any ex-slave, and David went home sometimes without his shirt because he knew how the law judged by appearances.

O to hear him sing the lake Isle of Innisfree,
now become Harvey River, near Lucea.

"Down by the Sally Gardens." My mother used to sing that song in a funny short-of-breath style, and looking back now I realize how many Irish words and phrases like "cute hooer," referring to a deceptive man or woman, were part of the language of the Harveys. They must have picked their Irishness up from the sailor who jumped ship in the Lucea Harbour and fathered my maternal grandmother with a woman of African descent who became the Guinea Woman in the poems and stories I would come to write.

The sailor was George O'Brian Wilson, who first saw Leanna Sinclair, mother of Margaret Wilson Harvey, when he went to call upon an Irish penkeeper on a sugar estate in the neighbouring parish of Westmoreland. He had jumped ship in the Lucea Harbour at the sight of the magnificent blue-green mountains of Western Jamaica. "The fairest isle that eyes ever beheld," is how Columbus had described this island. The intensely green landscape reminded George Wilson of parts of Ireland, but the weather here was much better, with its almost always hot, energizing sun and the warm clear blue seas with white sand beaches. Paradise. When he abandoned ship he took with him one thing, a woollen suit that had been woven and tailored by his own father. The wool had been dyed "rich black" by soaking it for a time in a boghole, then oiling it with goose grease before weaving it. That suit lasted him for his entire life, and he was buried in it.

George O'Brian Wilson was even more determined to stay in Jamaica once he landed and began to enjoy the rum bars and brothels of the small seaside town. This was the ideal place for men like him, and every white person he met seemed to have come to Jamaica to run away from some dark secret. No man gave a straight answer to any questions about his past life. So he let the ship sail without him and set about trying to locate and form alliances with other Irishmen, who gave him this advice: find and marry the daughter of some local Creole.

Whites born in Jamaica were not considered white by the English, because by now there was so much mixing of white and black blood; with so many black women giving birth to "sailor pickney," light-skinned children and jet-black children walking around with "good hair," Aryan features, and eyes the colour of semi-precious stones. Creole families needed to find white husbands for their daughters, for one day they all hoped to escape this place where they were outnumbered by Negroes and return to "the mother country," which many of them had never seen but which they nonetheless regarded as home.

It was not difficult for the Irish sailor to find a wealthy bride from one of these "anxious-to-upgrade-their-colour" families. Less than six months after he let the ship return to Ireland without him, he became a married man with property, the dowry of his Creole bride. Not long after his marriage, he went to visit another Irishman who worked as a penkeeper on a sugar estate in Grange, Westmoreland. It was there that he first saw Leanna Sinclair.

She was sixteen years old, just over five feet tall, and her skin was the colour of onyx. She had wide, amazed-looking eyes and a dusting of tiny warts that looked like beads of jet along the top of her cheeks, which is why she was called a Guinea woman. She was standing sideways when he first saw her, her face turned in the direction of the sea, standing on one leg like a Masai warrior or an egret, her other leg tucked up behind her. Her thick hair was hidden under a white headkerchief, and she gazed intently out to sea even as she served them.

George Wilson began to fear that she would drop the tray with the glasses of planters' punch called sangaree, and grow wings and fly straight over their heads as they sat there in their leather-backed planters' chairs on the wide verandah. He grew afraid that she would fly back to Africa before he got a chance to clasp her strange, wild beauty to him, and in that instant he became completely convinced that she possessed something that he needed in order to live, some powerful life force which he had to catch and absorb into him to enable him to make his way in Jamaica. He needed to cover her and be ready to catch it when it escaped from her throat as an ellipse of light. His fellow Irishman laughed when Wilson told him about how affected he was by the sight of this girl. "And you a newly married man and all!"

George Wilson, who would always refer to Jamaica as being "behind God's back," enjoyed parallel honeymoons. His efforts eventually produced Margaret Aberdeen Wilson, as he named her – he insisted on the Aberdeen but never explained why – who was born with his fair complexion, grey-blue eyes, and long straight black hair; and another daughter, Mary, who was born a few months before Margaret to his lawfully wedded wife and looked like nobody he knew. George Wilson grew to love the child Margaret more than he ever loved any other human being in his life.

One day when Margaret was a small girl, her father had called her his "little neega," which was probably his Irish pronunciation of "negro," and the child told him, "If me a neega, you a neega too, for you is my father, you a white neega." And that was true. He was much more in tune with the ways of the poor black Jamaican people than he was with the imitation English manners of the Creole class into which he had married. He had little or none of the graces of the well-to-do.

41

As the head of his new family, he was expected to behave like a member of the colonial ruling class, having to sit at table at night with the local gentry of Lucea, who talked about the "lazy, dirty Negroes" in much the same way that they spoke about the "lazy, dirty Irish" in England. He was much more at ease drinking in the small, dark wattle-and-daub rum shops with the thatched roofs which looked like the thatched sod and stone huts of his native county Galway, and he loved the robust African rhythms of the native music. He himself played a wicked fiddle and could sing so that it brought tears to the eyes. He would tell Margaret stories about Ireland, about the little people and the leprechauns. In turn the child would tell him stories told to her by her mother, about the trickster spider man, Anancy, from West Africa, and duppy stories about rolling calves. Wilson grew to admire Anancy's wily ways and he told her that Buddam, the village ne'er-do-well who was always being arrested by the village pan-head (which is what Jamaicans called district constables) for beating up people, had the strength of the mythical Irish warrior, Cuchulain.

When he grew old, George Wilson abandoned his family in Lucea, and came to live with Margaret in Harvey River in the small house that she and David built for him. In Harvey River, he plied his trade as a shoemaker and saddler, and my mother loved to tell the story of how he once made a pair of boots for a woman from the nearby village of Jericho. When he delivered the boots to the woman, he told her that the leather was rather tough, and that she should oil the boots before she wore them in order to soften them. He said this in his rich Irish brogue, and to the woman's West African ears the advice to oil her boots came out sounding like "boil your boots." She promptly went home, made up a roaring fire, put on a large cauldron of water, and boiled the boots until they shrank, so that they looked like footwear fit only for a small cloven-footed animal.

She returned to George Wilson in a great rage, insisting that he had told her to "bwile" her boots. He insisted that he had rightly told her to "aile" them, and then he probably told her that she should get her "bleddy eegnorant arse" the hell away from his shop before he shied his lapstone at her. The woman was thereafter called "Bwile boot, me tell you fi aile it, you bwile it" by the village children. My mother's people love beautiful shoes. In every photograph ever taken of the Harveys, they are wonderfully shod, no doubt a taste they acquired from George Wilson.

~

My great-grandmother was a Guinea woman. It seemed that, at best, Leanna Sinclair's feelings towards George O'Brian Wilson were mixed. While she was pleased by his attentions, she always felt as if her life's breath was being cut off when he covered her, and so she closed herself off tightly whenever he approached. She bore him two children, my mother's mother, Margaret, and a boy to whom he gave his own name, George, but who died when he was an infant. To capture her heart he tried flattery. "By Christ y'are the loveliest ting I've ever laid eye on."

"But you hate Jesus Christ, you tell me so youself, how you going swear by him and me believe you?"

He gave her gifts.

"I bought some ting for you, a fine red dress."

"I don't wear red. Plenty African get catch because them was wearing red and that is how them see them to catch them."

"Shut your focking mout and just do what I tell you."

George Wilson never did get to ingest that part of Leanna's soul which he visualized as a rim of light, no matter how hard he tried to make her cry out so that it would detach itself from her soul-case and float through her open throat into his mouth. He never did get to possess Leanna because she could always see far and she knew that George O'Brian Wilson was not her true love. If she appeared to be looking out to sea the first time that George Wilson saw her, it was because she was seeing a ship, perhaps it might even have been the one that was bringing those twin brothers to Jamaica. Leanna was able to recognize other people who could see far in this way, they always looked past you. Mostly they looked up to the sky. If they looked into your eyes, they often looked quickly away because they could see things about you that they did not want to have to see. Who wanted to be seeing people with perfectly good-looking faces change into animals when you looked at them? Or hear greedy people grunting, when to the ears of others they were speaking in dulcet tones?

One night when she was twelve years old, Leanna dreamt that she was one of the Africans packed into the hold of a slaver. In her dream, she was crouched and chained, wedged tightly against the bodies of other Africans squatting in their own excrement. The smell and the thick darkness in the hold was like no other darkness or smell in creation. It was shit and sulphur and the raw and rancid sweat of human fear, and aloes and bitters and the vile essence of degradation. The foul stinking air was rent by the hoarse cries of people calling out to different gods in many different tongues, calling upon ogun and shango and damballah, gods of iron and lightning and war, to fling down ancient curses upon their captors. Curses as old as the world itself. Curses employed by the first man and the first woman who suffered at the hands of other crazed beings who had flown past their nests, transgressors of the sacred law: do unto others as you would have them do unto you. Curses invoked by King David and King Rameses against their enemies. "Tear them from limb to limb, dash them against the rocks, smite them hip and thigh, maim and blind them, may their tongues cleave to the roofs of their mouths. May their own children suck out their eyes, their life breath, may dogs eat their entrails . . ."

And one or two more pious ones amongst them were praying to more compassionate gods to send mercy rain to soften the hearts of their captors, men who would reduce human beings to beast-state for the sake of gold and silver shekels and Cain's profit. Suddenly, in the midst of this terrible place, the people gradually became conscious of music being played. A music which took its rhythm from the waves on which the ship of darkness rode, a rhythm which rocked out and returned to its centre, conducting in its wake and movements the peace that passeth understanding. And for what seemed like an eternity, but was in fact only a few minutes, silence settled over the slaver. In later years, Jamaicans would call this beat Rocksteady.

Leanna had started to see the man who would become the love of her life just about the time that she entered puberty, and in her visions he was always walking towards her. Sometimes she would not see him for months and then she would be doing her domestic work up at the Irish penkeeper's house, polishing a mahogany table, and she would see an image of a young man, not too tall, but with strong legs and big hands, appear up through the wood grain of the table. For years she saw his image. Sometimes he would be walking across high blue mountains with people who looked like his mother and father, another time he would be making his way through cane fields, and sometimes he was walking by the sea. Once, he was lying down on the cold ground, looking up at the stars, gazing up at the constellation which looked like a big gourd in the sky, wishing for a drink of star water. Sometimes the young man was crouched down with the people who looked like his parents, hiding from someone or something in the bushes. But one thing was certain, he was coming towards her. And because Leanna knew this man was coming, she kept her heart tightly closed whenever George Wilson was near, so that he eventually grew tired of trying to make her yield up her essence to him.

~

After the trouble,
some with the name Bogle
catch fraid like sickness
and take panic for the cure.

John Bogle's people had found their way to the parish of Westmoreland after the Morant Bay Uprising, in 1865, when John's relative Paul Bogle — to whom he bore a remarkable resemblance — was hanged. Paul Bogle preached and he walked to petition the representatives of the British Colonial government on behalf of the starving people who were turned loose after emancipation and given nothing. No land, no money, no forty acres, not even one mule. The planters were compensated for loss of human property, but the men and women who had worked to build the great wealth of the British ruling class received not one farthing. On August 1, 1838, their first morning of full freedom, many of them had walked away from the estates carrying not even a simple hoe with which to till the ground. The ones who chose to stay worked for the lowest possible wages, out of which they then had to pay the estate owners for their keep. Then the sugar industry collapsed. Money was scarce and taxes high. Disease and famine, cholera and smallpox, claimed more than fifty thousand lives and then, like an additional Biblical plague, came drought. Domestic food crops began to fail year after year. Add to that a justice system that as a rule dispensed no justice to the majority of Jamaicans, a system administered by the estate owners and managers who were full of vengeance and wrath over the loss of their human property.

Paul Bogle, a child of enslaved parents, was a prosperous small farmer from Stony Gut in the parish of St. Thomas. Deacon Paul could speak with the tongues of men and of angels, but he was also a man of deeds. He led a delegation on a forty-five-mile walk from Stony Gut to Spanish Town to see Governor John Eyre, and draw his attention to the suffering, but the Governor refused to meet with them. George William Gordon was among the men of property who sympathized with the people's suffering. The son of a slave woman and a Scottish planter, he had worked hard to educate himself and had been elected to the Legislative Assembly in 1844. Bogle and Gordon, Baptists both, tried to petition the Colonial government on behalf of the beleaguered people. They tried and tried the peaceful way. They walked, they wrote petitions, even to the Queen herself. For their efforts they got a letter from Queen Victoria, which recommended the starving landless Jamaican people practise industry, thrift, hard work, and obedience.

Governor Eyre ordered Paul Bogle and George William Gordon to be hanged for leading the uprising that we were taught in school was the "Morant Bay Rebellion." Some four hundred desperate people stormed the courthouse in Morant

Bay and clashed with the local volunteer guards. Twenty-one men, mostly white, were killed. More than six hundred ex-slaves were executed and as many flogged in response to the uprising. A dispatch from Col. J.H.F. Elkington to the commander in the field went as follows. "Hole is doing splendid service all about Manchioneal and shooting every black man who cannot account for himself. Nelson at Port Antonio is hanging like fun by court martial. I hope that you will not send any black prisoners. Do punish the blackguards well." One month after, the Morant Bay River in St. Thomas was still stinking, polluted from the number of corpses floating in it.

After the Morant Bay Uprising, to say that your name was Bogle was to sign your own death warrant. Some of the surviving Bogles coined protective variations of their great name, such as Bogues, Boggis, and Bogey. John Bogle and his parents had walked across the island from St. Thomas to Hanover, removing themselves as much as was possible from what happened in St. Thomas. As far as the east is from the west, John's family travelled to the parish of Hanover, trying to keep their lives and to keep the great name of Bogle alive. But ironically they ended up being called Buddle instead of Bogle by many Hanover people. And one Sunday in 1875, as sure as fate, Leanna was walking towards the town of Savanna la Mar, and walking towards her on the main road was the same man she had been seeing in her dreams, leading a big grey mule. She began to laugh as she recognized him, and he began to laugh even louder. They met in the middle of the road, and he said to her, "If you was *my* missus, I wouldn't make you walk. I would give you this nice grey mule." From that day, they never lived apart, until John Bogle died. They lived, farmed, and flourished in Grange, Westmoreland, and Leanna rode her grey mule, wore her money jewellery, necklaces and bracelets

48

fashioned from silver coins soldered together, and lived a happy, prosperous life. When her mother married John Bogle, Margaret, who was six years old, told him, "You not my father." He said, "I know, but I am the man who will honour your mother."

"Me meet the man who intend to put him ring pon mi finger."

That is how Leanna Sinclair announced to George O'Brian Wilson that she was ending their relationship.

George Wilson, who had by then lost all interest in getting Leanna to surrender completely to him, said:

"Fock! So you're to be married then . . . well, way you go, just you have my Meg dressed, ready and waiting outside every Sattiday morning, for I'll not be setting foot in your goddamn yard ever again. I'll bring her back by nightfall . . . Oh, don't imagine tis you who's leaving me, truth is, I've no further use for you!" George Wilson never spoke directly to Leanna again. He did not feel any need to. She had given him what he needed to make his way in Jamaica. She had given him Margaret.

*M*argaret Aberdeen Wilson met David Harvey when they were schoolchildren. The fact that they both had black mothers and white fathers meant that they had a lot in common, and as long as they lived, they never ran out of things to say to each other. Their childhood friendship blossomed into romance, and when they became teenagers, David began to court Margaret. Leanna and her husband, John Bogle, would stay up in the small sitting room to make sure that the couple outside on the verandah "behaved themselves," so Margaret and David would sit on the verandah, which was lit with a smoky kerosene lamp, and they would talk about their friends, about what was happening in the village. She would tell him what her father had told her about Ireland, and he would tell her what his father had told him about England, all the while aching to fall into each other's arms. When it began to grow late, Leanna would rock her mahogany chair vigorously on the floorboards to signal to David that he should go home. David was a sensitive young man. He always took the hint, and he used this rocking-chair signal as his cue to perform a farewell suite of songs on his harmonica. Out of sheer mischief he would blow, "Nobody's Business but My Own," the anthem of the "don't-care."

If me married to a nayga man
turn round change him
fi one coolie man
nobody's business
but me own

Then he would play what became his and Margaret's sig-
nature song, "Beautiful Dreamer." He would raise the silver
harmonica to his lips, and it would flash in the half-darkness
of the verandah, where the small kerosene lamp rested on a
wicker table. He would play "Beautiful Dreamer," accompanied by the high alto chirping chorus of crickets, the bass calls
of bullfrogs, and the croaking lizard's response. His inspired
performance was illuminated by stage lights of peenie wallies,
or fireflies, and the thick country darkness formed an opaque
black fire cloth behind him. He would depart playing that
song, which Margaret would hear growing fainter as he rode
away on his horse, back to Harvey River, where he took her to
live after he married her when she was eighteen and he was
nineteen years old.

David's father, William Harvey, had given them twenty
acres of land and helped the new marrieds build their first
house. Margaret's father, George O'Brian Wilson, handcrafted
fine leather shoes for the bride and groom and insisted on
giving away his daughter despite the protests from his legal
wife and children in Lucea, to whom he was forced to say:
"There is not yet born the focking man or woman who is the
boss of me." He and Leanna Bogle did not exchange one word
at the wedding of their daughter, and John Bogle stood silently
by Leanna's side as the young bride, Margaret, who was dressed
in a long satin gown trimmed with wide bands of Irish lace
that George Wilson had specially ordered from England, walked

grim-faced — as was the custom of the time — under her sheer veil up the aisle of the Lucea Parish Church.

At the wedding reception, held at William and Frances Harvey's home in Harvey River, George Wilson played the fiddle and sang "Peg O My Heart," changing the words to "Meg O My Heart," for Meg was what he sometimes called his beloved Margaret. She and David danced while her father fiddled, and she blushed and tried to pull away when David danced up close to her. But he had smiled and insisted, saying, "We are now husband and wife, we can do whatever we please."

$\mathcal{B}$efore the children came into their lives, days in Margaret and David Harvey's household always began well before daybreak in the cool Hanover mornings. "Before night take off him black trousers, before cock crow, before the sun show it clean face behind the Dolphin Head Mountain." Margaret, like her mother, Leanna, was always the first person up in her household. She would put on one of David's old jackets over her long nightgown and walk barefoot through the sleeping house. When she reached the back door, she would slip her feet into a pair of his old boots and step out into the backyard and rap loudly on the window of the small outroom where the domestic helper slept. "Wake from thy slumber, Miss Lazy, arise and shine and catch up the fire." The fire that the sleepy-eyed girl would wake and start at 5 a.m. in the big iron stove would not be put out until evening. "The first thing that a good woman do when she wake up in the morning is to put on a kettle of water to make coffee for her husband and tea for her children." Margaret, like her mother, Leanna, lived by that rule. She always brought a cup of hot coffee to David first thing in the morning. He would drink it and then set off for his field. If it was a day when he conducted his village lawyer practice, he would rise with Margaret and study from his law books by lamplight before he set off to meet his brother, Tom, outside the town of Lucea.

Each day, David Harvey headed off into the world fuelled by large mugs of coffee, fried bammies or dumplings with codfish and ackee, cornmeal or hominy porridge, and thick white slabs of harddough bread. By mid-morning, a second breakfast was prepared and packed in straw baskets called "cutacu," and sent to him as he worked in the fields. Other men in surrounding villages took the remains of their first breakfast to the fields with them to eat at mid-morning, but in Margaret Harvey's household, second breakfasts were always delivered to David in the fields by a young boy from the village who ran errands for them. He was told to "run, run quick before the food cold, Mr. Harvey don't like cold food."

At midday when David returned from the fields, or in the afternoon if he had gone to his village lawyer practice, there was "dinner," the main meal of the day. From the start of their married life, David and Margaret's kitchen boasted some of the largest pots in Hanover, and as there were always relatives and friends visiting, the deep-bottomed pots swelled with rice, the smoke-stained pots boiled "junks" of yams, sweet potatoes, and dozens of green bananas with pieces of salt pork. There were huge cast-iron dutch pots in which slabs of mutton, beef, or pork, fresh from slaughter, were fried or stewed with garlic, onions, peppers, and salt. Midday dinners often lasted until early afternoon and filled the belly till supper, which was served at sundown, always with mugs of hot cocoa or "chocolate tea" and harddough bread and fried fish, or sardines and big, thick, sweet cornmeal puddings. A place was always set at the table for David as head of the house, and Margaret usually sat with him when he ate.

As more and more children were born to David and

Margaret, they ate in shifts, or they ate anytime they wanted to, using a variety of mismatched dishes. Fine china left over from Margaret's wedding set, pieces of which were broken by various helpers and children, were set out alongside ordinary "ware" plates, bought in Lucea. They used an assortment of cutlery. Some heavy, ornate silver knives and forks brought back from Cuba by David, bone-handled knives and forks brought from England by William Harvey, and more ordinary tin knives and forks bought from merchants in Lucea at various times. Except for Sundays after church, when the entire family always sat down to eat their Sunday dinner of rice and peas and chicken together, Margaret had no time for "frippery" like damask tablecloths. Raising eight children and feeding a steady stream of visitors did not make for "dainty living." "My children eat good food, plenty good food, as much as they want, no child of mine ever know hungry," Margaret would say. This no-frippery attitude was endorsed by her father, George O'Brian Wilson, when he came to live at Harvey River. He would tell Margaret about his days as a boy growing up in County Galway, where his family shared their small thatched stone cottage with the animals, and how the window taxes meant that his parents could only afford to have one small window and a half-door in their dark little house. Because of these conditions, one of his siblings had died of typhus.

Later in life, Cleodine tried to impose more "refined" ways of dining on the Harvey household. She would cook at home dishes that Mrs. Marston, the Englishwoman who ran a small private school for Hanover girls, had taught to her pupils as part of their training in the domestic sciences. Cleodine's attempts to improve the Harvey family cuisine was, however, not a success. "Look how she take the good piece a beef and stew it down to nothing, then cover it up with crush pitata as if she shame a it," was the verdict on her shepherd's pie from her brothers. "Country bumpkins, bungoes, you will never amount to anything," Cleodine said. Margaret and David, who usually let their first-born have her way, pretended that they liked the shepherd's pie, but they made no move to incorporate it and other English-style fare into their lives. "When I have my own house," Cleodine would say, "I will not be serving any of this coarse hard food." And Margaret, who drew the line at being "ruled" by any of her children, would answer, "When you get your own house you can do any damn thing you want, but don't forget that this is my house and I am the only big woman under this roof."

Margaret liked to think of herself as the undisputed boss of her house, and David made very few decisions without consulting her. The ones he did manage to make without her approval all had to do with him lending money or standing surety for some poor person, who invariably did not repay him. Margaret never let him forget these lapses. "If you did ask me, I could tell you that that man is a liar and a thief, and that any money you lend him would be a dead story, but no, you and you soft heart, you make everybody take you for a fool."

Her area of special concern, however, was the welfare of her daughters. Whenever some story of an unfortunate girl who had "fallen" reached her ears, Margaret would immediately blame the mother of the girl. "You see me? I watch my girl children like hawk! There is nothing that any of them do that I don't know about. I don't understand how a woman could say that her own daughter fall and she never know for months! I know how every one of my girl children stay at all times." When the Harvey girls reached puberty, they all received the same lecture from her, a lecture that was really a short threat: "What this means is that you can have baby now, and God see and know I will kill you if . . ." Margaret did not even have to finish her threat. The Harvey girls referred to the region below a woman's waistline as their "Bottoms."

Apart from witnessing the rough mating of farm animals, and blushing at the little rude jokes and songs of schoolchildren who were not above converting a hymn into a dirty ditty – "At the cross at the cross where I first met my boy and the burden of my drawers rolled away" – and the whispering about some village girl who "fall," the Harvey girls did not talk about sex. They were charged to remain virgins till they married, and to defend their virtues to the death. A charge which they all took very, very seriously.

*L*ate one afternoon Doris had gone to bathe in the river by herself. The riverbed was deserted of all the village women by the time she got there. Some had come early, after dispatching the men to the fields, bearing their dirty clothes in big bundles on their heads. Some went to the fields themselves and then did their laundry later in the day, but they all washed their clothes in the same way. Soaping them with iron-hard wedges of brown soap, making loud, strong rubbing sounds with their knuckles as they scrubbed the clothes clean. Young girls were told: "You have to rub the collar, the armholes, and the sleeves and make sure you turn the clothes wrongside, wash it clean, and rinse it at least two time."

White clothes were spread on rocks to bleach in the morning sun, while the coloured clothes were being rinsed in the swift moving water, then laid out on the rocks to dry. After doing the laundry, the women bathed themselves and bathed the children, often using the same wedges of brown soap on their skin, along with slippery green aloes to wash and condition their hair. That was the more open washing of clothes. There was a more secret "small clothes" washing that took place there too, small clothes being the term for menstrual cloths. This washing was done in pails of water drawn from the river, off to the side, under the shade of the bamboo which screened the river. Young women were told not to pour this "small clothes" water back into the river, so they used it to water the roots of the flowers growing on the riverbank. The bright red hibiscus and the red water grass seemed to benefit from this, and in turn they became useful, nurturing plants. The pulp of the hibiscus can be used to blacken shoes and to make ink for poor schoolchildren. The red water grass became a medicinal herb, good for bad fresh colds.

My mother never did say why she went to bathe alone in the river that day; maybe she wanted to do her own private washing in private and as it happened there was no one else there when she reached the river, so she took off her dress under which she was wearing her bathing costume and dived into the river. She was a beautiful diver, who never made a splash when she entered the water although she was a tall, plump girl. The water just seemed to part for her and to let her in. She swam bank to bank and dived deep once or twice to investigate what was under the rocks in her family river. She came up with a small crayfish but she threw it back. "Grow some more," she said aloud to the underweight crayfish.

"Who you talking to?" said a voice, and Doris looked up to see a strange boy standing across from her on the riverbank. He had to be a stranger, for normal river protocol dictated that if a village boy came across a Harvey girl bathing, he would leave immediately. Instead, this one stood on the riverbank, big and bold, staring at my mother, who had buried herself in the water up to her neck the moment that she realized that she was not alone. "Go away," she said. But the boy just stood there, grinning and staring. "You don't hear me say you must move, go'on, go 'way from here?" she said. The bold-faced boy, who was from Kingston and was visiting with relatives in nearby

Chambers Pen, had never seen a river before, much less a river with a pretty young girl bathing in it. He stood his ground, looking right at her, smiling an impudent, pleased-puss smile and refused to budge an inch.

The news reached Margaret and David before Doris got home. How she had been overheard cursing terrible badwords down by the river, "expressions" as she and her sisters called them. For my mother, taking the charge to defend her virtue seriously, had summoned up every curse word she had ever heard used by anybody in Harvey River, or on the streets of the seaport town of Lucea, and had flung them across the water at the leering town boy, who was so surprised by the stream of invective issuing from the mouth of the sweet-faced bather that he did exactly what my mother had been trying to get him to do, he fled.

"That's right, my daughter, I am proud of you." To her surprise, instead of scolding her for cursing badwords, that is what her father, David, said to her as he held her in his arms when she reached home.

"You do well, Doris," said Margaret.

"She did not have to stoop so low as to curse expressions," said Cleodine.

"Any port in a storm," said David, who then sent his sons to find the visiting town boy and to explain to him just how men were expected to behave when Harvey women were swimming in their river.

"Doris is not the prettiest one, but she is the one that everyone loves," her brother Flavius would say. "Dear Dor" they called her, for if Cleodine was pristine and as perfectly designed as an anthurium, Albertha a lily above reproach, Rose a fragrant damask rose by name and nature, and Ann gorgeous and intense as a bird of paradise, my mother could be described as a mixed bouquet. She was a little of all those flowers, with a good spray of common wildflowers like buttercups and ramgoat roses bundled in with hardy perennials and quick-growing impatiens, and she learned how to send her roots down deep when storm-time came.

Storm-time was the furthest thing from Doris's mind while she grew up as a daughter of the first family of Harvey River. She was an easy-going child who from an early age displayed signs of a quick intelligence and a love of hyperbole. Once, when her brother Edmund hid in a bush and jumped out at her, a frightened Doris declared: "Only Almighty God alone knows how my poor, poor, trembling, fearful little heart could stand such a great fright . . ." This she said with her eyes raised to heaven and one small hand covering her little palpitating heart. She had a way with words, words being one of the things she learned from her village lawyer father, David, from the vituperative Irish eloquence of her maternal grandfather, George O'Brian Wilson, and from the West African Guinea woman griot-style of her grandmother Leanna.

"Doris is really Mas David daughter." In the same way that her father literally gave the shirt off his back to people going to Court, and constantly loaned them money to pay fines, my mother was known as a "come to help us." Much as she loved her dresses, she would give them away to her cousins who admired them. She was the one you went to if you wanted to borrow anything. If you needed somebody to keep your baby while you went on an errand or if you were feeling sick, she was an excellent nurse. Once her sister Albertha's fingers had become so swollen and infected from excessive embroidering that she could do nothing for herself. It was my mother who bathed her and dressed her until her hands healed, and Albertha always spoke about her sister's ministrations with tears in her eyes. Everybody in Harvey River loved Doris; so on that September morning in 1920, after Margaret Wilson Harvey's husband and children had left the house, and she noticed a line of red ants marching along her clothesline – a sure portent of trouble – she did not expect trouble to do with Doris. In the late morning, she glanced across the valley, up to the hilltop, in the direction of the village school and saw what looked like a group of school girls in navy blue uniforms fluttering down the hillside like a flock of grass quits. Minutes later, when she heard the girls burst into the village with a great warbling commotion, Margaret hurried out into the square only to behold her daughter Doris at the head of the crowd bearing her long black plait in her clenched fist.

Back up the hill they went, this time with Margaret at the head of the crowd, carrying her daughter's once waist-length braid flung over her left shoulder. As they climbed the hill, she cried "this is like murder" and swore to personally punish the culprit who in a fit of adolescent concupiscence had sliced off my mother's hair as she sat in front of him with her head bent forward, concentrating on the rules of proper speech in her *Nestfield's Grammar*.

So devastated was Doris that she refused to go to school for weeks, staying close to home with her chopped-off hair hidden under a mob cap and bursting into tears anytime anybody said something like: "You *hear* what happened" or "*Here* is some money, go and buy a bread for supper," or "Didn't you *hear* me calling you?"

Harvey relatives came from far and near, bringing Doris little gifts, a nice ripe mango, a coconut cake, a shilling, gifts to help ease the misery of the loss of her plait, which Margaret kept, lying in state, on a table in the centre of the drawing room.

"Why these things always happen to me? Look how that nasty boy spy on me and make me curse those expressions and embarrass myself, and Almighty God, who seeth and knoweth all things, knows that I was innocently, innocently studying my book and that wicked wretch come and cut off my hair, why me? O Lord? Why me?" And then she cried out something that she had read in a novel: "My life is over, for a woman's beauty is her hair."

Margaret could not let that pass. "A woman's beauty? So you a woman now? The only woman in this house is me, your mother, so you better put this hat on you head and go on to school."

Eventually David dug a hole in the yard and buried the severed plait, saying, "It is only hair, it will grow back, it is not as if the boy took her life." "Yes, that is true," said her mother, "but it look like she have bad luck. Look how that renking little boy from town was peeping on her and now look this . . . her lovely head of hair shorn like a sheep."

*F*or months after the boy cut off her hair, my mother wore a broad leghorn straw hat whenever she went shopping in Lucea with her sisters. For these trips they would debate for days beforehand about what to wear in order to "cut a dash" when they entered the town. They favoured linen, crepe, and georgette dresses in cool pastel colours or romantic florals. Never dark colours; dark colours were for older, married women. Sooner or later they each would have decided on an outfit, always ones with skirts that buttoned up the side so they could undo the bottom buttons when they rode, two to a horse, into Lucea. But my mother would be changing her clothes up until the eleventh hour. Sometimes she would change into as many as ten complete outfits before her sisters threatened to leave without her as they rode the five miles into the town of Lucea. "Yes, Match-Me Doris, those black shoes go with that powder-blue dress and you don't have time to change them," says Albertha. And Doris, who did not like to be hurried, and was liable to become short-tempered if pressured, would certainly have told them, "Go on, go on and leave me behind, for I am not going into town looking like a poppyshow today. Furthermore my clothes are mine. I sew them, I can change them as much as I like." "You think you are the only one who can change clothes?" They would have argued, but once they got there they would become the five ladylike Harvey girls.

Lucea, the capital of Hanover, is situated on the western side of a horseshoe-shaped harbour that is approximately one mile wide. With the exception of the parish of Kingston and St. Andrew, Hanover is the smallest of the fourteen parishes in Jamaica. Hanover was almost named St. Sophia, in honour of the mother of King George I, but this name was voted down by the Legislative council in favour of Hanover, originally spelled Hannover. The name was chosen with reference to the German domain of the reigning family of England.

When the Harvey girls descended from their home in the hilly interior of Harvey River and rode into the town of Lucea, they never failed to look up in wonder at the Lucea Clock Tower, which held a red clock that looked like the high-domed helmet worn by German royal guards. Everyone in the town knew that the clock in the tower was brought to Lucea by mistake, that it had been destined for the island of St. Lucia, and that the captain of the ship which was transporting it had mistaken the Port of Lucea for the island of St. Lucia, and delivered it there in 1817. As it so happened, Lucea's town fathers had already ordered a new clock built, but it was of a more modern design, and not anything as grand as this German helmet. They decided forthwith that they could not and would not let the red helmet clock go and so they laid claim to it. It has remained there ever since.

After noting the time by the clock tower, the girls would dismount and leave the horses in the care of one of their relatives in Lucea, after which they would sometimes go to visit the Lucea Parish Church and pay their respects to some of their relatives who were buried in the churchyard. They would go by the Lucea Hospital at Fort Charlotte (named after George III's queen) and Rusea's High School, built towards the end of the eighteenth century with money left by a Frenchman, Martin Rusea, in thankfulness for the safe harbour and hospitality that he had found in Lucea. These were the town's main landmarks, situated fairly close together on the promontory overlooking the harbour. With the imposing Dolphin Head Mountains rising as high as two thousand feet, and an abundance of cabbage palms and tall coconut trees forming a lush backdrop to the azure harbour, the town of Lucea was a small but steady source of light.

The eligible young men of Lucea gathered to feast their eyes on the Harvey girls whenever they came to town. These included the young men who worked as clerks at the courthouse and as civil servants in the few colonial government offices in existence at that time, such as the Collector of Taxes. Some of them were apprenticed as surveyors in the Lands Department, and a few were members of Her Majesty's Jamaica Constabulary Force, but the Harvey girls would not consider giving the time of day to a policeman. For some reason (probably to do with their Irish grandfather, George O'Brian Wilson) their mother, Margaret, had a fierce prejudice against policemen and soldiers. Another of her edicts, in addition to "No child of mine will ever rule me," was "No policeman or soldier will ever sit in one of my chairs."

Dressed to the nines to come shopping for yet more fabric, the girls would go directly to Mr. Jim Reid's store on the Lucea main street. Mr. Reid, a slender, well-dressed, and soft-spoken man, was known for his exquisite taste. He stocked the finest cloths, lace, buttons, buckles, belting and trimmings, accessories, lingerie, and millinery, as he referred to his hats. Mr. Reid was unmarried. Such a pity, for any woman would have been glad to have him dress her every day. He adored the beautiful Rose. "Look Miss Rose, I ordered this blush pink crepe de chine with you in mind, and these carioca kid shoes are perfect, just perfect." Mr. Reid smelled nicely of Florida water. On Sundays he wore a crisp white drill suit and an expertly blocked Panama hat. He had a friend, Mr. Dixon, who owned a bicycle built for two. On Sunday afternoons, Mr. Reid and Mr. Dixon would go bicycling along the coast road, their well-seamed trouser legs secured by matching bicycle clips.

Shagoury's was the other store frequented by the Harvey girls. The goods there were not of the same quality as those stocked by Mr. Reid. Doris used the first one-pound pay-cheque from her job as a pupil-teacher to buy a pair of pumps from Shagoury's. Mr. Shagoury, who was not too long from Lebanon, recommended the shoes highly, saying, "these shoes strong, you wear them till they bark." Maybe that was a popular saying in his native country. But the shoes fell apart after a few weeks. The uppers and the sole separated, creating a flapping, gaping space in the front of the shoes when she walked. Her brother Howard said that was what Mr. Shagoury meant when he referred to the shoes "barking," for they now looked as if they had open mouths.

They would also shop at Emmanuel's Haberdashery, some-times for special linens and lingerie, for each Harvey girl expected to be married, and they each had a bottom drawer. After shopping, they would visit their Aunt Fanny's bakery on what was called Back Lane, to buy fresh breads and pastries to take back to Harvey River. The girls had a particular fondness for the small, flat buttery loaves called *gratto*, a word which was probably a corruption of the French *gâteau* in the same way that other French words crept into the language and had been reshaped by the tongues of Jamaicans. For example, Château Vert, a village in Hanover, was now called, *Shotover*, and the bunch of assorted vegetables — the legumes — that could now be bought in the local market for the Saturday soup were called *leggins*.

Aunt Fanny was their father David's sister, and she ran the bakery with her husband, a grim-faced man who had travelled to Panama and there learned the art of baking. In his case, he had learned the *secret* art of baking, for he refused to share his recipes with anyone, including his wife. He insisted on being alone when he prepared the dough for the buttery gratto and French bread, the meltingly delicious cashew and molasses biscuits, and the fancy pastries. All Aunt Fanny and their children were required to do was to place the privately prepared dough in the oven. The man died with his recipes unrevealed, and Hanover people claim that since his death there has not been baked a gratto as delicious as his.

Aunt Fanny had stood at his deathbed, accompanied by a few of her children bearing exercise books and pencils, saying, "Baker, Baker." She would have said that, for by now no one referred to him by his real name, and everyone called him "Baker" as if he alone had the right to this title. No other baker in Jamaica was as deserving of this name, not even "Nayga Bun," the cunning baker Bennett from Spanish Town who had invented the hot cross bun with the cheese hidden in its belly. Long ago at Easter time, some generous Christian masters would sometimes let their slaves have a hot cross bun as a treat, but they considered cheese to be too good for them, so Bennett hid the cheese inside the bun and marked those buns specially. Maybe he made them odd-shaped and thick-faced so that the aesthetic sensibilities of the mistress of the house would cause her to reject them (and allow the enslaved to have them). Maybe he made the rugged crosses on them with heavier dough. But whatever the case, he and they both came to be known as "Nayga Bun."

"Baker, do, I am begging you as your wife, to tell me how you make the gratto. How many eggs do you use to make a baker's dozen, Baker? How much flour and salt and so, what else you put in them to make them so nice?" The children stood ready with pens, pencils, and paper, poised to take down this precious recipe for the golden gratto. No answer. "All right Baker, since you won't tell me how to make the gratto, what about the biscuits? How much molasses? How much ginger and flour and other things you use in the biscuits, tell me nuh, Baker? Please, I am begging you as your wife, the mother of your children, who are going to starve if the bakery closes down." And Baker, who had a flat yellow face like a stale, spoiled gratto and who was really dying from a spiritual illness brought on by a "croomooching" nature, turned one jaundiced eye in the direction of his wife and children, then turned his face to the wall and swallowed hard. In this way he committed to his knotted bowels all his knowledge of the efficacy of egg whites, the cloudlike consistency of thrice-sifted flour, appropriate measures of leaven, and just how high dough should be allowed to rise before you punched it in the face for being too puffed up.

After his death, the bakery had to be closed down, for no one could replicate the bad-minded baker's creations. Poor Aunt Fanny had to move to Kingston, where one of her sons died from falling out of a tree at the Kingston Race Course, when the great Paul Robeson was giving a free concert there.

On their way past the blacksmith's forge, the Harvey girls would often have to push their way through gangs of schoolchildren who loved to stand outside the door and chant rude words in time to the ring of the blacksmith's hammer on the anvil:

> Lulu Bing
> Sally Bing
> Sally Bing
> Lulu Bing
> Morning Lulu Bing
> Morning Sally Bing
> Look up under Lulu Bing
> Look up under Sally Bing.

The Bing sisters were two spinster ladies from England, and this coarse jingle must have been a source of mortification for them, as no doubt they had never consented to having anyone look up under their modest cotton dresses. Now they had to put up with having their good names being bawled out in the streets by bands of dirty, uncouth ruffians, who had even added a second verse to their vulgar ditty:

> Lulu Bing
> Sally Bing
> Lulu Bing
> Sally Bing
> Me love Lulu Bing
> You love Sally Bing
> Me we married Lulu Bing
> You can married Sally Bing.

The Bing sisters were almost as famous in the town as the Mares, the Steers, and the Hoggs, three families who lived as neighbours in a section of town the locals called Animal Hill.

After spending a Saturday morning shopping, the Harvey girls would pass by Animal Hill to have lunch with one of their relatives. Maybe their cousin Lily Musson, who was the daughter of one of their father David's half-brothers. On their way to her house they would go by a house called Glenmore, at the corner of Cressley Lane. This spot was once the site of the Jewish burial ground, and in the yard there could still be seen some scattered tombstones, one of which bore an inscription to Mr. Moses Levy, who died in Lucea but was born in New York.

Sometimes the girls would see the Englishman Walter Jekyll parading through the streets of Lucea. Jekyll, called "Jake Hell" by the Hanoverians, was a flamboyant figure given to wearing sheer white diaphanous costumes when he went for his baths in the warm Caribbean sea. He carried his notebooks and pens in a type of straw basket favoured by the peasants, and he was often accompanied by one or two beautiful local lads. What was known about him was that he was born into the British upper class and educated at Cambridge University, and had been a minister of religion who had renounced holy orders and moved to Jamaica, where he developed a strong interest in Jamaican peasant culture. In 1907, he published "Jamaican Song and Story," based on the Anancy stories and folk songs he had heard from African Jamaicans during his travels throughout the island. He lived for a while in Hanover at Riverside, in the same village where Cleodine would later live as a married woman.

This character Jekyll was the mentor of Claude McKay, the great Jamaican poet and novelist, who would sometimes list Jekyll as his father on the forms he had to fill out while he lived in the United States. McKay became a leading figure in the Harlem Renaissance, and he wrote the sonnet "If We Must

Die," an anthem of black resistance that Sir Winston Churchill quoted in a speech to rally the people of England during the Second World War.

> If we must die let it not be like dogs
> hunted and penned in this inglorious spot
> while round us bark their maddened dogs
> making their mock at our accursed lot.

At the end of a day's shopping in Lucea, the Harvey girls were always met outside of the town by a family helper who would have been sent to assist them with carrying their parcels back to Harvey River. The girls would ride home full of the latest news from Lucea and laden with purchases – from lengths of fabric, stockings, hats, and lingerie to bottles of Lydia E Pinkham's Vegetable Compound for "female" complaint. They always brought back some small gift for David and Margaret, usually a bag of cakes and pastries from Aunt Fanny's bakery that were more "refined" than the substantial cornmeal and potato puddings that were baked every weekend in the Harvey household.

Many years later, my mother and her sisters would continue to fall into their fabulous-Harvey-girls-get-dressed-to-go-to-town routine whenever they were together. Even when they were old women, they were still the fabulous Harvey girls.

After she had reached sixth class, the highest class at the village school, my mother's oldest sister, Cleodine, was sent to Mrs. Marston's special school for young ladies, the closest thing to a finishing school that David and Margaret could afford. Her siblings watched in awe each morning as their big sister unbuttoned the five buttons – from hem to mid-calf – of her long skirt, mounted upon one of her father's horses and rode off sidesaddle to go and learn how to become a proper young lady. Cleodine liked it when they waved to her.

In no time, Cleodine began to affect a perfectly upright walk, because she was made to wear a backboard. This being early in the twentieth century, the Englishwoman instilled in the handful of elite village girls who attended her school good Victorian principles. She taught reading and writing, with great stress on proper penmanship, along with art, music, religious studies, and domestic science. Cleodine excelled in all these subjects to such an extent that, years later, she was able to perfectly hand-letter her wedding invitations, design and sew her own gorgeous wedding gown, demonstrate to the organist just how she wanted the wedding march to be played with loud flourishes, and supervise the craftsmen in the renovation of her marital home, which her husband had named "Dunrovin'."

After Cleodine directed the remodelling, she re-christened the house "Rose Cottage" and filled it with the finest mahogany furniture of her own designs as she became the wife of a man she did not love.

Cleodine was dressed in her long, white crepe de chine gown. It was fitted all the way down to her hips and then it flared out so that she looked like an inverted lily. Her veil of illusion tulle frothed out from her face and then rose and fell behind her. Her head was ringed by a circlet of orange blossoms. Her face glowed as she wept, "I do not love this man that I am about to marry." A little voice rose up inside her, asking, "Was there ever a sadder bride?" "No," Cleodine answered the voice. "No," she said out loud, "I am the saddest of all brides."

They are preparing the wedding feast. The aroma of good country cooking hangs like a spice canopy over the village. The domestic perfume of seasoning: top notes of curry; sharper notes of garlic, onions, and pimento; base notes of black pepper and thyme, which flavour the flesh of cows, goats, and chickens. Feast food is being prepared in big, black three-legged pots. In kerosene tins they are boiling a fierce pepper soup, made with the rubbery genitals of bulls, a cow cod soup to make the groom potent and virile. At the thought of this, Cleodine wants to vomit.

Over the front gate they have arranged an arch of June roses intertwined with asters and arum lilies. In the centre they have hung two silver bells, from whose mute clappers stream white and silver ribbons. Under the arch the bride will pass, going out of her parents' house a virgin. She will go to the parish church and return, passing under it again, as a wife, a married woman. She does not love this man Clement Campbell, this man who is fifteen years older than she and who has been travelling and working in Cuba and Panama, who has come back to the neighbouring village and bought land and built a big house with a sign on the gatepost that said, "Dunrovin'."

This man had come to her father and asked him for her hand before he ever had a conversation with her. At first she outright refused to marry him, but in the end her mother, Margaret, insisted, saying that Cleodine had always had her own way from birth and that she thought she was better than everybody else, and that it was her father, David, not she, Margaret, who had encouraged her to think like this. "You mark my words, you will pick and pick till you pick shit," said Margaret, sounding exactly like her father, George O'Brian Wilson. "Who do you want for a husband, the king of England? This man is a good man, a fine-looking man, he will be a good provider, what the hell more could you want?" It was all well and fine for her to be doing pupil-teaching up at that Englishwoman's school, but it was really high time for her to get a husband who could support her queenly tastes and show the way for her sisters.

When he came to call on her, he brought gifts that he had bought during his travels: three yards of pink silk cloth, three scented white soaps in a box marked *Muguet du bois*, two pairs of silk stockings, kid gloves, and then the diamond-and-opal ring. Cleodine had read in a book that it was bad luck to wear opals if they are not your birthstone, that opals should be worn only by people born in October under the sign of the scales. The stone in the ring reminds her of her mother's left eye when a spark leapt from the fire on which the workers were boiling sugar and put out the life in it, leaving a white cloud over the pupil for the rest of her life. This is what the stone in this ring reminds her of, and it sets her to remembering other things, other times, another man.

I have imagined that there was a man named Alex Marston, and when he was brought home from England, in 1915, nobody in the village saw him for weeks. They said that he was kept sedated with laudanum to see if sleep and rest could knit up his ravelled nerves, which had become shell-shocked during the war. Every time he woke up they fed him on soup made from one whole pigeon with the neck wrung, not severed, so that the blood did not drain out but stayed inside the body to be boiled down into the soup. When the bird was cooked so that its flesh fell away from its bones, they added red wine to the soup and his mother fed it to him herself.

One afternoon the eight girls who attended Mrs. Marston's school were sitting outside on the front verandah doing embroidery, cross-stitch, faggoting, drawn-thread, and the stitch called hardanga. Once, the hardanga stitch was lost for years and it did not resurface until an old seamstress from Westmoreland dreamt how to do it again. After that dream she woke in great excitement early on a Sunday morning, applied her needle to the bodice of a plain blue linen dress, and drew up the hardanga from oblivion, where it had languished for more than seventy years in the land of lost stitches. It had slipped off every seamstress's needle at exactly the same time and date in the same way that other stitches were lost by ancient Indian tribes, Inuit peoples, and Celtic craft workers. Every once in a while, when the culture of a people undergoes great stress, stitches drop out of existence, out of memory. The hardanga had disappeared when the great Jamaican freedom fighter Sam Sharpe was executed in 1832. Perhaps the women who had stitched his flowing white garments had hidden the hardanga stitch in the seams. These women, who had washed the clothes whiter than any Biblical Fullers soap with the foaming suds of blood-red ackee pods, had ironed the hardanga into the seams of Daddy Sharpe's robes, causing the stitch to be shut up there for three-score years and ten.

The girls were sitting on the verandah embroidering away while Mrs. Marston read to them from Jane Austen's *Sense and Sensibility*. Mrs. Marston always reminded them of how kind she was to start this school, to teach a select handful of girls how to become proper young ladies. Mrs. Marston also needed the money that their parents paid her, because her husband had taken up drinking in a serious way.

Alex appeared at the doorway in his pyjamas and dressing gown and stood there watching his mother reading to the girls. Cleodine, who was now a pupil-teacher at the school, was supervising the embroidering done by the younger girls, and looked up and saw him. His uncombed dark hair and wild eyes made him look like Heathcliff in *Wuthering Heights*. Mrs. Marston got up hurriedly and led her son back inside the house. After a few weeks he seemed to be much better, because Cleodine saw him exercising the horses in the pasture. One afternoon she was walking home alone, having stayed behind to help Mrs. Marston finish a dress. She was a better seamstress than Mrs. Marston any day, but the Englishwoman always tried to make her feel as if she was conferring a great honour upon her by allowing her to help. There were still things she wanted to learn from the Englishwoman before she stopped coming to help with the teaching of the younger pupils, so Cleodine fixed her face in a wry half-smile whenever the woman said things like "It is not often that I allow anyone from the village into my private quarters, but I'll make an exception in your case, Cleodine."

When she had walked down the hill leading her horse after helping Mrs. Marston with her dress, the style of which she thinks is utterly unsuited to Mrs. Marston's short thick body, she finds Alex waiting for her at the end of the long driveway.

"Hello, Cleodine."

"How do you know my name?"

"I asked who was the tall, slender girl with the legs like a colt."

She knew how to heal him. He said that whenever the battle erupted inside his head with gunshots and sirens and death screams, if he heard her singing, the noises would go into retreat. He would often pass her notes which read: "Sing for me and push back the enemy, my precious Cleodine," and she would find a reason to say to Mrs. Marston, "I need to practise a song that I'd like the younger girls to learn." Then she'd go to the school piano and play and sing, ostensibly for the younger pupils, but she and Alex knew who the songs were for. Once he wrote a song for her, using words like *anodyne* and *columbine* and *adamantine* and *love-divine* to rhyme with her name. She helped his mother with the school for two years, two years in which she saw him almost every day until the noises in his head got worse and they sent him back to England.

She did not love this other man whose hands were rough and calloused from years of hard manual labour in Panama and Cuba, who affected the manners of a Spanish gentleman and peppered his talk with Spanish words. His "aie Cara and aie chica" meant nothing to her, but she will never settle for becoming an old maid, never.

They came into the room and found Cleodine alone, staring at her image in the mirror. She had ordered everybody to leave her alone for a few minutes before the wedding, but they came barging in anyway, the wedding bessies, Tinnette and Marie, two sisters who looked after every bride of consequence in this village. They themselves had never married, but they knew every single thing that a bride is supposed to do or not to do on her wedding day.

"You must never let your groom see you in your wedding dress before the wedding."

"The bride should always carry money in her shoes or in her bosom on her wedding day, to make sure that she has a prosperous marriage."

Marie begins to fire questions at her. "What do you have on that is old?"

Her grandmother Frances's pure silk slip, given to her by her husband, William, who imported it from England. It was embroidered with raised roses on a vine trellis. It had been kept wrapped in a piece of tissue paper with white roots of fragrant khus khus grass and mothballs in a big brass-sided trunk for the wedding day of her son's first daughter.

"What do you have on that is new?"

Her crepe de chine and Brussels lace wedding dress, which she had made herself with the help of her mother and her sisters. They beaded it with rhinestones like false diamonds and more than three hundred teardrop pearls.

"What do you have on that is borrowed?"

The mother-of-pearl buckles on her shoes given to her by her godmother who lived in Falmouth, in the parish of Trelawny. Cleodine had thought of running away and going to tell her godmother that she could not go through with this wedding because she did not love this man. They say the man she loved is crazy, and now they have sent him away to England; but her godmother sent her those buckles with a letter that said she could not be happier that she was making such a good marriage.

"What do you have on that is blue?"

"Don't ask that. Just don't ask."

Marie stood up and faced her with a glass of dark red wine in her hand. The wine was so red that it looked like pigeon's blood. She told Cleodine to drink it. Cleodine tries to find her commanding voice, the one that made her siblings shudder and hurry to do her bidding, but she cannot.

Marie advanced towards Cleodine, holding out the pigeon-blood red wine, then she made as if to throw the wine all over the wedding dress, and Cleodine thought "if she throws the wine on my dress, then there can be no wedding," but how could she give these common Hanover people reason to drag her name from one corner of the parish to the other? In any case, she now had no one else to marry. She would drown herself in the sea before she gives these ignorant people reason to laugh at her.

So Cleodine took the wine and swallowed it down, beginning to feel as if she was floating on her veil of illusion tulle.

*A*lbertha, or Miss Jo, made only one friend at school: a girl who also came from a large family from the nearby village of Mount Peace. The girl's name was Pamela Samuels and the two became good friends because they had two things in common: they were both skilled embroiderers and they took life very seriously. They sat together in school and walked home together, swapping embroidery patterns and shaking their heads at the crude, ignorant ways, the out-of-orderness of the other children. They embroidered, embroidered, embroidered. Tablecloths and pillowcases and sheets and doilies by the dozen, which they stored in their respective bottom drawers because they both hoped one day to marry cultured, refined, and serious men. By the time they finished sixth class, Pamela Samuels and Miss Jo both became worried about what the future held for them in the little parish of Hanover, on the small island of Jamaica, with none of the men around refined enough for them. Together they made a pact to rise up early one Easter morning to do what young girls all over the world, anxious to know what the future held for them, did. They agreed to break eggs into white saucers and to stand outside under the slowly rising Easter sun, studying the shadows cast by the sun in the egg yolk and albumen. They both saw the same thing – ships.

Before the end of that year Pamela immigrated to Montreal, a move which may have had to do with her being a Presbyterian. The Harveys were devout Anglicans, pillars of the Church of England. David was the catechist at the Eton church and each Sunday the entire family attended worship there, to recite appropriate creeds and collects from the Book of Common Prayer, and raise the great hymns penned by masterful English wordsmiths like George Herbert and John Keble. The Harveys delighted in filing up to the lace-and-flower-decorated altar, where they would kneel and take thin white wafers on their tongues and wash them down with wine dispensed from ornate brass chalices. Pamela Samuels's people went to dour Presbyterian meetings. No altar, no incense, no solemn bows and crossings of self. The Harveys did not want Miss Jo to become a Presbyterian. "My God, she is grim enough already," said her father. So they were relieved when Pamela Samuels immigrated, possibly at the invitation of a Canadian Presbyterian minister known by her parents and his family, who had suggested that she should come to Canada where she could become a sort of governess to the minister's nine children. But Pamela Samuels missed her friend and soon she wrote, encouraging Miss Jo to come and join her in Montreal. True, she explained, it was bitterly cold and most people spoke not English but French, but a refined, well-spoken, and serious person like Miss Jo could easily find work in the homes of well-to-do Canadians. Perhaps she could earn a living sewing and embroidering for chic French-Canadian women and in that way she could enjoy a more cultured and refined lifestyle, far removed from the "rookumbine" and "gal a wey you go a gully for?" culture of rural Jamaica.

David and Margaret were not sure at first that it was right for their daughter to go off and live in Montreal, Canada, but eventually they concluded that she just might become even more dolorous and grim if she were not allowed to travel, and even if she did go to Montreal, at least they would never have to witness her turning her back on their beloved Church of England, so they gave her their blessings and she departed by steamer to Montreal, from where she later sent for her sister Rose.

Albertha's solemn, almost stoic nature was to stand her in good stead during those early days in Montreal. In her letters back to Harvey River, she never told how she looked forward to her days off from doing domestic work in the houses of wealthy people in Outremont and Mount Royal. She did not reveal how hard it was for her, someone who had grown up in a house with domestic help, to have to do housework for strange people. Keeping strangers' large mansions clean, and looking after their demanding children who would call her not "Miss Jo" but Albertha. Come here Albertha, do this do that Albertha. How hard it was to work and live in the houses of people who were not interested in who she really was, or where she came from.

She would write only to tell her family about the wonders of snow, about the church services she attended at St. James Anglican Church, because, contrary to David's fears that she would become a Presbyterian, Albertha had in fact gone in the other direction and become completely taken with the liturgy in Latin, incense burning, High Anglican, almost Roman Catholic services held at St. James, situated in downtown Montreal. Once she mentioned a bus trip that she and Pamela and a few other young women who also worked in service had taken to the Laurentian Mountains, but, for the most part, her letters were short, contained not one word of complaint, and always had Canadian dollars folded into them.

When she was forty years old, Albertha was introduced at a church social held at the Christchurch Anglican Cathedral to a Barbadian man named Geoffrey Seal, and to the horror of her sister Rose, who by then had joined her in Montreal, she began to walk out with him on her days off. Rose could not believe the change that would come over her older sister whenever the portly Barbadian appeared. Miss Jo would become animated and talkative and would often gaze affectionately at the man who was almost as wide as he was high. She even took to repeating his little gems of wisdom: "You know, Mr. Seal told me something this evening when we were having dinner in the restaurant at the Hudson's Bay store, he said that Montreal is the Paris of Canada," this said as if everybody, even the smallest child in Canada, did not know this for a fact.

Mr. Seal and Miss Jo were married within the year. None of Miss Jo's friends or relations could understand how she who had held to such high standards all her life could have married a man who fell so woefully short of their youthful ideals. An unkind person could have said "Seal by name and nature" when they saw a photograph of Miss Jo's groom. In addition to not being blessed with fine looks, Mr. Seal did not even have a great sense of humour. He, like Miss Jo, probably had never once cracked a smile at a rude folk song or laughed out loud at the slack wine-up way of country people. He was, by all accounts, dour and dull, but he was completely besotted by Miss Jo and she with him. His life was made complete when on their wedding night he discovered that Miss Jo, at age forty-one, was completely chaste and unspoiled. He proceeded thereafter to tenderly love and care for his virgin bride so that the serious, unsmiling Miss Jo became the placid and contented Miss Jo who did not give one row of pins about the disapproval of her family. Her sister Doris was the only one of her siblings who did not condemn her marriage, saying she was happy that Miss Jo had finally found love, after so long.

Cleodine

Albertha

Rose

— *The Fabulous*

Doris

Ann

Harvey Girls ～

From the day that Rose was abducted by the village madwoman, everybody in Harvey River watched carefully over her, and David and Margaret insisted that she should always be accompanied by one of her siblings at all times. Whenever this job fell to Cleodine, she would respond to the admiring cries directed at Rose by saying, "She is pretty, yes, but she is not as bright as me." Unlike Cleodine, Rose did not grow to be a brilliant or even a very competent student. She was intelligent enough, but she seemed to always prefer the company of younger children, and in classes at the village school, she was prone to long spells of daydreaming, looking out at the sky and the Dolphin Head Mountains with that sweet half-smile. And yet the teachers would never take a strap to her as they did to all the other children when she did not remember her twelve times table, or when she did not know how to spell words like *supercilious* and *peradventure*. It was as if it was understood that Rose functioned mainly as an icon, bringing joy, goodness, and light to her surroundings.

The true love of her life was a young man named John Clare, the son of a poor sugar estate worker, who had gone to school with her in the village. Intelligent and ambitious, he wanted to study to be a teacher; but his painful shyness always reduced him to silence in the presence of Rose's luminous beauty. He never could get up the courage to confess his love to her. How could someone so radiant love a quiet, knock-softly kind of man like him? She, for her part, kept wondering how come he never flirted with her or sent her mash notes, or invited her to go in a group to dances in Lucea and Montego Bay like the other young men. Could he not see that she saved her best smiles and warmest greetings for him? She did not care if he was poor, she would have worked with him to make a life, she would have borne him beautiful children. But all he ever did was stare at her and tremble, nervously brushing his hair back from his forehead, so she concluded that he did not care.

On the day she left the village for Montreal, to join her sister Miss Jo, he just stood in the square with hot tears running down his face, one hand pressing on his windpipe, as if he were trying to force out the necessary words to make her stay. He stood like this, watching her leave his life forever, all because he did not have the words. He did not know it, but he was the namesake and descendant of a great poet, John Clare, who had enjoyed some success in England in the eighteenth century, and then, because of his struggles with ill health and poverty, spent the latter years of his life in terrible misery. He wrote a poem called "Secret Love," and if only Aunt Rose's silent suitor had known it, he could have asked his poet forefather to speak to her for him.

> I dare not gaze upon her face
> But left her memory in each place:
> Where'er I saw a wild flower lie
> I kissed and bade my love goodbye.

When she had gone to apply for her passport, the officer processing Rose's papers had fallen in love with her, and tried all kinds of delaying tactics to discourage her from travelling to Montreal. He mislaid her application. He found fault with the way in which the forms were filled out, so that she missed the boat which sailed from Kingston to Montreal only every few months. It brought Canadian codfish, sardines, and wheat flour, and loaded up in Kingston with sugar, bananas, and rum. As there were not many people travelling to Canada from the West Indies at that time, berths were limited to a few on every cargo ship and Miss Jo, knowing of this, had gone to great trouble to secure her sister a place. Eventually the man did process Rose's passport, but only after her father accompanied her to the passport office and threatened to report the man to his superior officer, making him realize that Rose was not just a beautiful, inexperienced young girl from the country who had nobody to look out for her. And so Rose took the next ship from Kingston to join her sister Albertha in Montreal, and there she found work babysitting for a French-Canadian boy named Billy Lefèvre, whose alcoholic parents would often abandon him for weeks at a time. Invariably they would not have the money to pay for her services, so she would end up feeding and caring for the boy, who called her "Tanti." She would take him home to stay with her until his drunken parents resurfaced, and would often have to take him along with her on the other babysitting jobs she took in order to get money to feed them both. Eventually, after several such jobs turned out badly for her, she had to leave the Lefèvre boy behind with his unfortunate parents, and she found a job working in the household of a Mr. and Mrs. Lord. Mr. Lord was a newspaper magnate and Mrs. Lord was a patron of the arts. The entire family fell in love with Rose and they all became fiercely protective of her because every time she stepped outside their mansion, someone tried to take advantage of her luminous beauty.

Wherever she went in Montreal, men were drawn to her — always the wrong men. On the bus some bank clerk or a graduate student attending McGill University would sit beside her and get off at the wrong stop just to follow her home, calling out after her, "You are the most beautiful woman I have ever seen, I will die if I do not see you again." Her doctor fell in love with her, and kept arranging for her to come and be examined for sundry suspected illnesses. As a result of this unfortunate experience, she lost faith in the medical profession and pursued alternative forms of healing. She ate healthy foods and exercised every day and grew more and more beautiful and attracted more and more unsuitable men. Men who would forget to mention their wife of twenty years and their five children. Men who would threaten to commit suicide if she did not return their love, and who would then disappear after a few months, sending her notes that read: "My Beautiful Rose. You are too good for me, you deserve someone much better."

Perhaps the father of the son born to Rose when she was in her early forties wrote such a letter to her before he disappeared from her life. There was talk of an engagement; but nobody ever knew what really happened, for Rose carried the secret of his identity with her to the grave. But in 1951, Rose gave birth to a beautiful, healthy boy child, whom she christened David after his grandfather. When everyone saw a photograph of the boy, they all said he looked like an angel that had been sent to make Rose happy. Here was one man who would surely love her and stay with her as long as she lived.

*I*t could be said that uncle Flavius spent his life trying to find and keep God. His true quest began one Friday night in the village square, when he, being at a loss to find suitable amusement for himself in quiet, peaceful Harvey River, decided at the urging of his brother Edmund and other locals boys to accompany a band of mockers on a mission to harass a group of Salvation Army evangelists. This was the best that they could do to provide themselves with some form of Friday-night entertainment.

When they got to the meeting, the Salvation Army band was in full swing; the trumpets were blasting and the kettle drums were booming as the white uniforms of the Army members gleamed under the light of bottle torches. The band of mockers gathered and started singing along with the Salvation Army chorus, dragging out the words of the hymns. "I weeeel cleeeeeeeeg to theeee ooooooole ruggeeeeed crooooooosss," they sung, clinging to each other, shaking their heads and twitching their bodies as if convulsed by the Holy Spirit.

Flavius, like all other members of the Harvey family, was a talented actor, and he began wowing the crowd with a spirited virtuoso performance, causing his scoffer friends to laugh uproariously, ridiculing the efforts of the valiant band of

Salvationists who had walked miles across rocky roads to bring the word of God's army to the Hanover people. The leader of the Salvationists was a tall, indigo-skinned man with a powerful baritone voice. He wore steel-rimmed glasses that gleamed in the night. He had a shock of white hair and he played the big kettle drum. When the boys started their heckling, his response was to beat the drum hard. Harder and harder he hit the stretched goat skin until the drumbeat began to overpower the heartbeats of many of the people gathered in the square.

People stopped laughing at the mockers and stood transfixed by the power of the drum sound being pounded out by the man with the hair that stood out in the darkness like a halo around his head. The lenses of the man's glasses were throwing back reflections from the blazing bottle torches, so that his eyes looked as if they were on fire. He began to stare straight at Flavius, and the next thing you know, Flavius fell down, calling out, "Jesus, Jesus, O Lord Jesus." At first everyone thought that he was joking, still mocking the Salvationists, and then they all fell silent.

"Flavy, stop form fool now, the joke gone too far, come make we leave and go home before them lock we out," said his brother.

Flavius lay silent on the ground, unmoving, not responding to Edmund's voice or his gentle, then not so gentle, shaking.

"Lord have mercy, what is this pon me now. Flavy, gittup."

Eventually Flavius did stir, but this was only after people in the crowd doused his face with water and passed a bottle of white rum back and forth under his nostrils.

"Duppy box him. Me tell you say duppy box him, see how him rally when we sprinkle the white rum, everybody know say duppy fraid a white rum."

Flavius rose up and walked over to the band of Salvationists and asked if he could join them. He marched off singing with them into the dark Hanover night, returning late to his father's house. From that fateful night he spent the rest of his life seeking the Almighty with great zeal and fervour. During the course of his life he held membership in every known church in Jamaica, except for the Church of Rome and the African-based Myal, Revival, and Pocomania sects. Over and over again, he recreated that conversion experience as he joined one church after the other, each time convinced that he had found the perfect one to suit his spiritual needs. After much searching, he finally found a home in the Christadelphian Church, having fallen out over doctrinal differences with the Anglicans, Salvation Army, Baptists, Wesleyans, Moravians, Seventh-day Adventists, Jehovah's Witnesses, Pentecostals, and Brethren – Open and Closed.

His father, David, blamed Edmund for what happened to Flavius. "It's because of you why Flavius now has no abiding city, he would never go and tease any Salvation Army people if you did not put that idea in his head. Flavy is a respectful boy, he was perfectly happy in the Anglican Church, where he was born and raised. It is you, you Mr. Edmund, who encourage him in that mischief, now look at him walking up and down shaking tambourine – because he has no other musical ability – in a Salvation Army band!"

⁓

Although his father's anger at Flavius's conversion really made Edmund want to leave Harvey River – which Edmund had never liked in the first place – even more, his reasons for leaving soon became more urgent. It had to do with a girl from Chambers Pen.

"Fall her, your son fall my daughter, Mr. Harvey."

That is what the girl's father had said when he came to report his daughter's condition to David, who confronted Edmund about the matter when he came in late that night.

"You are going to do what is decent and honourable, as befits a son of mine."

Two weeks before the wedding, Edmund ran away to Kingston. Margaret accused David of chasing away her son. She wept and cursed her husband for days. "How you know if this child really belong to Eddie? What I was saying was we should wait till it born and see if it have the Harvey little toe, every Harvey child have the same shape little toe, if the child don't have it, it is not a Harvey, if it have it, then of course, Eddie must face up to his responsibility, now as it stands, you threaten him, him catch him fraid, and now him run gone and I might never see my boy child again!"

After Edmund fled Harvey River, it would be three whole years before they heard from him. He eventually wrote to his mother from Kingston, telling her he was now driving a big Ford taxi. Thereafter he would send her letters containing a few pound notes and the occasional photograph of himself standing with one foot on the running board of his taxi. But as they say in Jamaica, "what is fi you, cannot be un-fi you." Seven or so years after Edmund fled by night from Harvey River to avoid a shotgun wedding, he saw the woman who was to have been his bride walking up East Queen Street in the city of Kingston, where she had come on a shopping trip. And he could not do it, he could not just drive his taxi past her. He stopped and offered the mother of his son a drive.

He had been sending money to support the boy Neville, who was indeed born with the Harvey little toe, and who from his photographs one could tell was big for his age, bright, and well-mannered. Edmund begged the mother of his son a thousand pardons. He told her that people had told him things about her to turn his mind from her and that had made him confused. He apologized for the fact that she had been humiliated, shamed, and mashed-up by his desertion. She told him that she had read certain psalms for him in order for bad things to happen to him. She cursed him like a dog as she sat there in the front seat of his taxi and he kept saying that he was sorry. Then he asked her if she wanted something to eat. "My God, you must be hungry after you curse me so." And when he said this she had laughed. He took her for a meal at Arlington House Hotel, where Alexander Bustamante, who had come back from his stint in the Spanish Foreign Legion and who would later become the first prime minister of independent Jamaica, used to take his meals. She went home with Edmund that night and two months later he married her and a year later they had another son, Roy.

But the marriage did not last. Taxi men just do not make good husbands. They are always on the go, they don't thrive in normal domestic situations. Eventually, Edmund's wife immigrated to England and sent for their two sons. He never spoke of their brief marriage again.

All the river water could not cool
the fatal furnace within

*W*hen the soles of his feet remained behind on the floor-boards as he tried to walk to the front verandah, it was as if my uncle Howard had shed the last of the attachments that bound him to the earth. They were lying there on the polished mahogany as if he had traced his feet on cardboard and cut them out to send to Canada for his sisters Albertha and Rose to buy him new shoes. For weeks his skin had begun to appear more and more translucent, parchment-like and luminous. Then all his soft black curls fell off, and later his teeth and his fingernails came out. He died one January, after the feast of the Epiphany. When the three wise men were coming, he was going.

Except for my uncle Howard and, later, my aunt Albertha, the eight living children born to David and Margaret Harvey all died in the exact order in which they came into the world and they lived to be well over eighty years old. My uncle Howard died after a mysterious accident involving a woman and a stone flung one dark night by a jealous man. The stone broke his forehead open and let in fevers, confusion, and sickness so wasting that he became the first Harvey to jump the queue and disturb the order in which they all came into and departed the world.

"Mas Howie, don't bother to go to Lucea today. Today is Sunday, heavy rain might fall and you know how bad the road is when the rain fall." Margaret had told her first son this as he prepared to leave the house on that late October afternoon. He was whistling as he stood at the mirror in the hall, combing his slick black curls that were still wet from his bath in the Harvey River. Her heart "rose up" whenever she looked at him, so tall and slim-bodied, his skin the colour of a perfectly baked biscuit, his nose straight as a knife blade, and those brown eyes with the long sweeping lashes. None of her daughters had such lashes. Everybody said that he was the most handsome young man that anyone had ever seen, that he looked like God had made him personally with no help from assistant angels, so well put together was he. Margaret's grey eyes welled up every time she saw him. Imagine, that she could have brought such perfection into the world.

He had nice ways too. Affectionate, kind like his father, David. He was always funning and making jokes. He was the only one who could make such jokes with agate-eyed Margaret, who did not run jokes for spite. "Mummah," he would say, "come and dance with me," and he would hold her at the waist and waltz with her in circles as she protested, around the room. "Come and do the Lambeth walk with me, my sweet Mummah." "Boy, go away and find somebody your own size to play with," she would pretend to scold, but she actually did waltz with him, even as she swore that the only time she had ever danced was on the day of her wedding, and where did this boy come from, harassing his own mother so? "David," she would call out to her husband, "come and talk to your son." And David would stand there in the doorway and laugh as he watched his wife, who was not given to overmuch gaiety, being spun around the floor by their son who had grown taller than his father. He had the height of his English grandfather, William Harvey.

"Why you have to go to Lucea today, a Sunday, Howard?"

"Aye, Mother, I can't tell you my business."

He didn't have to tell her his business, for his business surely involved that woman, that red-head girl who had come from Lucea to attend a wedding in the village last week. The girl's skin caught fire from the time she saw Howard, best man for the groom, who was one of his cousins. All during the wedding reception, which was held at David and Margaret's house, the young woman was burning like a fire lantern. Her hair was coir red and her skin like burnished copper. She was a vamp from Montego Bay, who was now living in Lucea. Dressed in her orange voile dress, she looked like fire itself when she moved, her tiered skirt fanning out like flames around her as she insisted on dancing with him. "Come Howie, let me show you this move, I'm sure this step don't reach to country yet." Anyone could see she was just dying to lay herself careless before the first son of the first family of Harvey River, and he was like a rain-fly drawn to her flame.

When the red-head girl sat down to eat a huge plate heaped with curried goat, Margaret had stared in disbelief when the girl pronounced that the goat was not hot enough. The tender goat mutton had been seasoned and cooked by an East Indian man by the name of Gangalee, from the neighbouring parish of Westmoreland. Gangalee's skin was almost as black as that of the Africans. He was originally from Madras. "Me Madrassi," he would say. "You a coolie," said the African

Jamaicans. The night before, Margaret had watched him rub the curry powder into the pieces of fresh goat meat, curry that he had blended himself using turmeric, called tambrik by the African Jamaicans, coriander or curriana as the Jamaicans called it, cumin, sage, and his own secret special ingredients that the Jamaicans did not know, so they had no name for them. He had cut up onions, garlic, and what looked like dozens of hot country peppers and added this to the meat which had been left overnight to soak up the seasonings. The next day it was browned in iron pots of fragrant coconut oil and cooked down in big kerosene tins. You could smell the strength of the curry for miles. Gangalee was known to cook the best and hottest curry in the western end of Jamaica. Maybe it was the selfsame Gangalee who was immortalized in what became a popular Jamaican folk song:

> There was a coolie man by the name of Gangalee
> married to a coolie gal, them call her Cookie
> send her to go boil rice and ackee
> She disobey the order and boil rice and bajee
> Now bajee is a thing that take plenty water
> Bajee is a thing that take plenty fire
> Get you curry, get you curriana, get you mussy
> Get you mussiana, get piece a stick
> Put it pan the kibba, hinder bajee from boiling over
> Bamma beejee bajee, bajee o.

The girl demanded a Scotch bonnet pepper, which Howard brought to her. The pepper pieces fell from her fingers like burning sparks as she calmly sliced them into the already highly seasoned meat. Margaret watched in horror as the girl ate the red-hot flesh of one of the hottest peppers known to man, without calling for water to cool her tongue. Not a tear came to her eyes as she chewed the vicious hot capsicum. "Scotch bonnet pepper, you know, the girl eat one whole Scotch bonnet pepper!" Margaret had remarked to David afterwards. David had laughed and said, "She is a better man than me." For of all peppers, there are few as hot as the pepper shaped like a Scotsman's tam-o'-shanter; not the small deceptive little bird pepper, nor the hot finger pepper or jalapeno; maybe not even the wicked one called the habanero. It was this Scotch-bonnet eater that was causing Howard to go into Lucea that Sunday.

David and Margaret had warred over the way in which she was raising Howard. But he was not a child any more. "Leave him to be a man, what are you trying to do, turn him down? Keep him under your petticoat for the rest of your life?" David had also cautioned her against what everyone saw as her blatant favouritism. "How do you think the other children feel? They all think that you love Howard more than them."

If only she could have hidden him under her petticoat that day. That morning she had again seen a line of red ants marching along her clothesline and knew that something terrible was going to happen.

She watched her son leave, dressed in his dark trousers and a gleaming white shirt that she herself had washed and ironed. He was wearing a felt hat, rakishly skeeted to one side, and he was stepping smartly in an almost-dance as he made his way down the path to the main road to catch the truck going into Lucea. When he got to the gate he turned and threw her a kiss. It floated across the hibiscus hedge, skipped on the flat white river stones which paved the pathway up to the front door, and hopped over the windowsill into Margaret's lap. She picked it up, knotted it into a corner of her handkerchief, and tucked it into her bosom. As she did this she found herself singing one of her father's songs, "Down by the Sally Gardens, she bid me take love easy as leaves grow on a tree, but I was young and foolish and with her did not agree." Over and over she sung those lines.

When they brought Howard in, bleeding from the head that night so that the inside of his felt hat was lined with thick blood and his white shirt was now mostly dark under the light of the lamps, she was moaning, "But I was young and foolish and now I'm full of tears." They cleaned the wound with alcohol or overproof white rum, which caused him to cry out as it stung him even in his half-conscious state, and they bound the wound tightly with a clean cloth, torn from good white linen sheets, to try and staunch the head injury that was bleeding so profusely. How could one head contain so much blood?

All around the house on the acres and acres of land around them grew different herbs for bush medicine, a bush for every sickness, for every complaint. There was even a bush called "fresh cut" for new wounds. But who could find such herbs in the dark? Throughout the night they tried to doctor his head, to force teaspoons of sweet sugar and water down his throat to replace the vital energy draining away from him. They washed down his limbs with aromatic bay rum to quell the fever that was now rising through his pores, and David read psalms at the foot of the sickbed. Psalm after psalm, all except Psalm 90, which is the funeral psalm.

The nearest doctor was miles away, and Howard was in no condition to make the journey to the doctor's house along the rough, unpaved roads. It was best not to move him. All night they just kept staunching the wound and cooling his limbs until dawn broke. Now there was no choice. David went and found someone with a buggy who took his son, fevered and delirious, back into the town of Lucea to the hospital.

When he was brought back to Harvey River five weeks later, Howard was a shadow of himself. Margaret and David's handsome son had become a thin, gaunt, sad-eyed man who stepped tentatively from the back of the hired car that brought him home. Leaning on David's arm, he slowly made his way up the path to the front door, where he stopped, looked back, and gave a wan smile to all the friends and relatives gathered in the yard to welcome him. He raised his right hand in a feeble gesture of acknowledgement to them and then he went into the house, passed through the living room and into his bedroom, where he lingered for two months. Then one morning as he made his way towards the front door of the house, he stepped onto the floorboards and left the soles of his feet behind. Everyone knew that he would die before the day was over.

"Only a borrows, Miss Meg, you only got a borrows of him. He was God's own angel that God lend to you for a time." "You think that I don't know that? Nobody know that more than me," Margaret said to the woman.

David planted cinnamon and aloes near the grave of his first-born son. Cinnamon and aloes because they spoke of them in the Bible, in Proverbs 7:17: "I have sprinkled my bed with myrrh, aloes and cinnamon. Let us enjoy the delights of love." These words were spoken by loose women who sought to entice callow youths to their destruction. It was as if the words of the Bible had come to pass in David and Margaret's own lives. Their son had been killed by a man jealous over his red-haired woman, a man who was never caught and punished, for he fled and vanished into the thick country darkness the minute that Howard fell "like a wounded ox on the way to the slaughter house" (Proverbs). When Albertha and Rose returned from Montreal for a visit in the 1940s, they brought with them

David and Margaret Harvey in Harvey River,
on the occasion of their fortieth wedding anniversary.

bulbs of irises which they planted around Howard's tomb. The irises bloomed only as long as David and Margaret and their children lived in Harvey River.

~

For months after Howard's death, my mother's mother, Margaret, could be found sitting in her big bentwood mahogany rocking chair by the window in the front room of the house. She wanted the man who had flung the stone to see her. To see her terrible agony. Maybe if she sat by the window which faced the street, he would pass by and see her, pass by and be moved to confess by the sight of her raw grief. At night, she railed at her husband to use his village lawyer skills to find the murderer, but try as they might David and his brother, Tom, could not find him. Some people believed that he stowed away that same night on a ship docked in Montego Bay.

Margaret wanted no one to forget about the terrible injustice done to her. Day after day she sat by the window through which she last saw him fully alive, walking his young man's bopping walk, throwing her that last kiss. For hours she would sit by the window and rock and stare, sometimes moaning her father's Irish songs. "She bid me take love easy as the grass grows on the weirs, but I was young and foolish and now I'm full of tears." Sometimes she would imagine the body of the man who took her son's life hanging from a tree. Sometimes she would imagine her hands tight around his throat. Everyone passing by would comment on how hard Margaret was taking the loss of her son. Some would try to call out to her, sincere words of encouragement directed up the stone-paved path down which her son had gone forever. "Nuh mine, Mrs. Harvey. God knows best. The Lord giveth and the Lord taketh away."

These words, intended to comfort, did not reach her. She just sat there locked into her grief, rocking, moaning out across the yard and into the bushes, where her grief notes came to rest in the trees and became indigo-winged solitaires, making low piping loss sounds.

It was Margaret's father, George O'Brian Wilson, who eventually put an end to her public demonstration of grief. He appeared outside her window early one morning, having walked up from the small cottage that David had built for him near the main house. He waited outside in the front yard for his daughter's household to stir. When Margaret took her seat by the front window, her face drawn and contorted from her night's crying, she saw her slim, dark-haired father, who by then sported a long pepper-and-salt beard, standing in the front yard like a stern Old Testament prophet. "Get the fock up, get up out of that blasted chair, and get on with your goddamned life. Your poor husband says he's tired of talking to you about just sitting there because you don't countenance a word he says. Get the hell up, I never raised you to be a weakling, to have these eedjits jabbering about you as if you were the village lunatic, sitting there like Our Lady of Perpetual Weeping by the window with your house all going to hell. Because of you that assistant Queen Victoria Cleodine has become the boss of all, coming here every day from her Castle Rose Cottage to order us all around. Telling them at the bar to stop selling me my white rum, as if my drinking is her goddamn business, all because you are no longer present. The boy is gone, get on with your life. Get the fock up, or I'll take a whip to your backside."

That was the day that Margaret stopped sitting by the window and told Cleodine that it was too much work for her to run two houses and that she did not have to come to Harvey

River every day any more. Everyone agreed that George Wilson was the only one who could have made her get up from that window, reminding her that she had his Irish blood in her and that nobody, not even her grief, was going to be the boss of her.

George O'Brian Wilson, shoemaker and saddler, of
Lucea, Hanover, late occupation, bruk sailor.

*E*very year on the seventeenth of March after Margaret's
father came to live with her, the people of Harvey River would
congregate in the road to witness the annual St. Patrick's Day
party given by George O'Brian Wilson, for himself and for
other Irishmen in the area. He made it clear that this party was
not for anybody but the Irish, who would dress all in green and
gather from early afternoon at the Harvey house to drink, play
the fife, drink, play the fiddle, drink, sing, and drink.

With his half-Irish daughter Margaret as his assistant,
George Wilson would cook a creolized Irish stew, substituting
goat meat for mutton and adding turnips, onions, carrots, and
potatoes. As he added herbs like fresh thyme, he would lament
his separation from Ireland, often breaking into song as he
stirred. He served the stew to his guests before they got down
to the serious business of singing and drinking. Their Irish airs
and reels would issue across the Hanover cane fields as they
celebrated the day of their beloved saint, who, like most of the

people in Jamaica, had once been a slave. It is certain that some of these airs inserted themselves into the music of the Africans who were keeping the continent alive, "yerri yerri Congo," in the hills of Hanover and all over Jamaica. So every seventeenth of March, George Wilson and his friends would rise up and praise St. Patrick in sweet spiritual tongues until they fell down senseless. The morning after, everyone in the Harvey household would wake to find so many green men sprawled, stale-drunk and damp with dew, in the front yard, coiled at the roots of breadfruit and mango trees, flat out in the grass, or blissfully resting under flowering shrubs after their annual tear down.

A man who feared neither God nor man, George Wilson would sometimes stand outside the door of his small house in thunderstorms and fire off shots from his rifle into the heavens, answering each thunderclap with a gunshot, screaming, "God above, god below."

When he lay dying, George Wilson told his daughter that he was being plagued by the devil. Margaret asked him to describe in detail exactly how the devil was plaguing him. Always a practical woman, she intended to devise some drastic and appropriate strategy to defeat the horned one. George Wilson said that the devil was showing him two roads and advising him to take the shorter one. Margaret told him to tell the devil to go to hell because everybody knew that the road to heaven was the longer one. He thought it over and he seemed to accept this counsel. But a while later he asked the yardman to chop him some wood. When Margaret asked what he wanted it for, her father, being a man who was not averse to having a backup plan, said, "I'm going to build a fire and burn the devil's arse."

When George O'Brian Wilson died, my grandmother Margaret sent a message to his Creole family in Lucea to tell them of his passing. The family always made a point to never acknowledge Margaret or her mother, Leanna, and they did not acknowledge the message. So Margaret made arrangements to bury her father, whom she had tenderly taken care of in the last years of his life. On the day of the funeral, the entire village came out to pay their respects to the "white neega." There was a certain tension in the church, because in life George Wilson and church were like the devil and holy water. "When a man dead him just dead. Look how him just lie down there in the coffin and make them call up Jesus name over him and he don't get up and curse them," said the people of Harvey River. All through the funeral service there had been no sign of his legal wife and children. But at the burying ground, as they were nailing the coffin shut, Mrs. Wilson and her children drew up in a hired car and demanded that the coffin be opened so that they could pay their respects. Margaret remembered all the years they had refused to recognize her existence. She grabbed the hammer from her husband and drove the long ten-penny nails deeply and securely into the coffin lid, nailing it shut, and ordered that it be lowered into the grave at once.

part two

*I*t was a cricket match that first brought Vivian Marcus Goodison to Harvey River, where he fell instantly in love with my mother, Doris Louise Harvey.

All important events that occurred in the village of Harvey River took place at the Harvey home, and on this Sunday my mother's parents were hosts to a visiting cricket team. Slim and of medium height with rich copper-coloured skin, Marcus Goodison had a movie-star smile and a wonderfully engaging manner. He had driven the cricket team from Malvern in the parish of St. Elizabeth to Harvey River, where he immediately took note of the fact that in the Harvey household there were some very attractive young women. Upon seeing this, he surrendered his place on the team and never played the cricket match. He just gave up his turn as the star batsman to some aspiring hanger-on who would never ordinarily get a turn at bat, a reserve member of the team who was only chosen to make up numbers, a batsman prone to making "agricultural" strokes, a "yamlikker" who used the fine linseed-oiled willow like a crude hoe. Unlike Marcus, who did everything with finesse, whose strokes were poetry in motion. On that fateful day in 1930, Marcus had no time for cricket, for he had sighted Doris.

He had begun at first to sweet talk Ann. Then he looked to the far side of the yard and saw Doris, who was watering some of Margaret's special plants with cold tea left over from their breakfast. He had gone up to her and asked her for a drink of water, then he had set about charming her and her parents, and by the time he was due to drive back to St. Elizabeth he had succeeded. He explained to them that he was employed as chauffeur to the manager of Barclays Dominion Colonial and Overseas Bank just so they would know he was a responsible man; and to make sure that Doris wouldn't forget him when he was gone, he left behind his maroon-coloured beret, which completed his outfit. That outfit consisted of cream serge pants and a maroon blazer, worn with a white shirt and a pair of two-tone brown and white shoes. The next Sunday he drove from St. Elizabeth to Harvey River ostensibly to collect his beret, and maybe he left something else that day too because he soon became a regular visitor. In between visits he wrote her passionate letters.

> *I went to town last week and I stood up on King Street and looked, Dor, but not one woman in the whole Kingston was lovely as you.*

> *Dor, I hope and pray that you will consent to be my bride. If you say no, I don't know what I will do. Please don't hand me a left hand ticket.*

Marcus, as always appropriately dressed, arrived one Sunday to formally ask for Doris's hand in marriage. David and Margaret had been expecting this day for months. The young man was so obviously in love with their daughter. I mean you had to be in love to drive from Malvern, St. Elizabeth, to Harvey River, Hanover, almost every two weeks for a year. Driving over those rough, mostly unpaved roads, just to come and see a girl who was so shy that she never looked in your face when her parents were around for fear they might think her too bold.

David sees the car drive up and when he sees Marcus step out fully dressed in a navy blue suit and white shirt and tie, he tells Margaret,

"Mr. Man is here for your daughter's hand."

"Then she is just my daughter all of a sudden?"

David goes to the door to meet him. He stands in the doorway and calls out to Marcus, whom he has never seen look nervous before.

"Mr. Man, where are you going so dressed up today?"

He loved the young man. He was a well put-together person, he made a good living, he was charming and possessed of a deep self-assurance, but at the same time kind-hearted. He was always trying to make the people around him happy. He would do his best to make his daughter happy, David felt that. But he couldn't just allow him to come in here and walk off so easily with his Clarabelle.

Marcus hears the serious tone in David's "Mr. Man" question. He is a little surprised because he has come to regard him as a friend and ally. He has become deeply attached to this man he hopes will become his father-in-law, because he never grew up with his own father.

Marcus dressed like a dandy because all he knew of his own father were the stories of the young man who changed his shirts two or three times a day, who always smelled of "4711" gentleman's cologne, and who favoured two-tone "John White" shoes, imported specially for his size nine feet. Marcus played the guitar like his father, Uriel; from him he got the gift of music. My nightingale-throat father could sing too, and all wind and stringed instruments obeyed him. He was able to play virtually any musical instrument. He was glad of that gift from his father. So this is the Marcus who stands on the first of the three steps at the front door of the Harvey house.

"I have come to ask you an important question, Mr. Harvey."

"Yes, what kind of important question you have to ask me, Mr. Marcus Goodison?"

Marcus takes one step up and says, "I would like to have your daughter's hand in marriage."

"Which daughter would that be, Mr. Man. I have many daughters, you know."

"Your daughter Doris, sir. Doris is who I want to be my wife."

"You think that she will want you as a husband?"

"I hope and pray so, sir, because I . . . ," and here he almost breaks down crying, "because I have never met a nicer, kinder young lady in all my life, and my life will be worth nothing if she won't consent to be my wife, sir."

And these last words he says in a low hoarse voice, looking up into David's face, begging with his brown eyes for him to accept him, to intercede for him to Doris, because for a man who lost his mother when he was a teenager, his heart tells him that this is the woman he needs to show him what kindness and caring are. He knows that if and when he lays down to sleep beside her he will rest as he has never rested before, that his absent father, who was named for one of the archangels, will come to him in dreams and say, "My own boy, you have chosen well."

"Just know one thing, Mr. Man. If you form the fool you will have me to deal with."

"I would take my own life before I hurt her."

Marcus climbs up onto the top step and stands next to David, who then says, "Come my son, let us sit inside and talk."

Marcus's own father, Uriel, was the second son of the wealthy Goodison family, who owned acres and acres of red lands in St. Elizabeth, lands that were eventually sold to bauxite mining companies. Some say the first Goodisons were two English buccaneers who settled in Jamaica and married Creole women, so Marcus's father was one of the playboy sons descended from a line of retired buccaneers. Some say that the Goodisons were Jewish merchants and that the family name means "Son of God."

Marcus's mother, Hannah, had copper-coloured skin, blue-black hair, and deep tranquility. She looked like a painting of an Arawak Indian. She, like the Arawak Indians, had died early. Uriel, his father, also died young, and St. Elizabeth people said that his entire estate was meant to go to Marcus, who as far as anybody knew was his only child. But people also said it was squandered by Uriel's brother, an even bigger playboy than him, who hurried on his own end through riotous living in night clubs and brothels from London to Kingston and Havana. My father had received just enough money from his father's estate to buy himself a house in Malvern and a second-hand Model T Ford car. He was considered by the women of St. Elizabeth to be a good catch.

With her parents' consent, Marcus presented Doris with a diamond ring. My mother told me that for days after her engagement, all the young women in the village would come to the house and ask to see her diamond ring. However, not all of them were happy for her. At least one woman in Harvey River was overcome by jealousy, and envied the love that had found Doris. This woman was a distant cousin who wanted to be married more than she wanted anything else in life. Someone swore that they once heard her say that she would give her life to be married just for one day. Well this young woman had looked at the engagement ring and had not been able to say anything except to ask how did they know if the diamond was real. She was overheard saying how unfair life was, that imagine, instead of herself "this little gal" was going to be the one to become a married woman.

My mother says that she fell asleep one afternoon wearing her ring, which did not fit tightly. When she awoke, the ring was gone. Such a commotion followed, with her bawling like a baby at the loss of her brilliant diamond engagement ring. Memories of her "bad luck" persona came back to her, the Clarabelle persona who cursed expressions and embarrassed herself, the girl whose long hair was chopped off had now lost her diamond engagement ring, she had come back to displace lucky, happy Doris, who was in love with and loved by a hand-some young man named Marcus. Everyone searched the house and the yard, to see if it had slipped off while she did her chores. My mother kept crying, and insisting that she was wearing the ring up to when she fell asleep. She was sure of this because she had been staring into its centre, and had dreamt that she was bathing in a crystalline pool of water. But the ring was nowhere to be found. Doris was inconsolable. What kind of cross was this, what kind of sign, for sure this was a terrible omen!

But Margaret told her that she was not to think such thoughts. "What this is, is envy and bad mind," she said, "and my dead father is going to see about it." That was all she said; but she said it loudly enough for everyone who had come to help search for the ring to hear, and those who heard told those who had not heard. Doris found her ring at her front door the next morning. They say that the woman who was possessed by envy flung the ring, knotted in the corner of a handkerchief, onto the verandah of the Harvey house that night. Somebody said they saw her run past the house at great speed and throw something that arced like a white bird across the night sky, as she ran without stopping out of the village.

The task of preparing Doris for life as a refined married woman had been given over to Cleodine at Rose Cottage, where white damask tablecloths, bone-handled knives and forks, and monogrammed sheets were in everyday use. My mother had approached her sister's house with a very heavy heart. Once before, she had been sent to Rose Cottage to undergo "finishing" by Cleodine. That earlier visit had ended with Doris packing her bags after one week, and walking back to Harvey River in tears. When she reached home, tired, miserable, and covered with dust, she had entered the Harvey house sobbing. "She want to kill me. She make me wake up at five o'clock every morning, she make me knead dough till my hand want to drop off, because she have to have fresh bread every day. She make me draw her a hot bath every evening, because cold water cannot touch her skin. She make me iron about a thousand crochet doily to put on her chair and tables. 'Antimacassars, Doris, have you ironed the antimacassars?' Then she have to tell me again that an antimacassar is to keep hair oil from rubbing off on the chair upholstery, as if I care.

"Every time I try to sit down she say, 'There is nothing worse than a slothful woman,' and she find something else for me to do. 'Make me a cup of tea. The water must be boiling, and you must rinse the teapot in hot water before you put in the tea leaves. Not more than three minutes, the tea must not steep for more than three minutes and then you are to pour it through a strainer, I am not a tea-leaf reader, so don't bring any cup full of tea leaves to me.' Stew guava and orange to make jam and marmalade. Learn to steam fish just the way she like it, because she don't eat meat. She read in some book that she have, how people who don't eat red meat live long, so every day all she cook is fresh fish, fresh fish and so-so fresh fish and stew peas without meat. She say that white bread is like poison. 'Brown bread has roughage, Doris, roughage!' Every day she telling me how I must eat roughage, so she ordering me to cut up cabbage and eat it like rabbit. But is when she order me to iron one of her husband drill suits that I pack my bag and come back home. I tell her, 'He is your husband, you should iron his clothes,' and she box me, so I leave, Mummah and Puppah, please, don't make me go back to Rose Cottage."

But it was there that my mother was sent to stay before she married my father.

Rose Cottage was set on five acres of land in a rolling valley in the village of King's Vale. "Castle Rose Cottage," as George O'Brian Wilson often referred to his granddaughter's house, could not be seen from the main road, and visitors had to make their way down a set of steps cut neatly into the hill-side, until they came to the large white-painted, three-bedroom house built high on stilts. The house was called Rose Cottage because the entire garden was planted with fragrant pink, white, and cream rose bushes which bloomed in profusion from their neat, rectangular beds. Along the verandah, in special round clay pots made by a woman in the district called Congo Lou, Cleodine cultivated African violets. Indigo and purple and scarlet, brooding intense violets that were so strongly coloured you could stain your fingers by touching one

of the petals. Cleodine tended these herself, and all the brides-
to-be were given strict orders by the yardman, as they sat there
on the side verandah waiting to be shown into Cleodine's presence, never to "touch Miss Cleo's roses," meaning the violets.
Like many Jamaicans, he called all flowers roses.

By the time of my mother's marriage, Cleodine had become
one of the most famous makers of brides in western Jamaica.
Women came from as far as Montego Bay, Savanna la Mar, and
Falmouth to be transformed into fabulous brides by Cleodine.
The brides-to-be were rarely young. By the time they made
their way to Rose Cottage they were usually "big women,"
grown women who had lived for years with a man or with a
series of men and had raised their children (who would then
become attendants at the wedding) and worked and worked,
and saved and made a life, all the time looking forward to their
glorious wedding day. While they planted ground provisions
and vegetables in a field, they would sometimes pause and look
tenderly at bright potato flowers or garlands of yam vines and
imagine their own bridal bouquets. As they slept on mats in
the market, they imagined honeymoon beds, where all things
would be made new again. When they put up with a man's
wandering ways, wearing his hats and his shoes to show his
other women who was the woman-a-yard, they heard themselves saying, "I have the talk, for I have the ring." Every Sunday
when they cooked rice and peas and chicken and watched
family and friends gather round to eat and enjoy the taste of a
good woman's hand, they visioned the day when friends and
family, bearing presents, would come to raise a glass to "Mrs.
Bride and Mr. Bridegroom." And thereafter they would wave
with their left hand to all, and watch their ring finger grow
proud and stick out from the others on the left hand, for it was
now weighted with gold. When the time finally came for the

women to make their way to Rose Cottage, they were ready to be born again into beautiful virginal brides, and there was nothing that Cleodine liked more than being completely in charge of a wedding.

"Take a seat on the side verandah" the brides-to-be were told by Cleodine or by one of her maids. Never the front, for only specially invited guests were ever allowed in through her front door. "No, I will not be making that dress for you, that style is utterly unsuitable for you," she would say to some woman who had the temerity to come to her bearing a picture of a dress she had torn from a magazine. "All right Miss Cleo, anything you say, mam." "You are not trying on this dress until you go and take a bath," she was known to say to women come hot from the market to try on their wedding dress. "Here is a piece of soap and a towel, go and take a bath in the river before you try on this bridal gown," she would say. And surprisingly, big, independent women who were older than Cleodine, who ran their own households like tyrants, would go meekly to the river and cleanse themselves just as Cleodine had ordered them to do. Once or twice she was heard to say, "I don't cast my pearls before swine" or "I will not waste powder on a black-bird," as some rejected and dejected woman made her way from Rose Cottage, never to know the magic of being transformed by one of Cleodine's creations, for Cleodine on occasion would flatly refuse to take the custom of someone and she never would give any further explanation other than the one about the swine and blackbirds.

The centre of Rose Cottage was a large, high-ceilinged drawing room furnished with the elaborate furniture Cleodine had designed herself, and in pride of place, a pipe organ that she had ordered and had had shipped from England. Above the organ, just where she could raise her eyes to it as she pumped away, was a large gilt-framed photograph of John Wesley. Cleodine, in a gesture of modernity and independence, had upon her marriage formally embraced the Wesleyan Church, forsaking the Anglican religion of her forefathers.

"Well, Doris, I hope you realize that a married woman's life is not just a bed of roses," said Cleodine. They were sitting together in the gathering dusk on the front verandah of Rose Cottage. This time around, Cleodine had not ordered my mother about as she did on that disastrous first visit. She instead invited Doris to observe what she, the perfect example of a married woman, did with her days. "Everything must be done decently and in good order," Cleodine lived by these words. She rose early, because the Bible said that is what good women did. She washed herself in warm water which was brought to her by the maid, applied cold cream to her face and neck in upward strokes, dressed herself in garments that were demoted church dresses, and put on her high-heeled pumps. She was always the tallest person in her house, always. Thus prepared, she would emerge from her room and order everyone under her roof to participate in morning prayers and the singing of hymns before partaking of a healthy breakfast. None of those oily saltfish and hard food, morning-dinner type breakfasts were ever served in her house, ever. Only fresh brown bread baked the day before, new-laid brown eggs, New Zealand butter, wholewheat or oats porridge, homemade preserves and tea, lots of good black tea brewed in a warmed pot and served with milk and brown sugar.

"This is how you do it," she instructed as she showed my mother how to make a bed with the wrong side of the top sheet turned out so that the smoother right side is what touched you and your husband's skin when you lay down to rest. It is best to plan your meals in advance. You start the midday meal right after breakfast, so your husband never, ever has to wait on his food. Always make sure your husband's clothes are in good order. A badly turned out husband reflects poorly on a wife. Always tidy yourself to greet your husband at the end of the day and make sure his supper is ready and that he has clean pyjamas to sleep in each night. And on and on, everything done perfectly, just so, right from morning till evening when the household was called to evening prayers, the lamps extinguished, and Rose Cottage put to bed.

My mother had turned red when her sister said that a married woman's life was not a bed of roses. Just the word *bed* made her embarrassed. Then her sister dropped her voice, as if she was sharing a terrible secret. "You cannot imagine what a terrible thing is going to happen to you," Cleodine said, shaking her head from side to side and making clucking sounds in the back of her throat. "If you ever know what is before you," she whispered. What was before her was of course her wedding night. Her sister continued, "If you ever know, the pain that a man puts a woman through, in order to get his pleasure!" My mother burst into tears sitting there in the dark on the burnished front verandah. Cleodine had left the "what was before you" discussion until last. For the seven days that my mother had spent at Rose Cottage, being groomed for her life as a "proper married woman," Cleodine had made no mention of sex. She and her husband had separate bedrooms, and he was often "away" on business. Cleodine had shown her how to bake bread, how to spread a table for company, how to make perfect corners on a sheet, and how to iron a man's clothes. The proper ironing of a man's white shirt took an entire morning, with Cleodine sending my mother back to the ironing board three or four times until the perfectly ironed garment was produced. "No, the sleeves must not be seamed, the collar must have no creases, iron it first on the wrong side, open up the inside seams, then iron it on the right side." The ironing of a starched, white drill suit – with no creases in the sleeves of the jacket and perfectly straight seams in the trousers, and no creases on the fly – took almost one entire day. But there was no mention of sex.

Because the house was set in a valley, nightfall at Rose Cottage came early. Dusk then dark seemed to come to rest there before it reached Harvey River, and often, the Tilley lamps had to be lit from as early as 5 p.m. With dusk, an air of quiet melancholy often settled over Rose Cottage, with its shining floorboards, beautifully polished furniture, and everything in its right place. A heavy perfume of nightblooming jasmine, honey-suckle, and roses would waft in from the garden as Cleodine took her place at the pipe organ under the watchful eye of John Wesley, to play a selection of evensong hymns. It was after the organ recital that she would order all under her roof to take part in evening prayers before turning in for a long dark night.

The mahogany table in the dining room was always set with a place for Cleodine's husband, but often, when morning came, the place setting was undisturbed. "If it is too late, my husband sleeps in the room behind his businessplace," explained Cleodine, although my mother had asked nothing about the undisturbed place setting. After a long pause, she said, "At this time of the year, business is brisk, he is probably not coming home again tonight."

Except for the servants sleeping in the two rooms behind the house, my mother and her eldest sister were alone in Rose Cottage. By the light of the lamp that sat on the polished verandah table between them, my mother could make out her sister's profile that was growing to look more and more like Queen Victoria's. But on these nights, Cleodine looked like a very sad queen. By day, her strong face was set like stone under her upswept hairdo, and no one, especially not her "subordinates," dared to look directly into her amber brown eyes behind her gold-rimmed glasses. The tip of her middle finger, capped by a steel thimble, would drum steadily on the lid of her sewing machine as she issued brisk orders to the servants, "Go — tap tap — and fetch me — tap tap — a cup of tea." "My husband is a hard-working man, I am proud that he will do whatever is necessary to succeed," she said, then she was quiet for a moment, as if brooding upon exactly what her husband was doing in order to succeed. My mother knew enough about her sister to understand that this statement about her hard-working husband was one that was meant to stand by itself. One that did not invite any response from her, one that she was not welcome to comment upon.

My mother wanted to say something like "poor you." She always said "poor you," but she meant it as a genuine expression of solidarity and sympathy. She would have loved to have said to her sister, "Poor you, I hope that you are not too lonely," but she knew that her sister would have considered it an impertinent remark, so she just kept silent. She wanted to ask her, "Since you are the only one of us Harvey girls who is married, and since you have shown me everything about how to keep a good house, what can you tell me about what is before me?" and Cleodine must have read her mind, because she then said, "I think it best that you read this book to acquaint yourself with what is before you." In the semi-darkness of the verandah, she handed her a book entitled *Safe Counsel*. My mother, who always preferred a teaching story to any dry, fact-laden book, later said that she was too embarrassed to read it.

Marcus and Doris were married in the Lucea Parish Church on August 2, 1931. My mother frowned and wept during the entire wedding ceremony, because brides at that time were not supposed to look joyful. The worst thing a decent young woman could do was to look happy on her wedding day, for surely that meant that she was looking forward to the sensual pleasures of the honeymoon bed and only a bad woman would enjoy that. My mother wept copious tears. My father smiled broadly throughout. Albertha and Rose sent her a trousseau from Montreal. Included in this wardrobe for a new life were silk and satin nightdresses, some with matching bed jackets and nightcaps. Her flowing wedding gown of crepe de chine with silk godets and her chantilly lace train, fifteen yards long, was the talk of the parish for years.

The couple went off to live in St. Elizabeth, attended by Doris's personal helper, Ina, and laden down with trunks full of fabulous clothes and housewares. As was the custom then, my mother wore an elaborate hat and a long duster coat as she drove away with my father in his Model T Ford.

$\mathcal{N}$ow that all her other children had left the house, Ann became the object of her mother Margaret's homilies on how sorrow followed closely to joy as surely as the night followed the day, therefore one should not be so laughy-laughy, so quick to pop story and want to go to fairs and concerts and dances with unsuitable friends. She, Margaret Wilson Harvey, as everyone knew, always had a deep mistrust for anything resembling excess happiness, and just to prove herself right, look how she herself had gone and forgotten and been so happy over her son Howard, and had not God taken him from her? Had her other son Edmund not run away to Kingston, never to return to Harvey River? Had God not allowed a spark from the cane-boiling fire to cool into a cloud in her left eye? Had not George O'Brian Wilson's legal family been allowed to cut her out of his will, rob her of the house and land in Lucea that he had specifically willed to her after she had cared for him in the last years of his life?

Her daughter Ann needed to learn from her mother's misfortunes; and if she did not want to learn from her mother's misfortunes, she should at least learn from that cautionary tale about an own-way girl who had come to a bad end in a village near Harvey River. The girl, it was said, suffered from a powerful case of "don't care." She never listened to a word that her mother said, and she liked to laugh loudly and to "sit down bad"; that is, she would not sit with her legs closed and crossed at the ankles, preferably slanted to the side, so that others would not be able to look up under her dress. This girl loved to dance and she ignored her school work and took to sneaking out of her parents' house at night and going to dances in the company of some other no-good giggling Don't-Care girls from neighbouring villages, loud-laughing common girls. Well, one night she slipped out, and there it was she met her fate. The girl danced till near morning to the titillating beat of the "Merry Wang" and the frowsy rub-up "Mento." No doubt she danced to "Penny Reel O," a very slack song with lyrics like, "Long time me never see you, and you owe me little money. I beg you turn your belly gimme, make me rub out me money, penny reel O."

The dawn was rising over Hanover when she finally returned to her parents' house, but they had locked and bolted the doors and windows. So she sat outside in the yard on a stone, shivering in her long satin dance dress, with the back plunged low. As she sat there, it came to her that she should go and have an early morning bath in the river. She went down to the cool river, which in the dawn hours was a light jade green, the colour of young jimbelins. The water was deliciously cold and surprisingly warm in some spots, and she swam and swam until the sun came up fully over the village. She had no towel, so she rose out of the water and put on her dance dress over her wet skin, and to the eternal disgrace of her family, she walked home with her wet satin dress clinging to her voluptuous form, her hair long and dripping wet across her shoulders in thick ringlets. Cool and relaxed, she walked towards her parents' home and met them coming down the one street in the village, dressed in their church clothes. They passed each other in the square and never exchanged a word. But the entire village witnessed this shocking scene and by the time her parents reached the church, the parson had put together a fiery impromptu sermon about harlots and loose women. This incident was in fact a blessing for him, because he had planned to preach one of his old stale standbys about the prodigal son. Well, you know that terrible Don't-Care girl died soon thereafter, probably from pneumonia or TB which, according to Hanover people, she had contracted by wearing low-cut dresses which exposed her lungs.

But some other people claimed that the Don't-Care girl had met a mermaid when she went for her early morning swim in the river. They said that she had made friends with this "River Mummah," who had combed the girl's hair with her golden comb and taken her down to the deepest parts of the river. Down there, River Mummah had shown her where her golden table was spread with delicious things to eat, delicacies rescued from the holds of sunken galleons which had come from faraway lands, laden with spices like saffron and coriander. She had fed her on cured saddles of mutton and haunches of venison and special breads and light cakes which never went stale and never grew soggy underwater. She had introduced her to many water souls, some of whom had met aqueous deaths for love. Some had run away and chosen to drown themselves and live as restless water spirits rather than as wretched slaves. People said that the Don't-Care girl had not died from pneumonia or TB but that the mermaid had come for her and that she was living under the river, forever dancing now in its restless currents. Some people even claimed that on some Sunday mornings she could be seen walking through the village, dressed in her wet satin dance dress.

And do you know that even after Ann was told this story the girl still clung stubbornly to her joy, to her sense of humour and her dreams? She announced that she wanted to go to Rusea's High School to study, maybe to become a lawyer. Her mother pointed out that this was impossible because David had succeeded in giving away almost everything they ever had to people in need. Besides, she knew David did not believe that girls should be educated. Like many men of his time, he thought that it was a waste of money to educate girls, who anyway would just end up getting married and having children. All that they had left was some land which Margaret was not going to sell to finance Ann's dreams, so she had better do what her sisters Cleodine and Doris had done and find herself a husband.

For the rest of her life, my mother would compare any woman who was inclined to be stingy and controlling to my father's grandmother Dorcas, with whom they lived during the first few weeks of their marriage. Those early weeks of marriage had proven to be difficult for Doris and Marcus. The one-bedroom cottage in which he had lived his bachelor life was being made into a house fit for a married couple who expected to have children, and that is why they were staying with Dorcas. A tall, brooding, silent woman on whose land flourished a variety of fruit trees, she forbade anyone to ever pick so much as one lime without her permission. The sweet-sops, soursops, naseberries, starapples, oranges, and mangoes sometimes rotted under the trees because she did not feel like giving her permission for anyone to pick them. Sometimes she would gather baskets of fruit and hang them from the ceiling in her kitchen, where they would over-ripen, dripping their sour nectar down. Bees would buzz around these laden baskets of spite-fruit, mice would nibble on them, and fruit bats would slap their leathery wings against them, but she would not give them away if she didn't feel like it. My mother, who loved nothing more than feeding people, was stunned and appalled by Dorcas's miserliness. "Nobody in Hanover would ever do something like that," she would say, "these St. Elizabeth people are very peculiar."

On the day of Doris and Marcus's arrival in Malvern, the trustees of the Munro and Dickinson Trust were holding their monthly meeting, and the square was alive with horse-drawn carriages and several brand new Ford Motor cars. Doris did not fail to take note of the fine store that sold beautiful imported fabrics, and another dry goods store run by Cleve Tomlinson, who was Marcus's friend, and the fine courthouse building which, if anything, was even more impressive than the one in Lucea.

Marcus had many friends in the town of Malvern. Among them were teachers from the Bethlehem Teachers' College, and some were like the lively Gertie Holness, who ran the shop and bar situated on the main road and who was to become one of my mother's best friends. These friendships proved invaluable to her as she spent the first few weeks of her marriage enduring the tight-fisted ways of Dorcas, who considered Doris at twenty-three to be a mere girl.

The newlyweds attended church in Malvern on the first Sunday after their wedding to "turn thanks." It was and remains the custom in rural Jamaica that the bride and groom should always go back to church on the Sunday after their wedding to show themselves to God and the community and give thanks for the blessings of their new life. Doris took great care with her "turn thanks" outfit. She always described it in exactly the same words, the outfit she wore on this important occasion.

"I wore a dress of smoke-coloured Brussels lace with matching leather shoes that my grandfather George O'Brian Wilson made from my own last and a dusty pink cloche hat festooned with one blush pink rose."

All the marriageable women of Malvern had come out to see the stranger woman whom Marcus had chosen as his wife, the woman he had gone to Hanover and picked out over all of them. "They came to see a show that day," said Doris, "and they did see one." They returned to their homes defeated. Marcus had married a princess. Which woman in St. Elizabeth could dress like that? And her walk, that straight-backed upright walk which she had learned from her sister Cleodine, who had learned it by wearing a backboard. Many of the women who came prepared to hate her for stealing their most eligible bachelor now wanted to befriend her so that she could help them to look fabulous, sophisticated, and uncountrified.

All the women except for Patsy and Ramona O'Riley, sisters who had both had their eyes on Marcus as a prospective husband. "If I don't get him, then it must be Ramona," Patsy would often say. Marcus was easily one of the most attractive men in Malvern. He owned his own house and had a good job, and he could make anyone, even the dour Dorcas, laugh with his outrageous jokes. Marcus was the friend you needed to have if you were ever in a jam. He was the friend you could tell a secret to and you would never, ever, in a million years, hear it back. He would lend you money and forget it. He would overlook your worst faults. "We are all human," he would always say. "If Patsy don't get him then it must be me," Ramona said.

In those first weeks of living with Dorcas, Doris suffered greatly from homesickness. She missed her mother and her father, her sisters and brothers, more than words could say. Sometimes at the dinner table, sitting down to one of Dorcas's frugal repasts, she would cry softly and lament out loud something like, "I wonder, oh I wonder what they are having for dinner today."

Marcus became anxious, but he was doing everything to make sure his bride was happy. They were putting the final touches on their house, which was now redesigned with the rooms situated one behind the other like the boxcars of a train, a house with high ceilings, separate living and dining rooms in the centre, and four bedrooms, two joined to the living room, two to the dining room, and the kitchen and bathroom behind. A big well-fruited yard with flowerbeds and its own water tank. Everything was being put into place in their new home. He so wanted Doris to be happy.

"How is Mrs. Goodison?" asks Marcus's best friend, Stanley Parsons.

"She not so bright today, I think she a little low. Miss her people, you know."

Stanley was secretly relieved that Marcus had not married Patsy or Ramona. He was hoping to land one of the sisters himself and he did not stand a chance if Marcus was around. He had a good reason to call upon them.

"Patsy gal, it look like that stranger woman that Marcus go and find clear a Hanover, head not so right you know. I hear the big woman just bawling like a child night and day for her mother and father."

The next week Doris and Marcus go to church, and after the service people come up to ask her if she was feeling any better.

"I am fine," says Doris.

"Oh, I thought I hear that you are suffering from melancholy."

And so it went on. Any little personal thing that Marcus told Stanley made the rounds via the bush telegram operated by Patsy and Ramona.

"What kind of mixed marriage that is anyway. Marcus should never married outside this parish. I hear the wedding had all kind of people mix up, whole heap of big shots siddown beside poor nayga." This was true, thanks to David

Harvey's egalitarian thinking, but some snobbish St. Elizabeth people who attended the wedding had not liked it.

One night my mother dreamed that she and Marcus were sitting down to dinner and that someone was cutting away the floorboards under her chair. She screamed loudly and the cutting stopped, then began again. This time they were trying to saw away the floorboards from under the entire dining room.

"Marcus, you don't see what they are doing?" she said as she related the dream to him. And much as he didn't want to admit it, Marcus soon realized that it was probably someone close to him who was behind all this, maybe even Stanley trying to destroy his new life before it had time to take root.

"So Marcus, how the Missus getting on?" Stanley asks him.

"That is she and the Mister's business."

After a while when their source of information dried up and more and more people began to speak highly of Doris's legendary good nature and kindness, Patsy and Ramona found other people to savage. For the rest of his life Marcus was careful to watch his words around certain people. In later years he would always tell his children, "The only person who can harm you is somebody close to you. Be careful who you choose to be your friend."

~

The parish of St. Elizabeth was supposedly named for Elizabeth, Lady Modyford, wife of the Governor of Jamaica from 1664 to 1671. On old maps of Jamaica the area was marked as "Elizabeth," and it is not certain exactly when Elizabeth became a saint. Before Columbus encountered the island of Jamaica, the parish was the site of significant Arawak and Taino settlements, where the peaceful native inhabitants lived planting cassava and corn and going far out in the Caribbean sea to fish in large, long canoes hollowed out from the trunks of tall trees.

Apart from shopping expeditions into Lucea, and one or two visits to Montego Bay and Savanna la Mar, my mother had not travelled far from Harvey River before she married and moved to Malvern. Whenever Marcus, who was referred to as "Doris's intended" after their engagement, described Malvern to her, she would try to picture the place that was said to have one of the most salubrious climates in the world. A place that was almost always cool and where the air was clear and clean. She took to reading any story in the *Gleaner* newspaper that had anything at all to do with her intended's place of birth. "Shakespeare donates silver pattern and chalice to Black River Parish Church" ran the caption under a photograph of a man handing over an ornate box to another man dressed in a bishop's robes. But even if it turned out that the donor of the pattern and chalice was only a very distant relative of the great William Shakespeare, the newspaper report was proof that Malvern could not be an ordinary place if one of Shakespeare's relatives lived there.

Over time my mother collected a great number of odd facts about the parish of St. Elizabeth, facts that she would feed to her children for the rest of her life. "Santa Cruz," she would say if she saw or heard the name of that town mentioned any-where, "Santa Cruz is a Spanish name meaning Holy Cross." Other Spanish names that intrigued her were "Hato De Pereda," which was what the Spaniards called the Pedro Plains; and "Lacoban," what they first called the Black River.

"When I moved to Malvern, in St. Elizabeth, I really missed the Harvey River," she would say, "for it is a parish that sometimes suffers from drought. Still, there are rivers and ponds there, and the Spaniards called one of those ponds 'Laguno Suco,' which means 'dirty lagoon,' but St. Elizabeth people call it 'Wallywash.'"

Cockpit Country, Accompong, Cuffie Pen, and the Land of Look Behind. This was Maroon land, bush domain of Maroon leaders like Captain Cudjoe, who along with Accompong signed a peace treaty with the British in 1738. German Town, called "Jahman town," is where blond, blue-eyed men and women, the descendants of German immigrants, many of whom came to join the constabulary force, live and talk deeply dyed Jamaican patois.

Any mention of pirates would cause my mother to relate how southeast St. Elizabeth used to be home to many buccaneers. "Yes," she would say, "when Henry Morgan, who was a wicked old pirate, converted from his sinful ways and became Governor of Jamaica, he laid down the law to all the other buccaneers that they were to follow his example and settle down too. He gave them a lot of land in St. Elizabeth for them to turn 'gentleman farmers.' Some people say the Goodisons were descended from such men."

"'Labour in Vain Savannah' is what St. Elizabeth people called a place where the red soil was so tough and water so scarce that no cultivation could possibly thrive. Speaking of farmers," she would continue, "St. Elizabeth farmers are some of the most hard-working and industrious people in the world, for dry as that parish is, they still manage to grow so much of the food that feeds Jamaica. You know those people will even set down straw at the root of the plants to catch dew water when rain is scarce! They grow the nicest Irish potatoes and sweet potatoes in Jamaica and the best peas, pumpkin, and cassava.

"The Arawaks were the ones who first cultivated cassava,

you know, and there were Arawaks living in St. Elizabeth before Columbus came," she would say. "People who saw your father Marcus's mother always said she had Arawak blood in her. She resembled your father's cousin Estelle, the two of them had that same copper-coloured skin and that jet-black hair."

~

It was the arrival of her sister Ann that completely cured Doris of her homesickness. "Doris, I long to see you till I short." "Ann, you was always short," replied my mother, as they hugged and giggled in the front yard of the house in Malvern. Ann's talent as a mimic immediately found fresh material in the miserly character of Dorcas and the vicious troublemaking of Patsy and Ramona, whom she christened the cerassee sisters, cerassee being a local bitter herb. It was Marcus who had suggested that they invite Ann to come and spend time with them in Malvern when their own house was ready, for he knew that there was no one who could make my mother laugh like Ann. "Doris," she would say, "you remember 'Steevin, yu see mi drawers?'" and my mother would begin to laugh till long eye-water ran down her face, until she began to gasp for air, and her laughter and lack of breath became a series of whoops. Ann did not even have to finish the rest of that "Steevin, yu see mi drawers," a joke they had laughed about from the time they were small children, when on their way to church one day they overheard an exchange between an elderly couple who lived in a little house right on the main road:

Old woman: "Steevin, yu see mi drawers, the one with the crochet round the foot?"

Old man: "But now now Jemima, yu no tink yu damn fast, wha me know bout yu drawers?"

The compelling presence of the fabulous Ann drew all the eligible bachelors of Malvern to their house like a magnet. Suddenly all the young men in St. Elizabeth seemed to be "just passing by" the Goodison house from the time that Ann arrived. She flirted with, and made fun of, the best of them and she and my mother giggled like Don't-Care girls as they fixed up the newly renovated house. In between the giggling, Ann confided in Doris about the difficulties of being the last child left at home, how Margaret and herself were now always at war, especially since their father, David, was now confined to bed. He had nearly drowned when the small boat that was ferrying people from Havana, Cuba, to Lucea, capsized one Saturday night a mile outside the Lucea Harbour. David was a skilled swimmer and would have easily made it to shore but for one of the passengers, a large, loud-mouthed woman who could not swim. She kept holding on to him, and David just could not leave her to drown as all the other passengers had done, but laboured with her clinging to him like a massive remora that long water mile, giving her his strength, hauling her great weight through the dark Caribbean sea.

Most people agreed that my mother and father were not, as her father, David, would have said, "unevenly yoked." That they were a good match. That she was lucky to find such a kind and charming husband who was a good provider, and that he was lucky to find such a caring, industrious, and gifted wife. Her siblings all seemed to be happy to welcome Marcus into the Harvey clan. Everyone with maybe the exception of Cleodine. For if any one of David and Margaret's children was going to have an outstanding marriage surely it would have to be her, no, she could not, would not cede that honour to Doris.

Ann, in her later years, once referred to Cleodine as "Cleopatra Queen of Denial." For Cleodine had found that the way to cope with the disappointments in her own life was to simply deny that they existed. She solved the problem of ever witnessing my mother's happiness first-hand by never paying her a visit in her new home in Malvern. She would sometimes write to my parents, usually to inform them of some new piece of property her husband had acquired or of some important addition they had made to his place of business or to Rose Cottage, but she never came to visit. Ann and Flavius, however, would often over the years come and stay with their sister Doris in Malvern, and would always keep her abreast of the latest news in Harvey River. Once, Rose and Albertha came back on a visit from Canada, and they all had a big happy family gathering up in Malvern, without their older sister Cleodine.

Shortly after they were married, my mother had gone with my father to visit the capital city of Kingston, where he often went to the Kingston Industrial Garage on Darling Street, to buy parts for his garage business. He had taken her with him, because he said he wanted to show her something. He had driven past KIG down to a squatter settlement near the garage. "I know how you like an unusual sight, Doris, so look there."

My father pointed at a sprawling village built entirely from wooden packing crates. Everywhere as far as the eyes could see was the word FORD FORD FORD FORD FORD FORD FORD stencilled on the sides of the little wooden shacks.

"Ford ship the Model T in parts in one big wooden packing crate, and when the dealers assemble it, they use one side of the crate to form the floorboard of the car, and the rest of it the Henriqueses give away to whoever asks for it." My mother's eyes filled with tears when she thought of their nice comfortable house in Malvern and her family home in Harvey River. "Oh Marcus, God bless them," she said. "You have to give our people credit for being enterprising."

It was on that occasion that he had taken her to the Ward Theatre, where my mother for the first time in her life saw a moving picture. As she sat in a plush, velvet-covered seat in the balcony of the cool, dark theatre, sipping a cream soda that tasted like water from some sweet invisible fountain, she was as happy as she had ever been in her twenty-six years on earth. There in the dark, she kept glancing over at the profile of her handsome husband. Even in the dark, she was aware of his distinctive profile, his high forehead, his "Roman" nose, his smile, oh his wonderful smile. She still experienced that little shiver of excitement when she saw him smile. His smile and the smell of his 4711 cologne. She was immensely proud of the way he sat there perfectly groomed, wearing a white shirt that she herself had ironed. She admired the way his fingernails and toenails were always clean and well-trimmed. "A clean man," she always said to her children, "your father is such a clean man." There in the Ward Theatre, looking by turns at the screen where the grainy black-and-white film rolled, then back at her husband, her future, without a doubt, was bright. A woman with a high upsweep hairdo that trembled when she struck the keys sat in the orchestra pit and pounded out accompaniment to the movie on an upright piano. My mother leaned over close to my father and whispered that the woman was good at her job, for she knew how to play fast when one of the actors was running for a train, and to play slow and soft when the lovers on the screen were kissing. When she said that, my father kissed her.

My Lord, if only everybody in Harvey River could see her now. "What a token," her father, David, would have said about moving pictures, using the word that the King James Bible used to describe signs and wonders. That day in the theatre she felt certain that she could live happily anywhere on this earth as long as she had her husband beside her. She, who had frowned and wept all throughout their wedding ceremony because, as she always used to say, "It was a brazen bride in those days who smiled," was freely returning her husband's love, there in the dark.

The next day as she dressed, she changed her outfits over and over, asking him, "How you like this?" "How about these shoes with this dress?" and unlike her sisters, he never lost his temper with her, he just sat on the bed in the guest house and smiled and smiled and told her naughty things like, "Yes I like that blue dress, it shows off your nice bosom, and every man on King Street is going to grudge me if you wear it." She had changed outfits until she had come up with the perfect look to go shopping with him on King Street, with its rows of sophisticated department stores, stocked with every imported luxury item imaginable. "Cleo, Miss Jo, Rose, and Ann should be here today," she kept saying, when she saw the top-quality fabrics, shoes, hats, handbags, housewares, and toiletries sold by elegantly turned-out salesmen and women over genuine marble counters. On the arm of her handsome husband she had ascended the wide staircases to the upper level of Issa's department store and had lunched on the balcony of what was then probably the finest department store in the Caribbean. This outing had made her shopping trips into the town of Lucea seem small. The streets of the bustling big city had made my country-girl mother nervous. Although she had stepped jauntily in her fine wine-coloured pumps, which complemented her cream-coloured linen dress with just a touch of hand-embroidery in the form of a wine-red rose on her left shoulder, she was happy to cling tightly to my father's arm on that visit as the great crowds swept them along, up and down King Street, happy that he was such a fine and reliable husband who would always protect her from any harm.

*

$\mathcal{M}$y father did not consider his job as a chauffeur for the English manager of the Black River branch of Barclays Bank as a destination in life. His intention was to open his own garage, and along with Doris to run a fine guest house.

My parents were married in the month of August, but when December came around they realized that my father was going to have to spend his first Christmas away from his new bride, because the bank manager was a bachelor who always spent his Christmas holidays at the Liguanea Club in Kingston. The Liguanea Club was then an exclusive members club which did not admit black people. The only black Jamaicans who set foot on those grounds were the waiters, maids, and gardeners. The club's membership was comprised almost exclusively of expatriates, mostly Englishmen, who ran the affairs of the country when Jamaica was still a colony of Britain.

With a sad heart, Marcus left his new bride in the care of his grandmother and drove the bank manager into Kingston, depositing him at the Liguanea Club. He found accommodation for himself somewhere in downtown Kingston, and he spent all of that Christmas and New Year in the city driving his employer to various functions, waiting all night out in the car until the manager was sufficiently soused and ready to return to the club. He had celebrated Christmases like this before driving for the bank manager, but as a bachelor himself he had not minded hanging out with the other chauffeurs while their bosses drank and bad-mouthed the natives, who were usually outside bad-mouthing the expatriates. But that year he felt different. He was now a married man, and a married man belonged in his house with his family at Christmas. When he returned from Kingston, he promptly resigned from his job and went into partnership with his cousin Charley. Together, they opened a garage, something my father had always dreamed of doing. Like all young men born early in the twentieth century, they shared the same passion, a love of motor cars. Unfortunately, the business did not last.

Charley had been born in Africa, where his father had been posted as a member of the West India Regiment. His wife had accompanied him, and their only child, Charley, was born in Liberia. The first time that my mother met Charley was when Marcus invited him and his wife, Minnie, to dinner in their newly refurbished house to meet his new bride. Doris had prepared a sumptuous Sunday dinner of rice and peas and chicken and pot roast. Using all her new bride things, she had spread the table with a snow-white damask cloth and used her dishes decorated with a bird-on-a-flowering-branch pattern called "Pareek," made in England by the Johnson Brothers. For years to come my family would talk about this meal. They had barely said grace when Charley fell upon the food. "Piece more meat, man," "more rice and peas," "put the gravy on the rice . . . the rice!" he would say. Then he would bend his head again over the mountain of food before him and work away at it, swiftly and deftly levelling it while tapping his feet in a craven, gormandizing dance.

Out of embarrassment, Minnie began to kick her husband

under the table. Only then did he stop eating to demand loudly of her, "What the hell are you kicking me under the table for?" Close to tears, the embarrassed Minnie pleaded with him. "Charley, please, look at Marcus, he is such a gentleman." To which Charley, lowering his head once again to work away at the mountain of food, replied, "Marcus does not know how to eat food."

The first time my father saw a motor car, he had been blinded by the light. It was just after dark, and the light came from a lantern that was illuminated by burning carbide and carried on a pole by a proud young boy who walked ahead of the vehicle. The Leyden brothers, three wealthy planters from Black River, St. Elizabeth, were said to have imported the first motor car into Jamaica in 1903, a four-cylinder "New Orleans," manufactured in Twickenham, England. Perhaps this was the same car that was now making its way through the streets of Malvern, and my father, like the little boy in the nursery rhyme, "stood in his shoes and wondered" at the sight of the magnificent horseless carriage.

My father never forgot how, years before, he had seen his first car, he had been sent as a small boy on an errand by his mother to deliver freshly laundered vestments and altar cloths to the home of the local Anglican minister. All over St. Elizabeth, horse-drawn carriages were a common sight, and to accommodate them there were huge wooden drinking troughs in almost every town square. Marcus's mother, Hannah, who had a gift for washing and ironing white clothes into pristine cleanness, had undertaken to launder the vestments and altar cloths without payment as a kind of temple service from the time that she was a young girl. The job of delivering the clothes to the manse on Saturday evenings soon fell to the child Marcus.

It had been a scorching hot Saturday morning, St. Elizabeth was in the grip of a long and hard drought, as a thirsty, sweating little Marcus trudged through the town square bearing a basket full of holy laundry. Suddenly he heard a great commotion, and when he looked he beheld a group of boys who had stripped themselves naked and were splashing gleefully in the waters of the horse trough:

"Hey Marcus, come bathe wid we."

He didn't think twice; he just put down the basket and, taking off his shirt and short pants, jumped into the cooling waters of the horse trough. He was having such a good time that he did not see his grandmother Dorcas approaching. She snatched him out of the horse trough, slapped his bottom right there before everybody, and made him put on his clothes, retrieve the basket of laundry, and walk before her to the manse, where to his terrible shame, she reported to the minister that he was a wayward and sinful child. The minister then proceeded to give him a long, long lecture and concluded by saying: "My son, do not be like the horse or the mule which need to be bridled." My father never felt warmly towards anything to do with horses after that.

But when he saw the car, he knew that his life was somehow bound up with this machine, which was powered by a noisy motor, instead of with an animal that ate grass, produced stinking manure, and needed to drink from a water trough. Marcus had joined the band of youngsters following the boy who held the lantern to light the way for the car, and when the car stopped he watched in awe as the driver descended and handed a tin can with a long spout to the boy, who gave the lantern to another boy to hold while he went in search of water. My father stood there, gazing intently as the driver took out a set of tools, knelt down, jacked up the car, and unscrewed one of the wheels to change the thin narrow tire that had suffered a puncture. The boy with the lantern held the light high so the man could see to do his work. The first boy returned with the tin can filled with water, took back his lantern-bearing job, and the driver lifted the bonnet of the car, poured water into the engine, and closed it. Then he did something else, he took his leather belt from his waist and used it as a replacement for the fan belt which had snapped. When all these repairs were done, the driver swiftly turned the crank handle to restart the car, jumped in, and departed with the light-bearing boy running ahead of him into the night. My father would have followed them to the other end of the island had he not feared his grandmother's wrath.

So he went home instead and dreamt of the horseless carriage; and he knew that one day he would, like the driver, know how to give it water and to change the tires and replace broken parts and keep it going, for to him the car was more beautiful than any horse he had ever seen. So when big people asked him, "What you want to be when you grow big, Marcus?" he would reply, "I want to be a driver."

Cars were brought to the island of Jamaica by wealthy estate owners who imported the luxurious machines along with great steel drums of gasoline to power them. For years after, the great steel drums that had contained gasoline could be seen, abandoned, in open fields, gleaming under the hot sun, defying nature to break them down.

Because Marcus was so determined to become a driver, his mother had sent him to one of her relatives to learn how to drive a truck. By the end of one week, just by observing what his cousin did, my father was able to drive. His cousin was amazed when he, partly in jest, said to him, "Show me how you woulda drive, if you coulda drive," and the thirteen-year-old

Marcus got behind the wheel – half-sitting, half-standing, because he was not that tall – and with a smile of pure joy, drove the big old truck until it reached a steep incline.

"All right, all right driver," said his cousin, "gimme back mi truck, for me can barely manage this hill, what says a new driver like you."

Driver. He had called him *driver*, and the word fell like a benediction on the young Marcus's ears. After that my father set out to learn everything about cars and trucks. He would walk from Malvern into the town of Black River to seek out the company of the older men who had been trained to maintain the island's first motor car. Men who were happy to share their knowledge, to explain what made the horseless carriage run and how to keep it running.

Life was good for my parents in those early years. Unlike her mother, my mother had no difficulty conceiving, and went on to have nine children in all, one every two years from the time she was in her mid-twenties until she was in her early forties. After a year and a half of marriage, she gave birth to the beautiful and intelligent Barbara; two years later a son was born and named Howard, after her beloved brother; and then came Carmen Rose, whom we called Betty; and then Vaughn, who did not like his name, so he christened himself Bunny. (The five remaining children were born in Kingston, in the following order: the twins Kingsley and Karl, then Keith, me (Lorna) and Nigel.) Their house in Malvern became filled with children and friends always coming and going. There was plenty of domestic help with raising the children and doing the laundry and keeping the house clean, but my mother maintained strict control over her kitchen because my father always claimed that he could taste the difference in the food that she cooked as opposed to food cooked by anyone else. "I can taste your hand, Doris," he always said.

Christmas was the most wonderful time of all. Everyone wanted their car in top shape for the great season of party-going, and the garage was busy day and night. Even the most hard-pay customers would settle their debts in the season of Peace and Goodwill, so Marcus was always able to buy wonderful presents for Doris and the children. Toy pianos that played real tunes, lovely sleeping dolls and spinning tops and music boxes. Fabulous lengths of silk and soft shoes for Doris and more and more lovely furniture for their house. Their house, which always smelled of delicious food cooking, where the Salvation Army choir would stand outside and sing carols and Doris would invite them in and give them Marcus's famous Christmas eggnog as a thank you for serenading them. The Bible promised seven years of plenty, and that promise was made good during those prosperous years before they moved to Kingston. "In those days, we had the very best," my mother always said. And then war broke out in 1939.

My father had feared his grandmother's wicked tongue too much to tell her when his business began to lose money. "You pass you place, Marcus, to go and want to have garage business. You see me, I know my place, you woulda never catch me a eggs up myself bout me a open business. High seat kill Miss Thomas' puss! Nayga people must know dem place, what a way you bright fi go open garage business, is better you did keep you good, good work with the bank manager, it serve you right. Is that Hanover woman you go married to who encourage you inna that damn foolishness."

As it turned out, Marcus was to lose everything he owned. In the late 1930s, car parts and gasoline became increasingly scarce, and many of my father's customers were forced to convert their cars into horse-drawn carriages by removing the engines. Also, Uncle Charley, who was supposed to look after the bookkeeping side of the garage business, drank and spent money in the same manner in which he ate.

Marcus never told his grandmother when the business closed. When she sent to call him, it was a week after he had had to padlock the gates himself, and pay off the two mechanics who worked with him. Dorcas had summoned my father when people in the village had brought her news of his failed business. He received a message from her that said: "Come and see me, but don't bring your wife." He went to see her and found her sitting up in her rickety old iron bed, her airless bedroom lit by one small, irritable little kerosene lamp. The room reeked of her old lady musk smell, the camphor oil she used to anoint her creaking limbs, and the kerosene oil from the lamp. She spoke these words to my father through the semi-darkness:

"I decide out of the goodness of my heart that since you fall so low, you can come back here and live with your wife and children and help me to plant red peas and cassava. But, you and that Hanover woman and your damn children will have to live under my jurisdiction. Although you are a big married man now, I am still your grandmother and under my roof, my word is law." The old iron bed creaked and groaned as Dorcas threw herself into her homily on the sins of flying past your place. She all but stood up in her bed in order to remind my father how she had never failed at anything in her life, because, "He who is low, fears no fall." She repeated her offer to have my parents come back and live with her, an offer she accompanied by the thumping of her fist on her bony chest to underscore the phrase "My word is law." My father responded by leaping up from the chair in which he was sitting, and as he strode out the door, he said, "Don't worry about me, don't worry about me, my wife, or my children. We will be all right."

"I would prefer to die than to live under her roof again," he had said to my mother of Dorcas's offer. After Marcus's refusal, his grandmother took his name off her will and bequeathed her land to the government. Going to live in Harvey River was out of the question; there was no way to earn a living there. So my parents decided that their only alternative was to move to Kingston.

They had had one last dinner party in their Malvern house. One last big dinner party before the new owners came to take possession, before the truck that would take them into Kingston backed into the yard, drove over one of the flower-beds, and parked by the front door so that they could load what was left of their house filled with fine mahogany furniture onto the back. For that dinner party, my mother had cooked their favourite meal. Pot roast and rice and peas and brown stew chicken and fried plantains. And because no party in Jamaica is a party without curry goat, they had said to hell with the expense and purchased a young kid, and slaughtered and curried the tender flesh. As she spread the table with the damask tablecloth Cleodine had given her as a wedding gift, and put out all her fine wedding things, remembering all the "daintiness" that her sister had taught her, my mother was overcome by the knowledge that this was the last time that she would ever spread a table in this house where she had come to be so happy. A realization so final that she had to sit down suddenly in her seat nearest the door through which she would come and go to and from the kitchen to the table.

My mother remembered the morning they had bade miserly Dorcas and her house of meanness farewell. She had woken and found herself singing, "The strife is o'er, the battle done; Now is the Victor's triumph won . . . Alleluia!" She and Marcus had carefully assembled their possessions and packed them into a truck belonging to one of their friends, on the day their house was finally ready to be occupied. "Thank you very much, Grandma Dorcas, for your kind hospitality," they had said to the wretched, miserly old woman, and then they had practically run outside to the truck and driven joyfully to their own house. Marcus blew the horn all the way from his grandmother's house to theirs. They sang a song that newly emancipated Jamaicans sang on the first of August 1838. "Jubilee, Jubilee. Me get full free. Me can stand up when me want, siddown when me want, liedown and gettup when me want, for me free." Yessir, they were free to laugh and talk and sleep and wake as they pleased, to cook big dinners and entertain any number of friends they wanted. "Why the hell would I spendup my money to feed a whole heap of hungry-belly people who should stay home and eat at them own table?" was Dorcas's response to a suggestion my mother once made to her that they invite some of their neighbours over for Sunday dinner.

She was well-acquainted with every corner of this house, every door, every window. "Brussels" and "tarshan." My mother had carefully stitched every one of the lace curtains that were now being taken down from the windows of their house. She could identify a Brussels lace from a Venice or chantilly lace with her eyes closed. She would rub a forefinger over the surface and correctly identify the lace in question. She had arranged every bed, chair, and table in that house, where they had kept the front door open from morning till night because they so loved to see their home filled with guests. They had planned to one day convert that house in Malvern into a paying guest house, for nothing gave them more pleasure than to see their friends and relations enjoying hospitality Doris and Marcus style. But they never did get around to it.

"Doris girl, your nice life done," said a voice inside her. She walked over to the table and stared and stared at her place setting before her, trying hard not to cry. To calm herself, my mother rubbed the crest of the bird perched on a limb at the centre of the dinner plate. She ran her finger along the limb on which the bird sat, and a voice rose up in her. It said, "Doris, this limb is now broken." She imagined at that moment that the bird on the dinner plate flew up and out through the dining-room window from which the lace curtains were now removed. "You soon come back man, Marcus, and you cannot live in town, you just going to pay Kingston a visit," said their friends. My mother would remember little about that last dinner party in their house they were about to lose because she deliberately kept herself busy tending to the needs of their guests. The friends who were talking and laughing too loudly. The people who kept hugging her and saying, "We don't know what we are going to do without you." Some of them were even crying openly as she remained resolutely dry-eyed, but she would always remember one incident.

"Time for a song now, Marcus." My mother felt her heart fall when their friends began to say that. "You know we can't let you go to Kingston before you drop two tune, Marcus." O God why they want him to sing, Doris thought to herself. Why can't they put themself in his place? How would they feel if this had happened to them? Would they feel like singing? O Lord no, Marcus just tell them you don't feel good, tell them you not up to it tonight, of all nights. She watched his every move nervously, rubbing the insides of her arms along the sides of her belly, which had become high and wide after she had given birth to four children. "Say no, you not singing tonight." She shook her head and tried to get him to catch her eye, but he refused to look in her direction. Instead he headed into their bedroom. She hurriedly put down the tray of cold drinks that she had been offering to their guests, saying in a "put-on," cheerful voice, "Have a last drink on Marcus and me." When she saw him come from the bedroom with the guitar, she made for the open front door and stood in the doorway with her arms folded. He took a seat in the living room beside his prized gramophone, the second thing that he had bought for their house after their marriage bed. She could tell that he was determined to avoid her look, which she had learned from her mother, Margaret, that cross between a cut-eye and a stare-down look that she'd brought with her from Harvey River.

What she did not understand was that his heart was so heavy right then, that if he did not sing, he was going to break down and bawl like a baby. He reached up and lifted the big heavy-headed needle off the seventy-eight record. It was Leadbelly singing "Goodnight Irene." Before that night they would always listen to that record together, sitting side by side on the loveseat, the third thing that he had bought for their house. He always wanted her to sit on his left. "On the heart side," he would say, "I want you always near to my heart." Always with one arm thrown around her neck and his long fingers stroking her rounded upper arm, they would listen to Leadbelly, and Marcus would say, "Wait, wait, the nice part coming now." This was how they liked to wait for Leadbelly to reach that part in the chorus when he sings, "Goodnight, Irene, goodnight, Irene, I'll *get* you in my dreams," for when he reached that part, they would both turn and face each other at the same time and laugh out loud. Every time, they laughed together as if they were hearing Leadbelly's lascivious tone for the first time, "I'll *get* you in my dreams." They'd laugh till she caught herself laughing at Leadbelly's slackness, and she'd stop and say, "Marcus, you are too out of order," as if she had not become a little out of order herself, now that she was a married woman.

But that last night in their house, she could find nothing to laugh about as she watched my father carefully sit himself down alone on their loveseat so that the seams of his trousers fell just so. She watched as he held his guitar close to his chest, just like he sometimes held her when they were alone, and she knew she would never laugh at that song again. She watched as he shut his eyes tight and began to rock back and forth, and with a lump-in-his-throat voice, took up where Leadbelly left off. When she heard his voice begin to vibrate and break up, she stopped clutching herself and balled her hands into two fists by her side. She leaned forward, gathered up her strength, and began to call out to him silently, insistently from her place by the door. She felt herself begin to haul up strength from her belly-bottom, until she was almost standing on her tiptoes, and she strained towards him begging, no, commanding him without words: bear up. Don't break. Marcus, don't you cry before them. Not even if they are our friends, don't make them see you cry. "Sometimes I live in the country, sometimes I live in the town, sometimes I take a great notion, to jump in the river and drown: Irene goodnight, Irene goodnight, goodnight Irene, goodnight Irene, I'll see you in my dreams." That night she gathered up her strength and force-fed it to him so he could part company with Leadbelly. When he switched to his repertoire of rude songs, she touched her open hand to her belly-bottom in gratitude to her woman strength. "Bredda Manny O mi find a Candy, Bredda Manny O mi find a Candy, Bredda Manny O mi find a Candy dash it wey you nasty bitch a puss shit." That night he did make them laugh, he made them laugh, he made them dance.

Later, as they lay on their marriage bed, without having bothered to remove the white candlewick bedspread, he had cried then. "How many times must I lose, Dor?" he had asked her. "How many times?" It was then he told her how his mother had lost her land. She had lost it, he said, because of him. He had gone as an apprentice truck driver at the age of fourteen to work in Port Antonio and there he had fallen sick with malaria fever. They had sent a message to his mother to come to him in the hospital and she had, in the emergency, used her house and land as collateral for a loan of thirty pounds from a Mr. Russell, the justice of the peace of that parish. Her son was sick, she was in a hurry, she did not read what she signed and that is how she lost her land, in the same way that thousands of poor Jamaicans have lost their land for nearly two hundred years. When she came back to Malvern, after a month of nursing her son, Russell had foreclosed on her house and land. She had taken her case to the authorities at Black River Courthouse, but Russell's friends who sat on the bench had found in favour of Russell. Everybody said it was the loss that had killed her.

"How many times must I lose, Dor?" And then it was she who was holding him close to her chest, saying, "no mine no mine no mine," and assuring him of the many opportunities that existed for him in Kingston, the businessplaces just begging for a good and capable man like him to come there and work. It was she who was saying that everything happens for a purpose and that one thing she was looking forward to (although she was not an idle sort of person) was going again and again to the Ward Theatre to see moving pictures and concerts.

The more she thought about it, growing up in Kingston would make the children grow bright and uncountrified. Barbara, their brilliant first-born, could go to a very good school like St. Andrews High School for girls. But she had also said, as he kissed her in gratitude, that if after experiencing all the wonders of Kingston, they still really didn't like it, they should move right back to the country, where they would buy another house after they had worked and saved enough money. That night she knew in her heart that from then on, she was going to have to be the strong one, the one who would have to adopt her sister Cleodine's straight-backed walk and grim determination to move forward, come what may. And then he said to her, "Dor, let us make sure we keep our business to ourselves." My father had learned his lesson from the early experiences of their marriage and the mischief-making of his friends, like the cerassee sisters, and thereafter he always declared that what happened between a husband and a wife was strictly their personal business.

All the children in the Harvey household had grown up seeing their mother and father in agreement on most matters affecting the family. Sometimes if they disagreed openly and Margaret became loud and belligerent, as she was wont to do, David would suggest that they step into their bedroom and close the door and argue it out there. Sometimes as they lay in bed at night the children could overhear them talking about whether David should keep going to Cuba or not, or whether they should sell some of the land, whether David and his brothers should take a certain case, because everybody knew the accused had done what they said he had done. But before the children it was always, "Your father and me," or "Your mother and me think this or that." When Margaret did not get her own way, she would say, "Mr. Harvey and I think this or that so." And so Doris began to rehearse what she would say to anybody who asked her how could she leave the country for hard life in town. "We have decided to try our luck in Kingston."

part three

*O*n their first morning in the city of Kingston, before daylight, my father had woken up and dressed in the dark so as not to disturb her and the children. As he left, he whispered to her that he was going to return the truck that they had hired to bring them to Kingston to a driver who was waiting on Spanish Town Road so he could drive it back to its owner in Malvern. He said too that the same friend who had found these accommodations was taking him to see about a job and he wanted to be there early. She had murmured something like, "Where you going without breakfast?" and then she had fallen again into exhausted sleep. When sunlight, pouring in through the row of windows facing the street, made its way over the piles of furniture, across the wooden floor, and over to the small windowless room that was now their bedroom, my mother woke and heard the street cries of Orange Street for the first time. The night before, after entering the city of Kingston from the Spanish Town Road, when my father had turned the truck that carried them from St. Elizabeth up Orange Street, they had almost met with an accident. As my father rounded the corner, they saw thundering towards them a dray cart being driven at breakneck speed by two masked men! My father braked and pulled over suddenly as the cart flew by, trailing the smell of shit. These were the pit latrine cleaners of the city of Kingston, many of them descended from East Indian indentured labourers who had been born as untouchables and deemed fit only to clean sewers, handle corpses, and to do the lowliest work assigned to human beings. Although there was no law in Jamaica which made them untouchables, these men still elected to do the sewer-cleaning work done by their forefathers.

At the gate of no. 117 Orange Street, my mother's face had fallen when she saw what was to be their new home, a set of three rooms off a central courtyard, with an enclosed verandah. Still shaking from their encounter with the speeding cart of the latrine cleaners, she saw that the street was lined with rows of houses and places of business all jostling with each other for space. By the light of the street lamps, she could see that there was no room for trees on this street. The small wooden gate of no. 117 was reached by climbing a brick platform, via stairs set into it. When they had walked up the stairs, pushed open the wooden gate, and stepped into the vast brick courtyard, my mother realized that things had truly changed. For the first time in her entire life, she was going to share a living space with complete strangers, many of whom she could feel peering out at her and her family from rows of dimly lit rooms.

The friend who had found this place for them was waiting at the gate to hand over the keys. When he saw how my mother's face had changed when she stepped from the truck, he told her that they were fortunate to find a place like this because Kingston landlords don't like to rent to people with children!

Her four children lay asleep, wearing the clothes she had dressed them in the day before, on one of the two beds that they had hastily assembled last night. They were all exhausted from the long everlasting truck drive from Malvern to Kingston. All the way there the two younger ones, Betty and Vaughn, who rode with her in the cab, were restless. Betty kept asking where were they going over and over again, till my mother finally snapped and said, "What are you asking me for? I don't know," and she had felt bad the minute she had said it, for a remark like that would make her husband feel very small and ashamed because he had lost them their house. He did not respond, but just reached down and changed gears and stared hard at the road. In order to quiet the children and to change the mood in the cab of the truck, she had fed them biscuits and cakes and sweet drinks all the way to Kingston. The two older children, Barbara and Howard, rode in the back, seated on various items of furniture, happy to be having such an adventure. My father had made sure that they were secure by nailing a wooden gate across the back of the truck. Where were they going? She really, in her heart of hearts, did not know. This morning though, lying in this small bedroom in Kingston, she knew that soon the children would be awake and needing to be fed. Exhausted, disappointed, and overwhelmed as she was by her new surroundings, she felt guilty that for the first time in their married life, she had not prepared breakfast for her husband. She was not going to do the same to her children, so she ventured down into the yard in search of the kitchen. There was not a single tree in sight except for a headless breadfruit tree rising from the one unpaved space in the brick courtyard, its blunt silver-grey trunk bowing to the east. The only greenery in evidence sprung from discarded paint tins and old chamber pots arranged outside room doors and under the jalousie windows. These were planted mostly with mint bushes and common flowers like monkey fiddle and ram goat roses. My mother saw that her new source of water was to be a metal standpipe springing out of a low concrete cistern and she later found out that each of the tenants was supposed to take turns scrubbing it, a system guaranteed to generate no end of strife. Like the Harvey River, the standpipe was the place where residents gathered to collect water for all domestic purposes. Unlike the people of Harvey River, who found refreshment and blessings in their source of water, she would soon discover that the residents of the tenement yard regarded the standpipe as the site for loud quarrels and even the occasional fist fight.

"I would prefer to dead like a dog in the city of Kingston than to bruk mi back chop cane." That was the sentiment of all who had elected to "make life" in the city, to live in rented rooms and share the same cooking and sanitation facilities, to work and educate their children and to one day own their own house and land; they always said house and land.

"These damn hurry-come-up Kingston landlords don't like to rent to people with children." This is what the friend who had found the place for my parents had warned them. He also warned them how some of the people who had not too long ago come from rural Jamaica to find employment in the city were in the habit of declaring themselves "born Kingstonians," which entitled them to make fun of the latest arrivals from the country. "If they trouble you, don't pay them any mind, Dor, we are only passing through" was what Marcus had said.

As my mother made her way to the communal kitchen, one woman called out to her friend, "Mi dear you see mi new style gramophone?" and the other one replied, "Yes mi love, I see you have one that can only play pon verandah." As most of my parents' furniture could not fit in their now much smaller living space, they had had to pile much of it, even their precious gramophone, on the small verandah outside. When the other tenants woke that morning and saw the overflow of furniture on the verandah outside my parents' rooms, those whose worldly possessions hardly filled one small room immediately began to "throw words." Mocking phrases like "country come a town" rose up to meet her as she stepped down into the yard, saying good morning, good morning to everyone as she went, bearing a small newly acquired cast-iron coal pot stove that she intended to set up in the kitchen, which she identified as the long, low structure near the right-hand corner of the courtyard, with clouds of black smoke issuing from its narrow doors and windows.

"Ace-blank inna you arse" was what she heard as she stepped further into the courtyard. "Learn fi play domino bwoy." A group of big able-bodied men, including an old white-haired man dressed in a white sleeveless merino, sat crowded around a table, smoking cigarettes and drinking tea from large, battered enamel mugs as they slammed down bone domino tiles. It was 7 a.m. Women, some still in nightgowns, were plaiting the hair of small girls in the doorways of joined barracks-type rooms with narrow verandahs. One or two of them were vigorously beating children who were reluctant to go to school. "You duncey head little wretch you, you fi gwan a school, you want push handcart when you grow big?"

One young girl, who looked as if she had toiled all night somewhere, was slowly making her way to the farthest room in the yard, as two older children advanced towards my mother bearing brimming chamber pots. They were headed for the toilet that was housed in a ramshackle wooden structure to the left of the yard. The level of noise, and what her mother, Margaret, would have condemned as loud common laughter, nearly drove her backwards. She was tempted to turn and go back into her rooms and bolt the door, but she kept going.

"Good morning, everybody," my mother had said to the women standing stirring their cauldron-like pots in the dark kitchen. Nobody answered. Nobody made a move to make room for her at the "firewall," the sooty concrete counter where all the stoves sat. Chocolate, tea, coffee, ackee and codfish, rank corn pork, green bananas, boiling cornmeal porridge, and flour dumplings contested for scent supremacy in the early morning air. From the recesses of the dark kitchen, one woman immediately raised a bantering, mocking song, a song with words intended to wound. Actually it was more of a chant that had just one line that she intoned over and over, "How art the mighty fallen, how art the mighty fallen." The other women took up the chant, and my mother left the kitchen in tears.

"She think she better than we," the same woman kept telling all the other women in the yard as they squatted near the standpipe with their wooden washtubs. "Then if she better than we, why she and her husband and pickney have fi live here so?" The hectoring woman was named Vie and she had taken an instant and virulent dislike to my mother. My mother could hear Vie and the other women in the tenement discussing her and her family from her rooms in those first few weeks. She tried to keep her children confined to the rooms and verandah and to do her laundry late in the afternoon instead of early in the morning, after all the women had left the pipeside, but every day she still had to face the kitchen.

"How art the mighty fallen, how art the mighty fallen." Every time she went into the kitchen there was Vie, raising her "How art the mighty fallen" anthem. Eventually even the other women agreed that Vie took her hectoring and "throw-word" too far. How would anyone like it if every time you saw them they were saying, "How art the mighty fallen," when they did not even know you, did not know the circumstances of your life. Over time, Vie added to her chant a few other choice lines such as "Scornful dog nyam dutty pudding" and "High seat kill Miss Thomas' puss." At first my mother tried to ignore Vie, as my father suggested, and managed to make her way around the communal kitchen and bathroom arrangements by just watching to see when they were not in use. She also began to imagine that she was wearing her sister Cleodine's backboard every time she went down into the yard, her sister Cleodine, who would surely have a few things to say when she heard about where Doris and Marcus were now living.

In the 1650s and 1660s, what is now known as the city of Kingston, Jamaica, used to be Colonel Barry's Hog Crawle. The town itself was established on June 16, 1692, in acknowledgement of the importance of its massive harbour, said to be one of the seven largest in the world, its abundant good water, its proximity to natural resources, its fertile soil, and gentle breezes. Drawn up as a parallelogram one mile long from Port Royal to North Street, and half a mile wide from East Street to West Street, by 1716 Kingston had become the largest town on the island of Jamaica. According to travel writers of that time, Kingston was a city to be either hated or loved. Some writers found it to be one of the most backward and least attractive of southern cities, with narrow streets and dull, shabby houses. Others remarked on the handsome residences set far back from dusty roadways, showing white through shades of palm. Some referred to it as a city filled with hovels of low degree, dark with grime and populated by multitudinous negroes. But a little later, travel writer Ethel Symonette described it as a place with everybody on the go, tongues busy effecting purchases with the confused jingling of streetcar bells, joining with the clear ring of horses' hoofs, the shrieking whistle of the locomotive making itself heard. A bustling little place with rows of good business houses, nice churches, and passable shops where good English stuff could be bought at a ridiculously low price.

By the end of the nineteenth century, Kingston boasted hotels like the fabulous Myrtle Bank and the Constant Spring Hotel, also the ornate velvet-curtained Ward Theatre, where touring thespians from Britain gave regular performances. Then in 1907 an earthquake shook the city and fires broke out all over. The citizens swore that Armageddon had come. The Kingston Parish Church lost its steeple, and the owner of Nathan's, one of the largest stores on King Street, was killed when his store collapsed on top of him. By the time Marcus and Doris moved there in 1940, the population of Kingston numbered 150,000.

My mother rose early and ironed a shirt for my father to wear on his first day at work. She was pleased because she had ironed the shirt perfectly, with no seams in the sleeves and no creases along the collar. She was especially pleased as she went singing down to the kitchen because her husband had found a job, and that morning he was behaving more like his old self as he patted her on her bottom playfully when she passed by him sitting on the verandah, polishing his shoes. "Marcus, you are too out of order," she half-protested, sounding again like the young bride Doris, reacting to her frisky young groom for the first time in months — her groom, who was saying that maybe he would drop by to visit her in the telephone van that day when all the children were at school.

"Marcus, you mean we can soon move from here?" "I tell you we were just passing through," he had said. For the first time since they moved to Kingston the future began to look bright. He had gotten a job as a linesman at the Jamaica Telephone Company after weeks of job hunting, and my mother could not have been happier. She was singing, "God is working his purpose out" as she went into the kitchen. She did not give a damn about those lowdown Kingston women who were so vicious and unkind to her, for indeed God was working his purpose out. Her husband had found a job, they were just passing through, soon they would be leaving here, and just as she had that thought, Vie came buzzing around her like a damn rotten-teeth, one-frock locust.

My mother, who had been so excited and so anxious that my father should not be late on the first morning of his new job, would later swear that she heard George O'Brian Wilson's voice as she poured my father's tea into his favourite teacup while Vie bantered away in the background. Her grandfather's voice was asking, "Why the fock are you letting this eedjit bully you?" My mother turned and, like a great she-bear, slapped Vie, and my father's cup broke. Vie stood there stunned as my mother passed her, went upstairs, served my father a fried egg and bread, with no tea, which he ate standing up in the doorway before hastening to catch the tram to the telephone company. Then she fell on their bed in that cramped Kingston room and bawled like a baby, with two of her four children crowding round her, the two eldest having been dispatched to school early.

"What happen, Mama?" they kept asking until she had become irritable and told them to shut up and keep quiet. She could not tell them that she was crying because she never in her life had lived under such rough conditions and that she never in her life had ever had to stoop so low as to slap somebody just to be able to live in peace. No wonder country people called Kingston, "Killsome." As far as she was concerned they could not pass through quickly enough. But strangely, after she slapped Vie, the rest of the women began to be quite civil to her, especially after the business about the one-pound note.

It was a one-pound note, it was definitely a one-pound note. The reason my mother was so sure of this was that it was the only money she had to her name and it was all that stood between her and my father's next payday. She had sent one of my brothers with it to the shop to buy a loaf of bread, a tin of condensed milk, and a tin of cocoa for supper. He came back with the change short. My mother sent him back to tell the shopkeeper that there had been a mistake, but he returned from the shopkeeper with a message that said it was not one pound that my brother had brought to the shop, but ten shillings. She hardly ever left her house in those early days, mostly because she was still getting used to her surroundings. Sometimes as she carried her wooden bathboard, which my father had bought for them to use whenever they used the communal shower, she wondered to herself how and when did she go from being a Harvey of Harvey River, to wife of Marcus Goodison, living in their wonderful open house in Malvern, to sharing the same kitchen and bathroom with jaze-ears Vie? Could be worse, could always be worse, but while there is life, there is hope, because God is working his purpose out. But this time she was forced to work it out herself. She just could not afford to lose that much money, so she tidied herself and ventured out to explain to the shopkeeper that he had made a mistake. So there she was, this tall, shapely, attractive woman in a flowered navy blue crepe dress, worn with soft black leather pumps, walking quickly along with her children trooping behind her as she went to confront a thieving shop-keeper who had robbed her of the money she needed to send her children to school the next day. But when she got there, the shopkeeper insisted that it was ten shillings that my brother had tendered. My mother insisted that it was one pound, and the shopkeeper said that perhaps my brother had taken the money. My mother said she was sure that he had not. "If some people so great how come them have to be living right there on Orange Street, mixing up with poor nayga?" asked the shop-keeper to his wife, who stood silently supporting him. He began to make more and more really offensive remarks about people who thought that they were better than other people.

"Don't let them haul you down to their level. Walk away from them." It was strange how at times like these she relied on the queenly ways of Cleodine. So thinking about what her sister would have said and done, my mother turned to leave the shop, conceding victory to the shopkeeper, who was undoubt-edly about to haul her down, but then she turned back and faced him: "You know, you should not do this to me. I am a mother, and that was my children's lunch money." As she said this, tears rolled down her face.

In later years she would always half-seriously tell people that whatever they did they should try not to make her cry because her tears would bring down grief on whoever caused them to fall. Maybe she was not really joking because a few mornings later there was a loud knocking at the door of their three rooms. It turned out to be one of the women she'd seen in the yard who was going from door to door to tell everyone that the shopkeeper's place had caught fire. My mother did not say a word. She just walked with the woman down the street to where a crowd had assembled to watch the large wooden shop burning down to charcoal. Some of the people were still wearing their nightclothes. There were little children in their father's old shirts, even a few small boys wearing their mother's old dresses, looking like short kings in tattered robes; men in merinos and underpants; and one or two daring younger women wearing only slips, who had jumped out of bed when they heard the alarm. As my mother stood in the crowd, she heard people saying what a thief the shopkeeper was, how for years he had overcharged them, and how the fire was pure retribution. As she stood there, no doubt telling people around her how just a few days before he had cheated her out of her children's lunch money, the shopkeeper walked over to her in the crowd and without a word, he handed her a one-pound note.

When my mother awoke from one of her dreams, a dream in which she saw herself and her husband and children firmly planted like banana trees growing from the brick courtyard of the tenement, she said to Marcus, "We will never leave here if only you alone work." This is what she said, "Don't believe that I'm not grateful, but we can't live and save enough to move to a better place on just your wages." My father had said nothing. He had just folded up the newspaper and left for work. And every morning my mother rose early and made him his breakfast before he went off.

In those days she would buy a fresh loaf of bread from the Huntingtons Bakery's horse-drawn cart and a newspaper from the vendor for my father to read as he ate his breakfast. Later, after he left for work, she would sit and read for half an hour or so before she began the housework. She always read the obituary columns and she always read the want ads. "In yesterday's *Gleaner*, there was a notice for nurses out at Bellevue," she says. "We're just passing through, Dor, just passing through" is what he would say when he came home to find that she or his children had suffered some indignity from one of the other tenants, "We're just passing through." But her dreams never lied. Her dream showed them stuck, planted right there, rooted, never to move.

"There was a notice in yesterday's *Gleaner*, they need nurses out at Bellevue Asylum. I will get somebody to keep Betty and the twins for me in the days. Barbara, Howard, and Bunny will be at school," she said later about the ad.

"You? Go to work at the Asylum? Doris, that place is a living hell, you can't manage a situation like that. How can a woman like you ever manage a situation like that? Your father would kill me if he ever found out that I take you out of his house to make you go and work at the Asylum."

"I'm going out there on Monday morning. We will never make it on your paycheque alone." My father is silent. When my mother got like that, she looked exactly like her mother, Margaret, as if her face was carved from granite. He knew better than to try and talk her out of it.

⁓

The Lunatic Asylum (Bellevue) had been established in 1862, through the compassionate efforts of men such as Dr. Edward Bancroft and Dr. Louis Q. Bowerbank, to replace the old Lunatic Asylum, which was part of the Kingston Public Hospital and was described in a report to the Jamaican Assembly in 1851 as "nothing less than a chamber of horrors." In the years before Bellevue, new patients were stripped of their clothing, had their heads shaved, and were issued with short, tattered gowns marked front and back with either MLA (Male Lunatic Asylum) or FLA (Female Lunatic Asylum). Sometimes one small bug-infested cell would house as many as fourteen patients at night. They slept on bare wooden platforms without covering, or on cold stone floors. Male and female patients were often flung together in these cells, resulting in everything from pregnancies to murder. Two large tanks were provided for the inmates, with patients of both sexes bathing in the same water in the tanks.

Patients were fed rotting food and dirty water. The staff were generally unprincipled, uncaring, and indifferent. One matron was found guilty of using patients as her personal servants, and many of the nurses spent only a quarter of their working day on the premises. The patients were abused and ill-treated by all categories of staff, including washerwomen and labourers who beat them and forced them to do manual work and other labour both inside and outside the institution. The report described inhumane forms of punishment such as "tanking"; that is, holding down a person by force under water until he or she gasped for breath, sank unconscious, or sometimes even died.

Great care had been taken with the selection of the site of the new Lunatic Asylum, to be located along the Windward Road, and although it took more than ten years to complete, mainly because of the indifference of the then colonial government, the new facility was designed for patients to benefit from the sea breezes and from a more efficient and humane system of asylum management that sought to provide inmates with occupational and recreational facilities. In 1862, conditions at the new Lunatic Asylum stood in striking contrast to those at the old one; but by the 1940s, when my mother worked there for a short time, conditions had again begun to deteriorate.

As they rode together on the tram that first morning, my father kept asking her, "My God, Doris, you sure that you can handle this? I hear that place is a living hell, you know? I will try to get more overtime, you don't have to do this." She just said, "Don't make it any worse." And he had looked as miserable and downcast as the day they had driven away in the truck loaded with their worldly possessions from the house they had lost in Malvern and headed for Kingston. So they had ridden to the Asylum in silence, for try as she might, my mother could not find the right words to say to him to make him feel not so small, not so inadequate. Because to tell the truth, she was frightened at the thought of going to work at Bellevue, and bad as she felt for her husband, she needed to be silent and to pray for herself, to ask the Lord who was her shepherd to walk with her through the valley of the shadow of the madhouse.

And so my father went with her through the massive iron gates and stood with her outside the door of the matron's office, where about two hundred waiting women were applying for the twenty or so positions as psychiatric nurses who would be trained on the job.

"Are you sure you will be all right, Dor?" He looked wretched.

"Go," she said, "I will see you at home this evening."

But before he left he made one attempt to cheer her up, to make her laugh. He could always make her laugh. "Dor," he whispered. "Look at that woman over there in the red dress," and my mother looked over and saw a very tall, thin woman dressed in a tight red dress wearing a close-fitting green hat. "She don't look like a bird pepper to you?" asked my father. "Maybe she should go down to Spur Tree and apply for a job at the pickapepper factory." And that made my mother laugh and say, "Marcus, you are too out of order," and then she said, "You don't have to wait with me, I will see you at home later."

"To subdue the lunatics, you have to be very strong," said the Matron, a big, tall woman whom my father would later say always looked like she was carrying a spear and a shield. "Very strong, I am looking for very strong women to train as nurses, so if you are weak you won't make it here."

My mother was trained as a teacher of young children, but she probably was taken because she was physically so strong. And yet nothing could have prepared her for the sight of rows of prison-like cells, in each of which was a sick man or woman, their bodies barely covered by short gowns made from flour bags. Sometimes more than one person was locked in a cell; some were lying in their own filth. Her pet goat, her Grandmother Leanna's mule, her mother's donkey, her father's horse, Nana Frances's pigs. Any one of those animals in Harvey River seemed better off, better cared for than these poor so-called lunatics. As the matron had told the ten women she employed on the spot, the role of an Asylum nurse really was similar to that of a penkeeper. And nothing could have prepared her for the truly terrifying sight of the superintendent of the facility who, convinced that lunatics were dangerous criminals, was to be seen patrolling the premises armed with a gun.

"You not up to this my dear, you might as well go home now," said the matron to one of the new nurses who had vomited at the sight of the caged patients. This time it was not Cleodine's backboard that helped my mother, it was not George O'Brian Wilson's rage, it was the compassion of her father, David, telling her to "treat them as sick children, that is what these poor people are, they are like sick children." "Sick children," she said later, "I made myself think of them as sick children, and those who mess themselves, I cleaned. Those who needed a bath, I bathed. And I mash the food and spoon-fed those who could not feed themselves." The rest of the time she spent trying to unknot and delouse the heads of women whose hair had not been combed for weeks and she pared toenails that had grown into claws.

"What is your story, little miss?" my mother said to a girl who was about thirteen years old, who, though she was dressed in the short ragged gown of a mental patient, seemed to be behaving quite normally. If it were not for her age and her dress, she could have been a nurse, so caring was she of the other patients. "What is your story, little miss?" she asked as the girl helped her to spoon-feed an old woman who was convinced that the asylum was really a brothel.

"I am not living any whoring life, you think I don't know why you have me in here?" said the old woman. "You want me to sell myself to those sailors over there in the white clothes, and you are trying to bribe me with cornmeal porridge, but I am not eating it, and I'm not selling my good, good pumpum to any nasty dirty sailor."

"No, dear," my mother explained, "the men in the white clothes are doctors, not sailors, and you are too old to be talking like that."

"Oh yes," said the old woman who was bony and haggard as a yard broom, "Oh yes? It's because you don't know how the men dem go crazy for me."

The young girl was the only one who could get her to calm down. "Come Grandma. I won't make them do you anything," she said, and the deranged old woman, who had come to see the young girl as her granddaughter Beatrice, would say: "I am so glad you have come, Beatrice, these godless, worthless people want to come and turn me into a prostitute."

"Drink your porridge and don't pay them any mind," the young girl would say, and the old lady would quietly obey her. Once, the girl had even changed out of her flour bag uniform into a short dress that was too tight for her, and had gone off the premises, but she had come back before evening to help feed the older patients.

"What is your story, little miss?" my mother asked her.

"My mother get a new boyfriend after my father leave, she

start to send me to where him live to carry dinner for him sometimes when she have to work late. One evening I carry the dinner and him say I must come inside him room and wait till him finish eat and then him would give me back the carrier. When I was waiting on him, him start to look at me funny and ask me if I have boyfriend, and I say no, I am still a child, and him say I look big for my age. But when I go home and start to tell my mother what him ask me, she say she don't want to hear nothing from me. The next time she send me to carry dinner for him, I say I was not going, but she beat me and force me to go and him hold me down, and after that, I bawl and bawl till them say I was mad, and my mother boyfriend say is lie I tell on him, and my mother call police and lock me up. Matron say I can go home now, but my mother don't want me to come back. I wasn't mad you know, I wasn't really mad."

My mother persuaded the Matron to release the girl into her care, and she brought her home with her one evening, where she sat quietly on the verandah, touching everybody who passed by and whispering the same words over and over, "I wasn't mad you know, I wasn't mad." The young girl looked like a different person once she started to wear the dresses my mother sewed for her; and as soon as she could, my mother sent her down to Harvey River, where she lived among the Harveys for years, telling everyone who heard her story, "I wasn't mad you know, I wasn't really mad."

"There but for the grace of God," my mother would say. "There but for the grace of God, go I. You know how many of those people come to Kingston just to find work and hard life mashed them up?" Some of the patients who were collected enough to give her a name and address got my mother to write letters to their families telling them where they were, and how they were doing.

However, her job at the Asylum did not last very long. One day she came home from work to find that in her absence my sister Betty, who had been plagued by epileptic fits from the time she was a baby, had begun to have full-fledged grand mal seizures.

"*I* never knew hard life until I came to Kingston," my mother would say as she gazed at her hands. "I used to have the most beautiful hands." Hard Life. When she sounded those words they became a fierce giant, a merciless enemy whom you had to struggle against. Hard Life was the hurry-come-up, ex-slave landlord who, now that he owned some property in the form of a tenement yard, wanted his turn to play busha, or slave master, to delight in lording his owner status over you, to extract exorbitant sums of money from you for the privilege of living in his dry-weather premises. To inform you loudly that he normally did not rent to people with children and that he would be coming every Sunday morning at 6:00 a.m. to beat upon your door and demand his rent, which you had better have or he would turn you out onto the street.

Hard Life was a levelling teacher, anxious that no pupil should ever outstrip him, who liked to shame you before your class, to expose your errors and mistakes and poor judgment to the mocking scourgings of those you thought were your friends before you got marked down. Hard Life was an ill-mannered visitor who came to call on you in order to search up your cupboards when your back was turned, so that they could go and tell everyone how things were bad with you. To lie about you, that you had no sugar for your tea and that you had to trust or credit food. It was a vicious old hige who liked to suck out the secrets of your broken heart and regurgitate them before your enemies. Hard Life was a pyaka, a cantankerous flying spirit who fed on the bitter seeds of the bad-mind tree, who lived only to fly about and broadcast to others that you mash up, mash up, mash up. Hard Life was a gravalitous grudgeful John Crow who kept pressing its black suit for the day when it would attend your funeral and give a eulogy which picked at your remains. A lamentation over poor you. Hard Life was a Cyclops whose cast-eye you had to blind with psalms in order to escape from the dark cave in which it wanted you trapped, and he would have trapped you were it not for your own strength and for the ties of blood, the generosity of some of your relatives, who as soon as they heard that you were now living hard life in Kingston, began to send you regular food baskets. Country baskets filled with ground provisions, yams, potatoes, vegetables, fruits, corned beef and pork, bottles of coconut oil, baked goods, peas, cassava, plantains. These baskets were the Jamaican equivalent of the manna fed to the Israelites by Yahweh as they wandered in the wilderness.

All over the city of Kingston, happiness and contentment would be generated in cramped tenements with the arrival of these baskets sent by friends and relatives in the country. Families would partake of generous oily-mouthed feasts, and children would be told stories about life in the villages where this food came from. Normally ill-tempered mothers, nerves frayed from hard life in town, fathers burdened by hard work or lack of employment, would become carefree children again as they enjoyed the sense of ease and plenty generated by the largesse of those back home in the country. "See this soursop here, it come from a tree that my grandfather plant and my navel string bury at the root." These food baskets were brought to Kingston on the backs of market trucks, or labelled and loaded onto the train and watched over by kind, considerate conductresses who knew they were doing a form of angel-work by delivering them. The conductresses knew how gratefully, eagerly, the people of Kingston greeted the arrival of the country baskets filled with fresh, life-sustaining things to eat. Our family began to receive regular baskets from Harvey River as soon as my mother's relatives found out that she was living in Kingston, and first thing that she would do when she opened one of them was to pass on some of the food to others who were even more in need.

～

First, you put something soft under my sister Betty's head, like a pillow or a rolled-up blanket to keep her from battering her head bloody, and then you try to force a spoon between her teeth to stop her from biting and swallowing her tongue. You should also try to put some salt in her mouth to stop her from foaming. The seizures take my sister with no warning. She will be walking along and in midstep it will be as if some great unseen beast has taken her in its jaws and is just shaking her to and fro. "I fell out of the car in Malvern when I was carrying her," my mother would say. "Your father was driving and as he turned a corner going into the town of Black River, the car door swung open, and I tumbled out of the passenger seat. I was young and strong, I just got up and said no harm done. But I was wrong."

My mother would dream of life in Harvey River on days when her child had as many as four seizures, the days when she saw unspeakable things at the Asylum. In her mind she would return to the place where everyone called her "dear Dor," where life in her father's house was so easy, where she never had to work hard, where she was one of the fabulous Harvey girls. They used to sew their own bathing costumes in Harvey River, short loose tunics or bloomers with loose-fitting camisole tops. She often envisaged herself in her favourite tunic of bright red cotton with tiny green and white blossoms. She would braid her hair into two long plaits that would become undone as she swam and her hair would stream out behind her. She and her sisters, gorgeous mermaids cavorting in the river named for their grandfather, were washed by the cool green water, the bowing bamboo screen around the river protecting their privacy. "Dive now, Doris." And she dived deep, feeling the water cover her completely. While she was under its smooth, cool surface, she took some of the hurts and disappointments life had dealt her that were written on what would have been bitter-tasting scrolls carried in her bosom, and lodged them in the eel holes and crayfish dwellings in the river. She never, ever again mentioned her troubles once she had lodged them there.

She loved being a wife, but she really, really was born to be a mother. She sometimes fed her children like mother birds do, passing food from her mouth to theirs. Like her mother, Margaret, she was known to put her own mouth to the tiny congested nostrils of any of her nine babies and pull mucus down to clear their heads. "A mammal is a warm-blooded animal that gives suck to its young." She had told this to her children as a fact, a piece of information she handed out from the great mine of facts she stored in her head.

"Mama, are you a mammal?" one of the children asked her. "Yes," she said laughing, "Doris is a mammal."

All the children in the yard seemed to know that Doris was a mammal because they were drawn naturally to her. They climbed the steps and stood outside the door, looking in at her seated at her sewing machine and called over and over, "Hello, Mama Goodie. Hello, Mama Goodie." All the children in the yard called her Mama Goodie. She fed them when their mothers, who did not like her, were not around. She called them sweet names like "precious" or nonsense names like "my little noonoonkum" and encouraged them to go to school. Even Vie's ill-cared-for son, Errol, adored my mother; she was always feeding him, making whatever food she had for her own children stretch.

Little by little, she put away the fabulous Doris. The one who was the clothes horse, the one with the beautiful hands who, along with her handsome husband and her lovely children, was going to run a fine guest house situated in salubrious Malvern, where she would direct the staff how to provide the best accommodation possible for guests as she changed her dresses to preside over every meal.

She put away the fabulous Doris who took such pride in her mahogany furniture, as gradually the chairs, tables, and the gramophone on the verandah were broken by the children, stolen by the tenants, or just destroyed from hard use. She watched as all her china was broken and her fine linen torn, stolen, or just worn out from wear. And apart from always keeping one or two damask or lace tablecloths to "pull shame out of her eyes," that is, to put on a small show if visitors came, she forgot what her sister Cleodine had taught her about running a perfect household and she never worried much about those things again.

She put away her dream to travel to Montreal to see and experience snow first-hand and dress up and go shopping with her fabulous sisters. She began to live in two places: as Mama Goodie the mammal in hard-life Kingston, and as the daughter of David and Margaret Harvey in her memories of Harvey River.

Eventually my sister Betty's seizures became so severe that my mother had no choice but to stay home, where she could care for her. It was then that she decided to make her living as a dressmaker; and for the next thirty years she would design and sew her extraordinarily well-made garments, charging very little money, to every and anybody who needed her services.

Funnily enough, the terrible Vie became one of her first customers. Soon after my mother made it known to some of the women in the yard who had become friendly to her that she was now taking in sewing, Vie announced that she had been invited to the wedding of one of her sisters in the country. She wanted, she said, to return to her birthplace in style, to "cut a dash." To make all the people – especially her sister who had predicted, no doubt with good reason, that Vie would come to no good – see how well she was doing in town. Well, who better to help her cut a dash than Doris? So Vie waited for my mother to come into the dark kitchen one morning, and there, before all the other women, she apologized for harassing her. And my mother accepted her apology, sewed her a fine dress, and everyone agreed that Vie never looked better in her life.

In the evenings, when she finished with her sewing, my mother liked to sit by the window in her rocking chair, watching for her husband, Marcus, to come walking down Orange Street. He moved like a young man, shoulders back, taking long, easy strides. Every time she saw him strolling down the street it was as if she was seeing him for the first time when he came up to her in her father's yard and said that he was thirsty, and since she was watering the plants, could she give him something to drink too? As she sat by the window waiting for her husband, she remembered how nobody loved to see an unusual sight more than her father, David, who had died in 1942, after years of being confined to bed. And she wished that he was still alive so she could have described to him some of the really strange people who passed right outside the front window of her house in Kingston.

Take Elephant, for example, the terrible giant with limbs thick and coarse as the trunk of the banyan tree, who, it was rumoured, made up his bed at night in the Mullings Grass Yard on Spanish Town Road, where hills of fire coal rose black before the Blue Mountains. The mules that pulled the dray carts of Kingston were tethered there too, and they were said to be his only friends. By day, Elephant was to be found under the big trees in Victoria Park. He had a kind of open-air office there, where he was in the business of beating up people for pay. For a shilling or two, Elephant and Tom Pram and other "Big Tree" men would smite your enemies, hip and thigh. One day, as Elephant was lumbering up the street with a pack of children running behind him calling out, "Elephant, Elephant," he turned around like a great, wounded pachyderm and threatened to cut out their insides with a broken bottle, and we all had to run home and take refuge under our beds. When she heard about this, Doris ordered her own children to gather around her as she sat at her sewing machine. When we were all assembled, she told a cautionary tale about the children who had teased the prophet Elisha. "Go up you bald head," the wicked children had chanted to the great prophet, and he had caused two great she-bears from the woods to tear apart forty-two of the teasing children. After that cautionary tale, some of us never teased Elephant again.

Elephant still had feelings, unlike Bag O' Wire, who just stared straight ahead and never, ever uttered a word. He looked like a stone man covered with tar and pitch, and like Elephant, he carried a rank, filthy burlap, or "crocus," bag over one shoulder that had earned him his nickname. Bag O' Wire was Jamaica's national traitor. Everyone knew that. He had been an official in Marcus Garvey's United Negro Improvement Association and he had betrayed the great leader. His present condition was seen by one and all as divine retribution for selling out Mr. Garvey.

Then there was Bun Down Cross Roads, who, unlike Bag O' Wire and Elephant, still rose each day, bathed, and dressed himself in clean clothes, but instead of going to work in his office in Cross Roads, he now sold fruits from a tray on his head. Arson. That is what Doris told her children that he had committed. He had burned down his business to collect the insurance. After he got out of prison, he was reduced to selling fruits, but he called out his wares with the confidence of one who was to the manor born. That is, until anyone teased him, and then he would curse enough forty-shilling badwords – words that you could be fined forty shillings for uttering – to stain the air around.

"Why the young men always tease me?" Mother Muschette, the poor damaged woman who stood dressed in her wedding gown outside the Kingston Parish Church and waited in vain for her groom, a younger man, to appear, always asked my mother that question. In between stays at the Asylum, "Madda" Muschette lived on the street, pulling away from any man who passed too close to her. My mother could not recall if she had seen her there when she worked briefly in the Asylum; but every time Madda walked past our window, with the groups of jeering boys chanting, "Madda Muschette, where is your husband, Madda Muschette?" she would look directly up at the window to see if Doris was seated there, and she would cry out her sad question to her. My mother would order the boys to get away and stop tormenting the unfortunate woman.

But she would have told her father, David, that of all the people who walked the streets of Kingston there was none more tragic than Pearl Harbour, the long-haired, willowy, fair-skinned fallen woman. Everybody knew Pearl's story, how she came from a wealthy near-white family of doctors and professional people but now led the life of a "sport" or a "harlot." Pearl was often either moderately drunk or stone-blind drunk, and she possessed a scorching vocabulary that she had no doubt picked up from doing business with sailors. She was a terrifying sight, this woman who had once been a great beauty, as she lurched through the streets of Kingston during the day in her stained and rumpled nighttime dresses. She looked like a moon-in-the-gutter or a flung-down star that had been bombarded with black ice. Everyone taunted her and sometimes she cursed them, saying how their mothers were whores too, or else she pretended that she did not care what they said. For after all, she was "a living dead," too drunk to care. Even child-abusers, hypocrites, murderers of body and spirit, and robbers of widows and orphans all felt they were better than she, that they were entitled to use her as a vessel for their venom and contempt. Poor Pearl Harbour. Such stories, there were such stories about Pearl Harbour. Like how she had got her name when she serviced an entire man-of-war ship. But one of Doris's customers, a hospital matron for whom she sewed uniforms, had told her another story about Pearl. The matron used to work with one of Pearl's doctor relatives, who told her that as an innocent young girl poor Pearl had fallen hopelessly in love with a handsome ginnal, a trickster, whom she had followed to wicked Kingston. She had opened her soulcase to him, and he had rummaged in it, sold the contents cheaply, and then discarded her. This act of betrayal had drawn her down to utter perdition. She was now a walking corpse. "Back to back, belly to belly, I don't care a damn, I done dead already." They could have written the words of this song, "Jumbie Jamboree," for her.

Then there was the German watchmaker, Mr. Gruber, whom all the children loved to stand and observe performing his meticulous tasks. Mr. Gruber was a man who did things with balletic grace and precision. A short-statured, sandy-haired man of few words, he would sit in his small shop with his magnifying glass screwed into his right eye, and wield the delicate tools of his watchmaker's trade. He never acknowledged the presence of the children who liked to stand outside the door of his shop, but every day he would put on a spectacular performance for them. At 4 p.m., Mr. Gruber would carefully lock and bolt the doors of his shop, then wheel his shining Rudge bicycle out onto the street. He'd position himself alongside the bicycle and begin to tap his feet on the black surface of the hot asphalt. Soon he'd be tapping faster and faster until he is running on the spot. Then he begins to push the bicycle forward and to run alongside it, picking up speed as he goes. Faster and faster runs Mr. Gruber and then, when you least expect it, he leaps straight up into the air, hovers like a hummingbird for a fraction of a moment, before he lands squarely on the bicycle seat. He then bends over and with his rump in the air and his head thrust forward pedals furiously up the street. By this time the children are all cheering, "Spring mount, Mr. Gruber, take a spring mount."

A few doors up from Mr. Gruber's was Mr. Mead the chemist. Whenever my mother sent one of the children to buy glycerin for earaches, or a black, foul-smelling sticky ointment that was excellent for reducing swelling, Mr. Mead would send them back with exact instructions as to the proper use of these medicines. "Remember to tell your mother to use one and a half drops of this, no more, no less. You only need to use enough ointment to cover the top of a sixpence, not a shilling, a sixpence." Mr. Mead ran the drugstore at the corner of Orange and Charles streets and he must have discovered the fountain of youth back there in the curtained-off room behind the store where he filled prescriptions, for he looked the same year after year, a tall, dark man who wore a fresh, white jacket every day. Next to Mr. Mead's dispensary was what everyone called "The Hat Shop." But Doris had told her children that the two sisters who fashioned standoffish, pastel buckram and silk flowers into Sunday hats for ladies were "milliners."

On the other side of the street was Smith's Garage, where Mr. Smith once hosted a very formal cocktail party. All sorts of elegantly dressed people rolled up in cars that he had no doubt repaired, and entered into the transformed interior of his workplace, now scrubbed clean and festooned with crepe-paper decorations. An invitation had come in the mail addressed to Mr. and Mrs. Vivian Marcus Goodison, and Marcus, giving no sign that he was still troubled by the loss of his own garage business, had put on his suit and looked very dapper. Doris, for the first time in a long time, had made herself a new dress, and together they had crossed the street and attended the cocktail party. When they came back she taught the children the phrase "hors d'oeuvres," and she gave them some devilled eggs which she had wrapped in a napkin.

As Doris sits by the window, she hears the calls of the vendors and the servicemen who go up and down Orange Street, each with their own unique song. The bottle man who would ask "aaaaaaaaaaaaany pint bakkle?" and the travelling soldering man — who was probably the Jamaican incarnation of Ogun, the West African god of iron, now coming to weld the holes in the pots and pans and chamber pots of transported Africans — announced his presence with a hissing "Sssawdereeen." The mango sellers had complex calls, because more often than not there would be two of them pushing a cart laden with luscious, ripe mangoes. One would sound the call and the other the response:

Mango
　　Hairy mango

Number eleven
  Mango
Governor
  Mango
Blackie
  Mango
Sweetie come brush me
  Mango
Ripe and green
  Mango.

Theirs was the most melodious of all street calls, the most
poetic, except for the call of the Arab dry-goods seller, who
would chant:

Attar of roses, attar of roses
good for your noses
Come to you from me and Moses.

Sweet and sour of breastmilk, Johnson's baby talcum
powder, and the faint vinegar of perspiration, that was my
mother's perfume. I remember one of her two long grey-and-
white plaits had come loose from the crown into which it was
pinned across her head, and was dangling down one side of her
smooth face that was the colour of a biscuit (till the day she
died she never had a wrinkle). I reached out and held on to the
escaped vine of her hair. In this early memory of my mother,
she was breast-feeding my baby brother as I sat pressed up
against her in the big cane seat rocking chair, so I must have
been about three years old. For what seemed like a long time,
there was only the rubbery sound of my baby brother sucking
hard on her left breast, then I felt her soft body shift in the

chair as she shifted him from one side to the other. Then the cry of the soldering man came hissing in through the window that faced the street: "Sssawdereeen."

⌒

The children are all asleep. As always Doris watches by the window for Marcus to come home. It is the rainy season, time of hurricanes, June too soon, July stand by, August look out you must, September remember, October all over. It is a rainy August night, and Marcus has not yet come home. He has been out putting up the telephone lines that have been torn down by the high winds and the heavy rains, so that important people can communicate with each other again. In those days most people did not have telephones in their homes. Sometimes at night she falls asleep before he comes home. Sometimes he comes in and wakes up her and the children to feed them ice cream. Royal Cremo's Neapolitan Brick ice cream, vanilla-cherry, and chocolate-striped ice cream. These sleepy late-night celebrations took place unexpectedly, for no particular reason except for the fact that Marcus, like Doris, always loved celebrations and rituals.

Then as always she hears his footsteps coming up the stairs, and when he appears in the darkened doorway he looks like the logo on the bottle of Spanish sherry that one of his friends gave him for Christmas, featuring a silhouette of a man in a wide-rimmed hat and a flowing cape. She feels great relief. Only after he takes off his hat and raincoat and galoshes does he look like Marcus. The mysterious black-cloaked, hatted figure has disappeared, and he says something like, "This is not a night for man nor beast to be outside." "I worry about you out there in Kingston at night," says my mother. "You worry too much," he says. "I promised your father that I would not make you worry." He had promised her that she would never have to worry, that they would have a nice life. "I have certain dreams and plans," he had told her when he was courting her. "I want to have my own garage business and I'd like me and my wife" — when he said the words *my wife*, he had looked meaningfully at her, then repeated the phrase — "me and my wife, to run a first-class guest house up in Malvern," and then he had asked her if she had ever been to Malvern. She said, no, she had been only to Montego Bay and Savanna la Mar, but that she never stopped hoping one day to go to Montreal to visit her sisters and see snow for herself.

*O*ne evening Marcus arrived home from work and came in the door saying, "I brought somebody to see you," and lo and behold it was her brother Edmund, whom my mother had not seen since he had run away from Harvey River before my mother met my father. "I saw this man standing with one foot on the running board of a taxi on East Queen Street, a man wearing a felt hat pushed to the back of his head, just like in that photograph on your bureau, and I said to myself, my god that must be Edmund Harvey. So I went up to him and said, 'Hi, brother-in-law.'" My mother can't quite believe her eyes that after all these years she has met up with her runaway brother. They can't stop hugging each other. She immediately offers him some dinner, and he says, "Thanks, just as long as there is no yam in that dinner."

Uncle Edmund pushed back his chair from the dining table and lit a Four Aces cigarette. He recommended to my mother an iron tonic that he says all taxi men are taking. Taxi men exchange information that is vital to their business. They are always concerned about their health because they work long hard hours. They read the newspaper every day because they have to have good conversation with the passengers, especially tourists, who always have an endless list of questions to ask the taxi driver. "It's as if when they take your taxi they expect you to be the Minister of Information," said Edmund. "And although you don't want to be telling them any foolishness, then again, you can't tell them everything, especially when it comes to Jamaican politics. So when one of those tourist ask you something like, 'So don't you think that Jamaicans are lucky to be governed by England and have a Parliament and a British Governor,' you just say Oh yes and drop off the damn idiot at the Myrtle Bank Hotel and take the tip that he give you.

"'You are one smart Jamaican fellow, don't listen to all this crazy talk about Independence.'

"'You are right boss,' said the taxi man.

"I just make him go on none the wiser that I don't care a blast about England and Missus Queen and that I agree with Norman Manley that Jamaica should be an independent country," says Edmund.

"Taxi man have to know what is what," he tells my mother. "Taxi man have to know every bar and brothel in Kingston, every bank, government building, theatre, night club, statue, and monument. Taxi man have to know how to give the tourists what they want, and that is why I always said taxi man don't make good husband. We are always on the move. Morant Bay one day, Montego Bay by the same night, Port Royal next morning. Taxi man mostly live alone, we live cowboy life, so taxi man stay." Edmund draws hard on his Four Aces cigarette.

"So you going home to rest now, Edmund?"

"No sir, the night is young, I am going to catch a midnight show out at Majestic Theatre. Doris, you brother is a real Kingstonian."

After that, Uncle Edmund came to visit at least once a week and he was always telling stories to illustrate why Kingston was a more exciting place than Harvey River, where he swore he would never return, neither in life nor death. Kingston to him was the place where the most fantastic and fascinating things happened. Take, for example, the story of the old man in the yard where he lived, an old man called Tata, who had a bosun growing inside his pants, a swollen giant testicle the size of a yellow heart breadfruit. You could see the shape of it when he walked his rolling off-centre walk. Everybody said he should get it cut, but he believed that if they cut it, he would surely die. All the boys in the area claimed to have seen this terrible thing that grew underneath the old man's trousers. They gathered in packs and stormed the toilet when Tata used it. They peeped under the door, and the old man became hysterical. He threatened to kill them for their insolent out-of-order behaviour, their outrageous lack of respect for an old man. It was a kind of rite of passage. The boys would not be men until they had seen Tata's bosun, until they had stared at this awful, unnatural ball, and had walked away still seeing, not struck blind or dead. "The other day they give him one whole bottle of white rum to drink," says Edmund, "and two grandsons lift him up and carry him down to public hospital. The doctors gave him gas and cut off the bosun. They said it is the biggest one anybody ever see in Jamaica, maybe in the whole world, and them send it gone to England for the doctors over there to examine it."

My mother had a story of her own for her brother, one to illustrate how bad people from Kingston could be. She told him of a situation right there in the yard next door to where we were living, which had to do with a young woman named Lizzie who had come from the country to help her sister Bernice after Bernice had had three babies in two years and ten months. Lizzie looked like a baby duck, a dill-dill, because she had big wide lips and wicked bandy legs; and she spoke so badly that everybody laughed at her. She would say "guddung" instead of "go down" and "gittup" for "get up" and "tandey" for "stay there," and she called her sister "Sta Bernice." All the other women in the yard she addressed as "ma'am" . . . yes ma'am, no ma'am. Lizzie was always working. She washed line upon line of birdseye nappies gleaming white. She made "tie-leaf" or "blue-drawers," delicious portions of grated sweet potato, dark sugar, and coconut milk, spiced with nutmeg then wrapped in banana-leaf parcels and steamed. Lizzie cooked a fine mackerel rundown, flaked salted mackerel cooked in a spicy, savoury lick-you-finger coconut custard, causing Mr. Vincent, Bernice's husband, to joke that Lizzie was such a good cook that he should have married her instead of her sister. After a time, Lizzie stopped calling the other women "ma'am" so much. She also began to grumble, saying that her sister could help herself a little more instead of just lying down all day and complaining about how weak she felt.

Then one day Bernice said that she was going to the country to see about herself because she couldn't understand how she still felt so weak even after she got so much rest. She knew a man in the country who would give her a good bush bath and a read-up. She left Lizzie in charge while she was gone. Lizzie said that she heard from the country that the obeah man said that Bernice's case was a hard one. That somebody was working hard to keep her down because the obeah man said he kept getting a vision of somebody driving two long ten-penny nails into Bernice's right calf. "When Bernice came back from the country, nobody in the yard want to face her," said Doris, "because if the obeah man did not tell her that Lizzie and Mr. Vincent were now along with each other right out, then Bernice lose all around. But Vincent tell her himself. Tell her openly that Lizzie was a better woman than her any day and advise her to go back to the obeah man in the country. Bernice leave that same evening, but she come back the next morning when Vincent gone to work, and beat Lizzie till she soft. I guess she rest enough, and she was not feeling so weak any more."

"Edmund, you better take care, you hear. Kingston is not an easy place," said my mother, "a place where it is not easy to raise up yourself if you fall."

~

My mother found out first-hand that it is sometimes hard to raise yourself up because God knows there are always people who are eager to see you stay down. Like her oldest sister who hadn't come to visit her because she was not sure that her chairs were good enough. When she finally did come to see her, she came in a dream, shaking her head, saying, "Poor unfortunate you, you have no luck." This was Cleodine's greeting to her from the gateway of the Harvey home because in the dream my mother has been forced to return to her parents' house with all her children. "Poor unfortunate you," she repeats, but that is just the warm part of her greeting. "My dear, you are like a pipe, everybody just comes, turns you on and uses you and then walks off and leaves you," says Cleodine as she strides up the stone path leading to the Harvey house. Even the flowers in the yard seem to fold in on themselves as they hear these words. The bold-faced hibiscus shrink their red-and-gold petals and roll themselves into tubes, displaying only their pale undersides. The loud chirping cling-cling and grass-quit birds abruptly shut up, and a flurry of April butterflies who were flightily making the most of their short lives settle nervously on branches. Cleodine must have risen before dawn to put herself together for this visitation. She was wearing a gorgeous silk dress of cocoa brown, awash with gold-and-orange blossoms. Her dark brown leather pumps had been polished and shined by the yardboy, her brown leather handbag with its shining clasp looked positively plump with prosperity, her hair was styled in an upsweep, and her gold-rimmed glasses gleamed on her straight nose bridge. She decided against wearing a hat but carried instead an umbrella trimmed with ochre lace held high above her head.

Even in a dream it is hard to recover from somebody likening you to a standpipe. It is harder to gather yourself when they quickly repeat it. "Just like a pipe, everybody just come, use you and then walk away, you meet it my dear, you really meet it." And my mother wants to ask her what is this "it" that she has met and to remind Cleodine that she herself has met her "it." But she is doubled over by that lethal repeat, that vicious one-two jab.

But if Cleodine came to her in dreams to liken her to a standpipe, others came too, and for the rest of her life my mother lived by these visitations.

At first Doris had thought that it was the clip-clop of the breadman or the milkman's horse coming down Orange Street in the before-day morning. She thought to herself that maybe she should struggle up out of sleep, get out of bed, and wake one of the boys to go out into the street and buy fresh milk or a warm harddough bread. But the sound of the hooves kept coming, right up to the gate and then she heard them inside the yard. The hoofbeats then sounded as if they were climbing all the way up the steps and into the room and then she saw her grandmother Leanna sitting astride her grey mule right next to her bed, her long necklaces of silver coins soldered together, tinkling like bells. Just like she did when she was a young girl, Doris jumped onto the back of the mule and Leanna guided it out of the room, down the steps into the brick-paved court-yard, where all the tenants were standing looking in amazement at the tall flanked grey mule ridden by the jet-black old woman in a dress the colour of laundry blue, her silver money jewellery shining in early light.

Doris clung to her grandmother's waist, pressing her cheek to the woman's bony back, inhaling her strong body scent of cinnamon and escallions. She closed her eyes and time slowed down so that the short ride across the courtyard felt as if they were riding forever over the green pastures of Hanover and Westmoreland. As they rode, the guinea grass soaked with dew water flashed and bathed the soles of their feet and the night-blooming jasmine sprayed their faces with her last ounce of essence before closing her white vials. The early morning air carried the potential sweetness of green sugar cane before it hardened into iron stalks at the sun's urging, stalks so hard that a man could break his back trying to cut them down. They rode past men and women asleep in small huts and long barracks-type dwellings. This was the grace hour when they existed in dreams as ordinary men and women, free to lie down or get up whenever they wanted. This was the hour before they rose to meet cane. To seed and weed, to cut and harvest it. The hour before some would run away or stay and undermine it, withdraw their enthusiasm from it, throw words and sing bantering songs, and meet in secret at night to plot bloody overthrow of it. They rode past the time, before cane, when Jamaican people planted mainly corn and cassava, hunted wild boar and coneys, and went to sea in magnificent boats they had fashioned from trees; when their artists made sacred wood carvings that would survive for hundreds of years; when their scientists discovered how to extract poison from the roots of cassava; when they played an early form of soccer and lived mostly in peace, till three leaking ships filled with lost men came towards them bearing Hard Life.

Doris and her grandmother rode past all the amazed tenants straight into the kitchen where Leanna dismounted and used her riding crop to clear away a space for her grand-daughter's stove on the firewall. "Patience, you are going to have to study patience and take what you get till you get what you want," she had said, and then she had mounted her mule and ridden away, clearing the gate effortlessly. But not before she removed one of her money necklaces and draped it around my mother's neck. "Control the silver," she'd said. "You will never get any big money in this life. Massa will always hold that, so learn to control the silver."

Doris always said that it was after her grandmother Leanna came and made a space for her on the firewall that the women in the yard all started to befriend her.

"Doris, Doris, take off thy shoes from off thy feet, for the ground which thou standest on is not holy ground but hard work ground." Nana Frances Duhaney had come one night and told her that, paraphrasing the words of Yahweh to Moses. She had bent down and removed Doris's soft pumps from her feet because Doris, in a determined effort not to let herself go, had been wearing her leather pumps around the house like her sister Cleodine. Nana Frances had come, bent down, taken the shoes off her feet, and told her that the only way that she was going to be able to manage all the hard work she would now have to do to raise nine children was to go barefoot around the house. She told her to uncover her feet in order to draw up strong energy through the wooden floorboards and through the metal pedal of the sewing machine.

"You don't have to go to school today," Doris would say to one of the children or "be very careful how you play with such and such a child," or "give me that slingshot, somebody could lose an eye today." Her own mother, Margaret, had come the night before, serious and unsmiling. Invariably she came only when she had to warn her about some possible danger to one of the children.

Doris's father, David, had appeared, fully dressed except for his shirt, and stood right there in the yard, under the beheaded breadfruit tree, and had said to her: "Remember your confirmation promise, my daughter, don't forget your promise that was given you from Isaiah 43: Fear not for I have redeemed thee, I have called thee by name, thou art mine, when thou passest through the waters I will be with thee, and through the rivers they shall not overwhelm thee, when thou walkest through the fire thou shall not be burnt." And then he had turned to go, but before he left, he looked over at the men playing the seemingly unending game of dominoes and said, "How is this different from what rich men do up at the Liguanea Club, where black people can only pass through those gates as maids and waiters? This is a poor man social club," and then he pointed to the old white-haired man who seemed to be in charge of the ongoing domino game, and whom my mother heard everyone call Papacita. David said, "You see Papacita there, he worked more than ten strong men when he was young, cutting cane all over Jamaica, and then he spent years more in Cuba cutting hectares and hectares of cane. Nobody in the history of the world ever cut as much cane as Papacita. Let him play domino now, God knows he shouldn't do any more hard work." And David goes through the gate saying, "These people are no better or no worse than people anywhere, anything that you can do to help them, help them and you will be surprised to know how they will help you."

For weeks Doris puzzled over what exactly her grandmother Leanna had meant when she advised her to "control the silver." One Saturday she was buying food in the Redemption Ground Market and she found herself telling an old woman, from whom she was buying escallion, about the dream of her grandmother riding into the yard to see her. And the woman explained to her that there was a time in the history of Jamaica when all the silver coinage on the island had found its way into the hands of enslaved men and women, enterprising Africans who cultivated their food plots and sold their produce in the Sunday markets around the island. "Them had was to send away a England go make more silver money," the woman had said. She also said that many Jamaicans had bought their freedom and their own land by saving these small sums of silver money and that her great-grandmother had been one such Jamaican.

Of course George O'Brian Wilson had appeared to her from her earliest days in Kingston, and she always maintained that it was he who had instructed her to slap Vie. Whenever the Irishman appeared to her, she would wake up in a no-nonsense mood and woe betide the man, woman, or child who crossed her that day. "Take your damn cloth and go if you can't wait for me to finish sewing it," she would say to an impatient customer. And like her mother, she would remind any of her children in no uncertain terms, "No child of mine will ever rule me." It was a foolish, foolish child who would challenge that statement.

One of the women in the yard came to Doris and said, "I wake up this morning and drop and break my eyeglasses, Miss

Goodie, you think that you could just read this letter for me that my son write me from England?" Of course the letter needed a reply and her glasses still had not been fixed, so my mother wrote a reply. And so it went, with both women agreeing to blame the woman's illiteracy on her broken glasses. The woman began to do small favours for my mother, like buying food at the market for her and taking her clothes off the wash line, and she never did get her glasses fixed. Once it was known that my mother would read letters and never, ever mention the contents to others, and write replies to letters, again without mentioning the contents, and fill out forms and write letters of recommendation and give good advice, more and more people in the yard began to stand outside the door saying, "Hello Miss Goodie, I have a little favour to ask you." When their children came and stood outside the door and called to her, she began to invite them in and taught them what she taught her own children. Soon, even Vie's son knew that a T was like a telephone pole, and a G was like a water goblet that would pour forth fresh water if you tilted it.

I was seven years old when I first saw the place that had produced my mother's people and which was to shape my imagination for the rest of my life. In July 1954, I joined the great exodus of Kingston children sent to visit with relatives in the country during the summer holidays. I remember being wedged in the back seat of a small, black Morris Minor motor car with three adults all related to my mother and going on the longest journey of my life up till that point – fourteen hours from Kingston to the parish of Hanover. Stops were made along the way: for gas; for me to be sick; to put water in the radiator; for us to pee in the bushes; to fix flat tires; for them to wrap my chest in newspaper to seal my motion sickness; for food and drink, including a mandatory fish and bammy stop at Old Harbour. We finally got to the town of Lucea in the parish of Hanover late at night, and I slept at the home of my mother's cousin, whose name was Tamar. "Palm tree," my mother said, that was the meaning of her name. Tamar had four children, Wesley, Vivian, Joyce, and Lyn, but she still looked like a young girl. She was not tall and slender like a palm tree, she was short and neat-looking, dressed as she was when I saw her for the first time in a pink floral dress. I guess she was more like a flowering shrub.

Later that next day I was taken by car to the village of Harvey River, five miles from Lucea. Harvey River is set in the interior of Hanover, under the Dolphin Head Mountains. My mother's family home was a large wood-and-stone house set right off the village square. As we approached, I noticed that there was a beautiful flower garden flourishing in the front yard. The house was occupied by Aunt Ann and her children, Myrna, Colin, and Joan, now that David and Margaret Harvey were dead.

It was not a manicured yard like the gardens that I had seen in the suburbs of St. Andrew when my father took us on Sunday afternoons for drives from where we lived on Orange Street in downtown Kingston. This garden was thick with pink June roses and oleanders and red flowering hibiscus, and foaming white "rice and peas" bushes that stretched out and brushed against you when you walked up the short stone-paved path to the front door. I did not know the names of flowers then, but the first one I learned was "jasmine," the tiny starry white flowers which proceeded to perfume the evening with a lovely scent that was activated once it grew dark. Also, there was a large field of white lilies that grew behind the house, giving off a honey-and-spice perfume so fragrant that clothes which were hung on the wash line came in dry and sweet-smelling. When night fell and nobody made a move to turn on the lights, I became anxious. Tamar's house in Lucea, where I'd slept the night before, had electric lights, so I thought that all of Hanover was similarly lit. Instead, my Aunt Ann called her son, Colin, to bring the lamps. Several fat-bellied, glass-shaded kerosene oil lamps with the words Home Sweet Home picked out in white script between two lacy borders were brought. They were the source of light for the entire house. The lamps threw up tall, macabre shadows on the walls of the house that

I had imagined as a fairy-tale dwelling in the golden afternoon light. Now this same enchanted house seemed sinister and frightening, and I suddenly wanted to go home, back to Kingston, where there was no such garden but where there were bright electric lights. I started to cry softly, then I began to cry loudly, then I added a refrain to my crying. I want to go home, I want to go home. My aunt never said a word. She just told my three cousins to go to bed and leave us alone.

She let me weep for what seemed like a long time. Even when I drooled all over the front of my good pink-and-white dress, she said nothing to me. We just sat there at the dining-room table — she, who looked like a woman in a Gauguin painting, and I, a younger version of her, sat in the gathering darkness with the Home Sweet Home lamp casting a water-wash yellow light between us, arranged in a composition that could have been painted on velvet and titled "Crying for the Light." She said nothing, she just let me cry. When I sobbed myself into silence, she lifted me up and put me into bed with my cousin Joan, where I fell asleep at once. Early next morning Joan shook me awake, saying that it was time for us to have our morning bath in the river. For the first time I saw the river that was named for my mother's people. Then, it seemed like a huge wide green sea with the cleanest swift-moving water. My cousins could swim, they just ran down the riverbank and leapt into the water. And I jumped right in after them; but because I could not swim, I nearly drowned. So I quickly learned to stay in the shallows and watch them swim the river, bank to bank. But I was so happy. I felt somehow that I would never come to any harm as long as I was immersed in that water named for my family. I felt that I should allow the currents to sweep me along and whenever I sensed that I was out too deep, I would just wade back to where my feet could touch ground. When my cousins were ready to leave, I did not want to get out of the water. They laughed and said, "Think it's you wanted to go back to Kingston last night!"

For breakfast Aunt Ann had given us big mugs of chocolate tea with coconut milk. The chocolate was made from the cacao trees in Grandfather David's cacao walk. Rich, dark-brown like sweet mud, the chocolate fat floated on top, painting an oily moustache on your upper lip every time you put the mug to your mouth. There were hot toasted cassava bammies spread with yellow salt butter – cocoa like rich wine, and bammy like fresh host, a pure country communion after my river baptism. After breakfast, I joined the band of village children roaming all over the countryside, stoning fruit trees and eating fruit in various stages of fitness. Green common mangoes that you sliced and ate with salt (you always walked with some salt twisted in a piece of brown paper for just this reason), ripe common mangoes with names like blackie, stringy, number eleven, and beefy, and sometimes even good mangoes like Hayden, Bombay, and Julie, which were mostly cultivated in people's yards and did not grow wild in the bush. Common mangoes grew in the bush, and you ate as many of them as you wished, until you got a running belly, which would mean a visit to the pit latrine, which I dreaded as much as I did the lack of electric lights.

That summer I tasted fruit I had never eaten before. Small tart green jimbelins, fragrant rose apples that grew by the river, pods of musky stinking toe and slick mackafat. We heard stories, such stories. Under the shadow of the Dolphin Head Mountains is a cave. They said that there used to be a young man in a nearby village who disappeared one day as he walked home from school. The villagers searched for him for days and had almost given him up for dead when someone who had gone to gather firewood found him sleeping near the mouth of the cave. The story he told was that he had been walking home from school when he heard what sounded like singing coming from inside the cave. He went deep inside, following the sound of the singing, and there he found a pool, so he drank some water from it and promptly fell asleep. He was not sure whether he was awake or dreaming, when he sensed that the cave was filled with people in bright robes. They told him that the water in the pool was really palm wine. They sung to him and told him they were sorry because they had helped to sell his ancestors to the slave traders. They said that they wished to repay him for the terrible wrong they had done, and this is how they would make amends to him. From henceforward he would be very lucky: they said he was never to answer to the name Cyril again and that he was to insist from now on that everyone call him Lucky. After that the boy really became very lucky. He won every bingo and raffle held at church and school functions and he bought one cow from which he got seven calves. He went to Montego Bay and some tourists took a liking to him and sent for him to come and live with them in England. He went to London and, years later, married one of the Queen's relatives. All the children in the village kept going to the cave in the hope that they would see the apologizing Africans again, for all of them wanted to have Lucky's good fortune to travel and be loved by a relative of the Queen.

There was also a house there which they said was haunted. They said that a very wicked woman used to live there. She was an obeah woman and she had harmed a lot of people. Wicked, vengeful people would pay her money to do bad things to their enemies and to innocent people whom they wanted to "keep down." Before she died she asked that she be buried with her face turned down to the ground as she was too ashamed to meet the gaze of her Maker on Judgment Day. We were advised to run by that house while chanting the Lord's Prayer for protection, throwing pebbles behind us.

About noon we would return home for lunch, where we roasted breadfruits and big pieces of salted codfish over a wood fire. Then we would mix big mugs of "lemonade," made with sour Seville oranges, sugar, and water. We ate al fresco, sitting without shoes on the tombstones of the dead Harveys. At first I was frightened by this, but all my cousins did it. And my cousin Joan, who had been very close to our grandmother Margaret, convinced me that it was all right. She had played in the family plot for a long time and no harm had ever befallen her. It was true. She was very beautiful, slim, and graceful, so one day I sat beside her on our grandparents' tombstones; and though like any Kingston-born child I was frightened of duppies, after I sat there a while and nothing happened I became quite used to going to the family plot and sitting on the tombstones of all my Harvey relatives.

Soon after I returned to Kingston, we moved to no. 30 Studley Park Road, a move made possible by the fact that my two eldest siblings, Barbara and Howard, were now working and contributing to our family's finances. Barbara was at the Gleaner Company, where she would eventually become the editor of the evening newspaper, and my brother Howard went to work at the Jamaica Telephone Company. Everyone in our family was happy because, except for a nurse and her sister who shared the apartment downstairs, we were the only other occupants of our new home, which had three large bedrooms, a wide living and dining room, and a long enclosed verandah. The house was situated almost opposite the gates of All Saints Government School, which my brothers Kingsley, Karl, Keith, Nigel, and I attended. Even if it was not the prettiest of houses, no. 30 Studley Park Road provided the answer to our family's prayers, for there we had our very own kitchen, bathroom, and toilets. And there was the sewing room.

I took to sitting in the sewing room although I had no real interest in sewing, assuming as I did then that my mother would always be alive to make me fabulous dresses, and asking questions of my mother about the Harveys, those who were living and those who were buried under the stones on which my cousins and I used to sit.

*W*hen you came up the long flight of stairs which led up from the yard, you stepped into the living and dining room where a massive wooden table with turned legs occupied a good one third of the room's space. The table is where we ate all our meals, the older children seated on a variety of chairs, the younger ones on a long wooden bench. If you passed the table and turned left, you'd enter the room which was my mother's domain, the sewing room. It was here that the women for whom she made dresses sat and discussed "big woman business" as they waited for my mother to fit or finish their garments. This was also the room where my mother taught neighbourhood girls to sew, free of charge, so that they could as she always said "earn a bread and be independent." This large room had a high ceiling and one window which looked out onto the street. Under the window was my favourite seat, a huge brass-tipped trunk that was used to store fabric. It was one of the few things left over from my parents' earlier life. Two beds, three or four chairs for the women to sit on, and my mother's Singer sewing machine completed the furnishings.

My mother always sat with her back to the door, so that the light from the south fell across the cloth she was sewing. Sometimes for as much as seven hours a day, every day except

Sunday, she could be found in that room, her long bare feet tilting at the wide wrought-iron pedal, her right hand spinning the wooden handle, bobbin, shuttle, presserfoot, many miles of fabric passing under her hands, arriving as cloth and leaving as fine garments. She sometimes ran the sewing machine like a racing car driver, bending her head way down, her long grey-and-white plaits curled around her face like slow smoke.

There is a constant stream of people, mostly women, coming through the sewing room to see her. They are not all customers, some come to ask her to read or write letters, to ask her advice, for her help, her opinion. She mediates in disputes too, sometimes saying, "A soft answer turneth away wrath" but at other times: "Don't allow people to take any liberty with you."

That is what she must have told the woman whom she helped to run away from my father's friend Beadle, because one day, just like in those blues songs my father, Marcus, loves, Beadle woke up and found his woman gone. "Gone, Mrs. Goodison," he comes to the sewing room to tell my mother. "The woman pack up and gone." The sight of a grown man who has only recently moved to Kingston from Malvern, St. Elizabeth, openly crying like a baby renders all the women speechless. Even the flint-hearted Miss Mirry, our helper, who always had a bitter proverb to suit any occasion, is silent as everyone stares at the man whose workman's khaki uniform makes him look like a whipped schoolboy. Strangely enough, Doris, who is usually so sympathetic, says only, "This is all very unfortunate."

"Whatever happens between you and your husband is nobody else's business, except if he is ill-treating you, and God knows that wretch was ill-treating that poor woman," says my mother after Beadle has left. "Of course she is gone. I packed her suitcase for her early this morning, and I call my brother Edmund to come in his taxi and take her to the wharf. That ship has sailed by now."

She roughly turns the handle of the sewing machine and pumps furiously for a few minutes. Everyone in the room rides the waves of her indignation as my mother drives the sewing machine forward. Suddenly she stops. "He treats her like a dog. All his money goes to the rum bar, and when she has her period he orders her to sleep on the floor as if he was not born of woman. I am glad that I helped her to escape."

The other women are silent, gazing in admiration at her. They have never seen this freedom-fighter side of her before, the fearless Doris who has just a few hours before helped to spirit away a battered woman to safety. Then a slender pale-skinned woman who chain-smokes, wears matching red lipstick and nail polish, and speaks with an American accent says: "I was with a man like that once. I met him on the fourth of July at a picnic when I lived in Georgia, and talk about a hot love! I believed I'd die if I didn't marry him . . ." and here she switches into Jamaican patois, "but see me, and come live with me" – and, as if in a chorus, all the other women finish the proverb with her – "is two different things."

"Every time he beat me, he sent me flowers, or perfume, as if he was trying to cover up his stinking behaviour. Every time he black-up my eye, he would swear up and down how he would never hit me again. Till the next time." And then she suddenly stood and lifted up her dress to reveal a deep keloid scar running down her right thigh. The women make loud sympathetic noises and glance quickly away from the horrible sight. The woman from Georgia lets her skirt hem fall and then turns around and picks up her cigarette, which she had care-fully rested on the windowsill before she stood up. When she lifts the cigarette to her lips to take a deep draw of tobacco and menthol, her hand shakes and so does her voice.

"I knew I had to leave the son-of-a-bitch after he did that. So you know what I did? I got my sister to send me a telegram from Jamaica to say, 'Come quick, Mother is dying.' I bawled non-stop for two days until he said that he, *he* was giving me permission to come to Jamaica but only for two weeks. Well, I bid him one tender farewell at the airport, and I never went back. I left a house full of clothes, jewellery, and furniture, but what use would they be to me if I'd let him kill me?"

"I could never stand up and make a man just beat me so, me and him would haffi fight, after him not me father or me mother," says Betsy, who is jet-black and has a wonderful open face. Her gums are dark, almost purple, and she has perfect white teeth. Betsy is also almost six feet tall.

The woman from Georgia now has tears in her eyes. She blows a long stream of cigarette smoke through the window.

"When you talk bout beating, my grandmother give me one terrible beating with a tamarind switch the first time I see my period," says Edith, a cheerful young girl whom my mother was trying to teach to sew — without much success she'd often say — because Edith's world really revolved around blues dances. She lived for Saturday nights when she would boogie till dawn in various dance halls, dressed in tight blouses and wide swing skirts cinched tight at the waist with a broad belt that showed off her eighteen-inch waistline. Edith was always happily singing the latest Fats Domino song under her breath as she hemmed a dress or serged a seam but today she laughs a harsh, embarrassed laugh when she says, "She say she beat me fi warn me fi no get pregnant."

"Damn old-fashioned behind times foolishness," says the lady from Georgia. "After all, it's a natural thing that God made to happen to women." Then she snorts and says, "All the same, God seemed to save some of the worst things for women."

"Mind you fly in God face," says Betsy, who was sitting on the floor near my mother's feet. Betsy is a "Mother," a spiritual leader in a revival group. Doris sometimes sews the cobalt blue robes that Betsy wears when she preaches, all full of the spirit, on the street corner.

I was sitting on a chair in a corner where my mother could not see me. I was willing myself to be invisible, praying that everyone would forget that I was in the room and just keep talking so I could hear, so I could learn about big woman business. On other occasions, if the conversation was becoming too grown up, my mother would say, "just stick a pin right there" to whoever was speaking, and then she'd turn to me and say, "leave, this is not for a little girl's ears." But today she says nothing to me, so I just keep still, glad to be in on big woman business.

"You know, when I see my health," says Betsy, "my grandfather call everybody in the house and tell them that they were not to treat me like a child any more, for now I could be a mother; and him shake my hand and give me five shillings and tell me to buy anything I want with it because I was now a big young lady!"

I remember that day when at age ten I was part of the big woman group, how everybody in the sewing room nodded their approval when Betsy told that story, because it seemed like the proper thing to have done.

"You can learn a lot from old people," said Edith. "Is a old lady name Edna who always tell me that when things bad with you, when you broke and down-hearted is when you must dress up in you best clothes, for is better you make people envy you and grudge you than make them feel sorry for you."

That was the signal for everyone to contribute their own words for the big woman to live by.

Doris: "My mother, Margaret, tell me, Rose, Miss Jo, Cleodine, and Ann that a woman must always at all times have a good nightgown and a good clean panty put aside in case she have to go to the hospital."

Edith: "My grandmother tell me I must always keep at least one good woman friend who I can trust, who I can tell anything to and who won't turn round and disgrace me."

Betsy: "For there is nothing worse than when you friend chat out you private business; even when the friendship done, you mustn't chat out you friend private business. You see me Betsy, if you tell me a secret, me carry it to the grave, for the Bible say that if you betray you friend secret, that friendship can never in life ever fix again."

Doris: "That is true, it's like when a man stop love you; reconcile yourself to it. Know that it finish and done with, and never you force up on him, for the more you try and make him love you, the more he will hate you."

Betsy: "But some woman will do anything to make a man stay with them, you know. You see that American woman Miss Simpson? Me understand say is some a her pum-pum hair she cut and parch and sprinkle like black pepper over King Edward food and that is why him left the throne of England and married to her."

The woman from Georgia laughed so hard when Betsy said that, that she choked; and Edith, who was laughing till tears ran down her face, had to slap her on the back.

My mother frowned and glanced in my direction. Her look said, "you did not hear that." Then in order to bring the conversation back from the edge of the pit where Betsy's inside dish on poor Wallis Simpson had taken things, she told a story about her sister Ann to illustrate why a big woman had to be wise in order to protect herself in the world.

"When my sister Ann got married and went to live in Montego Bay, she had a lovely friend, a Mrs. Doris Melbourne, who lived next door. Well, my sister Ann's husband was not the best provider, and so when Ann get any money from her sewing she just give it to Mrs. Melbourne – who was separated from her husband – so that she could prepare meals for both families. When dinner was ready, Mrs. Melbourne made her daughter Elaine come to the fence and say to Ann, 'My mother is inviting you and the children to have dinner with us.' And Ann just take her children and go next door and have a lovely meal with her friend. When her husband come in late, asking, 'Where is my dinner?' Ann just say, 'There is no dinner because you never gave me any money to buy anything.'"

"Lord that one good," says Edith.

Then, my mother did something she had never done before, she turned in my direction and included me in the big woman circle. "You see Lorna, there? Up to yesterday I send her to go and help Mrs. Percy with something that will prevent her from going to the poorhouse one day."

I remembered that the day before my mother had answered the telephone and when she hung it up she said, "Go to Mrs. Percy and she will give you something." I liked going to Mrs. Percy's, which was above the grocery and bar run by her and her husband, for there was usually a quadrille group practising in the paved area beside the bar. I loved to see the dance – which I later learned had originated in the courts of Europe – being performed by neighbourhood people like the tall, elegant man known as Cubana and the local hearse driver the children called Bald-head Morty. When Mrs. Percy saw me she'd said: "Oh, your mother send you for the cloth to make my dress. Excuse me, Mr. Percy (she always called him Mr.), I'm just going upstairs to get some cloth to give to Mrs. Goodison."

Her husband just turned and scowled at her without saying a word. We went to their rooms above the shop, and she pulled out a drawer and took out a length of cloth. Then she reached into her bosom and extracted some well-creased pound notes, which she then folded into the fabric. She'd put the cloth in a bag marked "The Buzzer," the name of a store on King Street, and she'd handed it to me. I now knew the reason.

"Poor woman," said my mother, "she married to this man and work her fingers to the bone for him. By accident one day she find him will, only to discover that the man intend to leave everything to the children by him first wife. Well, from she find out that she is not in his will, she been taking money out the till and sending it to me to keep for her. Once a week she come here and collect the money and bank it. Imagine the poor woman have to be stealing out her own money because under the law a married woman have no rights."

"That is not thief, Miss Goodie. That is take, the woman taking what belong to her by right," says Edith.

There is silence in the sewing room after that story. I sit in my corner feeling very grown up to have been included in the big woman business for that day. I look over in my mother's direction in time to see her switch on the tiny light above the presserfoot of the sewing machine just before she finishes stitching the seven-inch zip into the placket of the hobble skirt.

"Oh, look at the time," says the Georgia lady.

"Here is your skirt, my dear, give it a good press before you wear it."

"You see me here swapping laugh for peas soup; I have to go get ready for church tonight," says Betsy, "so when I must come back to fit my dress, Miss Goodie?"

"Tomorrow midday," says my mother, "come and get some dinner and I will fit your dress afterwards."

"All right everybody, God bless and keep you till I see you tomorrow if life spare," says Betsy.

"Wait for me and I will walk with you to the bus stop," says the lady from Georgia as she folds her hobble skirt into a shopping bag marked "Nathan's Department Store."

"You can go now, Edith," says my mother, "try and come early tomorrow." And with those words my mother rises from her sewing machine and closes the room for the day.

"How you put up with Miss Mirry?" Everyone asked my mother that question. Miss Mirry had come to work with our family as a domestic helper shortly after my father started working two jobs, one installing telephones at the Jamaica Telephone Company, and the other, which he did on week-ends, as a driver to a doctor. She moved with the family from Orange Street to Studley Park Road and stayed with us for almost fifteen years until she walked off kissing her teeth one day and never came back. Miss Mirry was a short, stout, very dark-skinned woman who always wore a head-tie because her hair was grey and she did not like to look old. She had a face that seemed to be frozen in a permanent "kiss-teeth," so that her lips were twisted to one side, and her eyes squinched up. She had a large straight nose and sometimes she smoked cigarettes by turning the lit end inside her mouth.

Miss Mirry hated everybody, including the woman who came once a week on Fridays to iron our clothes because my mother said Miss Mirry needed help. Still Miss Mirry hated the woman and spent every Friday throwing words about "people who come to box bread outta other people mouth."

And there was Mrs. Hinsula. Only my mother seemed to feel any sympathy for the woman she once described in this way: "She used to be a real big shot lady, married to a rich man from Cuba, till her husband left her." And now Mrs. Hinsula — or Señora Hinsula, as she sometimes called herself — was reduced to living off the charity of others. Every Sunday for years she came to visit us exactly at dinnertime, and when she arrived, it was all that Miss Mirry could do to hand her a clean plate. But my mother always welcomed her warmly, and in addition to feeding her she would prepare a parcel with rice, flour, sugar, a tin of condensed milk, and a bar of soap for her to take away with her. One Sunday she added a nice thick slab of salted codfish to the parcel, and Señora Hinsula declared, "No, no, no, I cannot possibly take that saltfish, it would smell me up on the bus." Miss Mirry exploded and called Mrs. Hinsula "a poor show great" who still behaved like she was somebody when everybody knew that she did not have a pot to piss in or a window to throw it through. Her shoes were so worn out that my brother Keith used to say that Señora Hinsula walked not in, but beside, her shoes. My mother told Miss Mirry to stay out of her business, "I know what she is going through. She is just trying to hold on to her dignity. You have to hold on to your dignity."

Mostly Miss Mirry seemed to hate me. The sight of me made her crazy. We must have been enemies in a previous life in West Africa because without a doubt that is where Miss Mirry came from. All I had to do was to pass by her as she bent over our wooden washtub scrubbing our dirty clothes, or as she stood at the cistern washing dishes, and she would begin to fume and hiss like a steaming kettle, muttering words like *wutliss, facety gal.* I did not like Miss Mirry either, but we were not allowed to be disrespectful to her as my mother believed that children should be respectful to all their elders. That is why we called her Miss Mirry instead of just Mirry. Miss

Mirry twisted up everybody's name, even her own. Her name was Miriam Henry, but she called herself Mirryam Endry. She called my sister Barbara "Baba," and she said she came from "Ullava," which was really the town of Old Harbour. Most words in English just refused to obey her tongue, and she did not much care.

Miss Mirry had a weakness for younger men, and on our grocery list – which my mother filled out and sent to the Chinese grocery every Friday – we sometimes saw added the odd bottle of beer. Between items like twelve tins of condensed milk, ten pounds of rice, and ten pounds of sugar, there would appear two bottles of Guinness Stout that could not be accounted for by Marcus or Doris nor any of us nine children. But we all knew who it was that had "trusted" or charged these dark bottles of potent brew to offer as blandishments to some younger man. Once the Sunday chicken dinner arrived at the table missing one leg because she had secured the other drumstick for her latest love.

Miss Mirry did not permit us to eat the fruits that our father brought for us, his own children. The house at Studley Park Road had a long narrow room situated between the kitchen and the bathroom, a room she called the "buttery." In it, she would hide the bunches of ripe bananas or baskets of mangoes my father would bring home. To get at these fruits, my brothers devised a plan. They would go into the toilet, which was next to the buttery, and climb through the space above the connecting wall. They had to be careful when they jumped that they landed in the piles of laundry that she also stored in the buttery. After their soft landings, they would eat as many of the bananas as they could, stuff their pockets with the mangoes, and climb back over the wall into the toilet. They then pulled hard on the chain and emerged. One after the other they did this whenever they knew that Miss Mirry was hiding a bunch of bananas and a basket of mangoes. The best part came when she discovered that the fruits were gone and that there was just a pile of collapsed empty yellow skins strewn across the floor of the buttery. Then she exploded and called us damn thieves for eating the fruits that our own father had brought to feed his children.

It was Nigel, the youngest, who came up with an idea to get back at Miss Mirry. She could not read, and he would sit on the top step (where he didn't have far to run and hide behind my mother when Miss Mirry chased him up the flight of stairs that led up from the yard to our rooms) and spell out his curses at her.

Y-o-u i-s a d-o-g, a d-i-r-t-y d-o-g, a u-g-l-y d-o-g.

"Yu think I don't know what you calling me?"

"What I calling you?"

"Yu facety little boy."

Y-o-u i-s a d-i-r-t-y D-r-a-n-k-r-o.

Well it was all over now, because Nigel's spelling of John Crow, the bald-headed scavenger vulture, was making everyone hysterical. The rest of us were laughing at her, and Miss Mirry was foaming at the mouth, but she couldn't say exactly what was being done to her. Nigel, as far as I know, was the only person who ever got the better of Miss Mirry. But she once gave me a tamarind leaf bath in her washtub when I had measles, and she told me as she bathed my itching skin that "every sickness in the world have a bush to cure it."

Miss Mirry also said of the wedding of Lennie the yam man who married Miss Pinky, who was a hunchback, at our house, that "Every hoe, have a stick a bush." This agricultural analogy was an appropriate one for Lennie, and it was probably my mother's love for the great Lucea yams grown in the parish of Hanover that made her so tolerant of Lennie, the yam man who had come to bear a remarkable resemblance to the yams he sold. He was a large, thick man; *earthy* would be a good word to describe him. Lennie would come two or three times a week and announce his arrival by standing at the foot of the staircase which led up to our house, bawling, "Miss Goodieooooooooh." Lennie drank john crow batty white rum, a cheap, coarse, dreggy, and extremely potent rum, which was drawn from the bottom of the rum barrel, and he would sometimes burst into fits of loud crying when talking to my mother. Though her dreams of running a fine guest home never did materialize, in her house everyone was treated as an honoured guest. So, rising from her sewing machine, she would direct Miss Mirry to brew Lennie a cup of ginger tea. As she prepared the tea and then handed it ungraciously to Lennie, Miss Mirry would hiss and Lennie would drink in loud slurps, moaning through the cleansing sting of ginger tea, shaking his head from side to side, and muttering that only Gawd alone knew the crawse he bore. My mother would tell him to bear up, then she would buy Lucea yams from him.

The "crawse" turned out to have something to do with the ill health of his woman, Miss Pinky. But she was really the one with the crawse. When he brought her to meet my mother, we saw that she was hunchbacked, and looked like one of the last of the Jewish peddlers who walked about the streets of Kingston with a big pack of goods on their backs, a burden that caused them in the approaching distance to appear to be bent almost double. Miss Pinky was almost exactly half the size of Lennie. Her head came to a point just above his belt, and when she smiled she looked like a very young girl. When she took a seat in one of the chairs in our dining room, she swung her legs in circles above the floorboards.

Doris was pleased to meet Miss Pinky and told Miss Mirry to give her something cool to drink. Miss Mirry, who was undoubtedly the world's most ill-tempered person and did not like taking orders from anybody, had been making stabbing motions at the floor with the broom, pretending to be sweeping, in the hope of overhearing all about Lennie and Miss Pinky's business. When my mother sent her to get Miss Pinky something to drink, she shuffled off in my father's old shoes with the backs folded down, hissing and grumbling, muttering something in which the words "too much excitement" featured.

The next morning at breakfast, Doris announced her big news. Lennie and Pinky would be getting married in a few weeks. My father, who could not abide Lennie's coarseness, said he assumed the wedding would be held in the Redemption Ground Market. But my mother said no, she had told them they could have the wedding right here in our house. My father did not laugh. For the next few weeks my mother proceeded to make arrangements for Lennie and Pinky's wedding, including designing and sewing the wedding dress. She was proud of her reputation for being able to make garments to fit any kind of shape. Unlike her sister Cleodine, she never turned a customer away, and all her customers felt free to enter our house and to sit anywhere they pleased. My mother had sewn for many brides in her life. She was an artist, an artist who created with shining white bolts of slipper satin, crepe de chine, organza, chiffon, guipure lace, Brussels lace, and Venice lace. She hung "tears of joy" pearls, iridescent sequins, and diamond-like rhinestones upon her creations, which turned ordinary women into queens, ethereal bridal beings, their glowing faces framed by mists of illusion tulle flowing veils or fingertip veils. They floated up the aisle followed by cathedral trains. She sewed for many brides who were seven and eight months pregnant. For them, she had devised a cunning apron cum peplum, which artfully camouflaged the offending belly. She never discussed what dressmaking sleight of hand she employed to make Miss Pinky's dress fit her so well, but everyone agreed that Miss Pinky's gown suited her perfectly.

When the day of the wedding arrived, my father announced that he would be working overtime that night. My mother was in her element, grandly directing the proceedings as the mistress of the revels. She installed Miss Pinky in her bedroom, dressed her in bridal finery, and led her forth, transformed into a beautiful bride. Several large ladies, referred to as "eegla ooman" (higgler women) by Miss Mirry, came and took over the kitchen – which caused Miss Mirry to fume and hiss even more and mutter under her breath about never-see-come-see, hurry-come-up people – and soon the aroma of curried goat and chicken wafted about the yard, spicy harbingers of good feasting to come.

Miss Pinky looked lovely, everyone kept saying so. Everyone also kept saying that my mother had lived up to her reputation for being able to sew to fit any shape. The wedding was attended by scores of other women like the eegla ooman and their male equivalents. These women, who had grown quite well off from selling food in the market, were dressed in rich brocade and lace, "quality cloth" according to Miss Mirry, and the men wore dark suits and felt hats. The guest of honour was a doctor from the University of the West Indies Hospital, Pinky's doctor, and the guests kept remarking on how Doctor Goldman was just sitting there, laughing and talking like an ordinary man right there in our living room. The table was splendidly decorated, with pink asters and asparagus ferns pinned to its corners, and Doris's best cut-glass carafes filled with dark red wine. The wine-filled carafes glowed against the white lace of the tablecloth and set off the architecture of the cake, which was a tall four-storied creation, covered in thick, white icing and studded with flat silver discs, like nail heads. Several smaller round cakes branched off independently from the central one. The cake was rich with raisins, currants, prunes, and cherries and redolent of spices, overproof rum, and sweet Puerto Pruno wine. If you ate enough of it, you became deliciously light-headed.

Over the course of the wedding celebration, almost every single person stood up in my parents' living room and gave a speech, a toast, or rendered an item. As is the custom in Jamaican weddings, the bride and groom were showered with words to live by. Many of the older guests quoted passages from the Bible about how a man should leave his mother and father and cling to his wife, for in the same Bible, it said that it was not good for man to live alone. Some of the guests wished for Lennie and Pinky to be as well suited to each other's needs as a "tumpa knife and green banana" and also "like Isaac and Rebecca." I stood there with my brothers and sisters among the weddings guests and listened as even the eegla ooman and man who sold in the market confidently quoted line after line from poets such as Wordsworth, Keats, Shelley, and Claude McKay.

In thinking back, I realize many of the guests at the wedding that day would probably have taken part in poetry and elocution contests at meetings of Marcus Garvey's Universal Negro Improvement Association, enabling them to give the gift of poetry to Lennie and Pinky as a "a thing of beauty" to be to them "a joy forever." The last speech of the evening was made by Doctor Goldman, who spoke about "hope springing eternal in the human breast" and made references to how courageous the bride was and how it was necessary to have faith and be optimistic.

Afterwards, Lennie and Pinky opened the dance floor to Mickey and Sylvia's "Dearest." The dancing ended at about I a.m., and Doris got to keep one of the smaller cakes off the big cake and she took it into her bedroom for fear we, her children, would rise in the night and devour it.

A few months later, Pinky was operated on, but it was too late. She died, and they buried her in her wedding dress. Lennie was drunk for two weeks straight after that, and even Miss Mirry was moved to say that she felt sorry for him.

"Dear Mrs. Goodison, Would you please sweeten my mouth today with some of your dinner? Love, Teacher Bernard." Our house at Studley Park Road became a hospitality centre, much of which revolved around my mother's seemingly bottomless cooking pot. Teachers from All Saints School; our schoolfriends, many of whom became important Jamaican statesmen and entertainers; relatives visiting from the country, many in the process of immigrating to England, who had come to receive a crash course from my mother on how to look and behave stylishly in a new land, all came to eat every day from Doris's bottomless cooking pot. The main meal of the day, "dinner," was served at noon, and all the children came back from school to eat it. Marcus and our eldest brother, Howard, would drive up in the telephone company van and as soon as they arrived, the miraculous midday feeding would commence. Many of our schoolfriends who came to eat at our house did so to avoid eating Bullo slush, the free school lunch provided by the government for Jamaican schoolchildren. My mother began running a guest house of sorts after all.

Bullo slush came by handcart each day, steaming and sloshing from side to side in a big square galvanized tin. It was cooked in a kitchen somewhere in the city and dispersed to primary schools throughout Kingston to provide a hot nutritional meal for the city's schoolchildren. Bullo slush was a dark brown lumpy stew in which portions of gristly mystery meat moved like the fins of a shark. Many children claimed to get running belly from eating it. Bullo slush gave off a faintly medicinal smell, the same smell given off by the free cheese and milk powder distributed at school. There were rumours that iodine was added to all "government food" so that in case the schoolchildren had any cuts, this food would heal them.

Like her mother before her, Doris cooked huge amounts of food every day and much of the money she made from sewing went into feeding the multitudes. You could "smell her hand," as her father once said, from the moment you turned into the gate. She always cooked the midday meal herself. Miss Mirry acted as her assistant, cleaning the seasoning and picking grains from the rice. My mother believed in the culinary power of garlic, always scraped with the edge of a knife; and many white circles of sliced onions, pimento kernels, lengths of escallion were pressed hard to release pungent juices, and were added to with sprigs of fragrant thyme, sliced country pepper, black pepper, and salt. All these were rubbed into the meat with clean, bare hands. And the meat – beef or pork, mutton or chicken – was seasoned then browned in huge iron Dutch pots, then covered with just enough water and left to stew into succulence. To the bubbling gravy she added Marcus's favourite sauce, Pickapepper Sauce, whose bottles had on the label a rendering of a gaudy plumed parrot picking a red pepper. Then tomatoes and thyme were added to the bubbling brown gravy. She cooked deep pots of rice, steamed verdant leafy bundles of iron-rich calaloo, grated carrots, sliced tomatoes, because she believed in the importance of eating vegetables; and she fed all the children who came, including a few of my brothers' schoolfriends who had become Rastafarians.

～

Below All Saints School, along the gully bank, was a Rasta camp from which the sound of hypnotic drumming and chanting issued night and day. Neighbourhood rumours of dark deeds, from ganja smoking to human sacrifice, ran rife and fuelled my mother's fear that her sons might be drawn by some compelling, ganja-smoking force, to go down and join the Rastafarians. She prayed night and day to the God of the Church of England, and dispatched all her children to Sunday school at All Saints Anglican Church every week without fail. "The Church of England, all the Harveys were born into the Church of England," she would say, and she would tell her children again and again how the Anglican religion had brought the Harveys through everything from Uncle Howard's murder to the robbery by George O'Brian Wilson's legal family of the property willed to Margaret by her father, and because of their faith, the Harveys were still going strong. Surely, she said, it was the teachings of the Church of England that had kept her going when she and my father had lost their Malvern house. And in her early days in Kingston, what but the Anglican religion had helped her to rise up every morning and read from the Book of Common Prayer and choose a good Anglican hymn to sing to herself over and over as she faced the hostility of Vie and the women in the yard – "God is His own interpreter, and He will make it plain" – to help her to make sense of all the changes, the upheavals in her life. My mother could not see how an angry God, who had to be worshipped in clouds of ganja smoke, could help her or her children.

Fireball, thunder ball, earthquake, lightning, fire bun, Babylon, fire fi you, Babylon, fire fi you. On every street corner in Kingston in the 1950s, there had suddenly appeared fierce "Beardmen." Some of them said that it had been the great Jamaican prophet, Marcus Mosiah Garvey, who had announced "Look to Africa for the crowning of a black king. He shall be the redeemer." And so it was in 1930, Ras Tafari Makonnen, direct descendant of King Solomon and the black Queen of Sheba, was crowned Emperor of Ethiopia and given the title, Haile Selassie, King of Kings, Lord of Lords, Conquering Lion of the Tribe of Judah. And thus it was that the descendants of kidnapped and dispossessed Africans found a god who looked more like them.

My mother said she could understand why they felt this way, for slavery had been a terrible and wicked thing, but she did not want her sons to become Rastafarians. Rastas wore their locks like Samburu warriors. Dread, uncut locks because the Bible that they lived by said that a razor must not touch the hairs of your head. The Dreads, with their wild, red eyes, poured scorn and destruction on Babylon, Babylon being the system of government that Jamaicans as colonial subjects lived under, Babylon being Jamaica, a strange land to those who considered Africa to be their true homes.

"Rule Britannia, Britannia rules the waves, Britons never, never, never shall be slaves," sang the ex-slaves, the ones who celebrated Empire Day, the Queen's birthday, by going out and lining the streets in town and country, and waving small Union Jacks. When the children went to school on Empire Day, they were rewarded with a penny bun (a kind of coarse lump of the

Queen's birthday cake). Was there a special fund in the coffers of the colonial government to provide penny buns for the black children who sang that Britons would never be slaves? Some Calypsonian sang, "Build me a road make I walk on the sea to see my mother country." He did not mean Africa. Every New Year, the Queen gave Jamaicans a message. Sometimes she and her family came to visit and everybody lined the streets again and waved small Union Jacks.

My mother took all of her children to see Her Royal Highness, and when I said that I did not want to see the Queen, she said to me, "So you think that you are your own big woman now?" I remember standing there on King Street, totally miserable as the sun blazed down upon lines of Jamaicans waiting to see the Queen go by. When she finally passed by in a big topless car, we could see that she was a small woman who waved her gloved arm mechanically and smiled. All I kept thinking was that I really did not see why I had to stand up for such a long time to catch a glimpse of the Queen for such a short time.

The Dreads were capturing land all over Jamaica, seizing Crown land and building settlements and camps and sending smoke signals to young men in clouds of wisdom weed. There was explosive Nyabinghi drumming and chanting, days and nights of endless reasoning, reasoning upon reasoning, to turn Babylon's logic upon its bald head. But there were things about Rastafarians that fascinated my mother, who loved words, like the strange language they spoke with "I" as the centre of all things. According to Rastafarians, there was no separation between people, so you and me became "I and I"; even a great crowd of people became a multitude of "I's." "Africa is I father's home, Africa I want to go," cried the Dreads on the streets of Jamaica. They said there was no more understanding, for too long had Jamaicans been kept under so Babylon could stand, so henceforth the I and I would "overstand"; and "Bungo," which used to be a curse word signifying black and uneducated, would be a title of honour. Bungo Natty would be a high title because knotty hair offended the aesthetics of Babylon and the texture of black hair was something black people could not do anything about without causing great discomfort to themselves.

The reason for this subversion was explained to my mother by one of the young men, known as Phantom, whom she used to feed from her bottomless cooking pot. Although he no longer ate her food, because Rastafarians preferred not to eat salt, he always came to visit with her and to be received as an honoured guest, as she was known to receive everyone. Having nine children of her own did not prevent my mother from becoming very attached to other people's children, and Phantom was one of the many neighbourhood children for whom she cared deeply. He was honest, hopeful, and ambitious – qualities my mother found endearing in combination. "Phantom," she had asked him, "why a nice young man like you from a decent home, who went to high school and who your mother try with so, go and take up Rasta?"

"Mother Goodie," replied Phantom. "Babylon don't like how I and I talk, Babylon don't like how I and I walk, for I and I mouth too big and I and I nose too broad and I and I skin too black and as for I and I hair, I and I won't touch that. Everything about this kidnapped African is like poison to Babylon. So what Rastafari come to is this, block this game, turn over this table. I and I will not play by Babylon rule book, for that book no fair, I and I take I self outta this three-card game, and who want play it can play it, now mum is the word, parapinto is the game. I and I prefer not to eat no salt, and I and I will touch no part of pig, that is why the I cannot partake of that lovely plate of stew peas that the I has offered the I, because I and I foresee that a day will be coming when what sell in a shop will not have buyer, I and I will live close to the ground and grow the green herbs and eat the iron of the quick-springing ilaloo, and build our structure with ground provisions until that bright morning when I and I work being over I and I will fly away or will board the Black Star Liners which will come at last into Kingston Harbour. You know Mother Goodie, them arrest I last year and the first thing that Babylon representative do is to walk scissors through I head. Years now the I cultivate these dreads, no razor walk near these locks. I let them clump together as they see fit, grow like stout vines and hang long down I trunk. They accuse the I of breeding lice, rumour, and propaganda of forty-leg in the dread head. Mother Goodie, Babylonians are Delilah's descendants. The I watch I locks lying like woolly serpents at I feet, locks which were once woolly serpents alive on the I head, then I turn and see the grinning house slave holding up scissors like a forked spear, claiming him is warrior, him cut I down and conquer I. I drum for him, a funde mental mourning song, for his living death to come. Life set on a wheel and it will wheel, wheel and turn till the I turn come, must come. Come down Babylon, come down, come down offa Black Man shoulder."

Years later, we were told by a family friend from Ghana that at the same time Rastafarians were becoming a force to be reckoned with in Jamaica, in parts of West Africa, specifically in Cape Coast, in the town of Oguaa, dreadlocked men had also begun to appear. Wild-eyed men who lived apart from the rest of society, in remote places, by deep lagoons, who dressed in rough, woven crocus-bag garments and carried staffs would appear on street corners and chant.

"Wona nyi, wegya nyi. I am your mother, I am your father

Ahomaka wo mo. There is joy in it, papapahpa. Very well," cried the Dreads on the streets of Ghana, lending cosmic support to the Dreads of Jamaica.

Some of the neighbourhood boys began to disappear down the gully bank. You would see them on the street, dread-locked strangers with red eyes who stared past you because they no longer knew you. For fear that a similar fate would befall her sons, my mother prayed harder and harder to the God of the Church of England to preserve her sons from what she saw as a state of perdition, because once these boys "sighted up" Haile Selassie, it seemed they never again returned to normal life.

But ironically, it was the same Phantom who became one of the first converts to leave Rastafari and to take refuge in the land of Queen Elizabeth of England.

~

Phantom appeared in our yard one day carrying a cardboard grip. He was dressed in a brand new, tight-fitting continental suit made for him by the great Jamaican entertainer and tailor, Clancy Eccles. He was wearing a shiny pair of Three Castle shoes and his shorn head was covered by a "stingy brim" felt hat. This outfit in later years would become de rigueur for English entertainers, and this is gospel: it was introduced to Britain by Jamaican immigrants. Phantom had come to tell Mother Goodie goodbye and to bid a general farewell to us all, saying:

> People I am leaving, for
> Rasta-ism is "ism"
> Cramp and paralyze all "ism" and "schism"
> Rasta-ism is no ambition "ism"

Rasta-ism is ganja "ism"
Rasta-ism is live-like-dog "ism," Rasta-ism is old
nayga "ism"

At that point, a black Zephyr 6 taxi drew up outside and Phantom went out the gate, with my mother wishing him "travelling mercies" and giving him a large slice of cornmeal pudding wrapped in a grease-proof bread bag to sustain him on his journey. He climbed in and departed for the wharf, driving past the ice cream parlour operated by the beautiful Chinese woman named Cynthia, past Miss Dinah's grocery, and the barbershop operated by Sillo, a man who was proud to be an African, so proud that he called his barbershop Addis Ababa Shop. Phantom boarded an Italian banana boat called the *Ascania*, having paid a passage of seventy-five pounds, and set sail for England, leaving Rasta behind.

Everyone expected Phantom's ship to sink. We waited to hear that it had been swallowed up by the waves because there was a traitor to Rastafari on board. But it did not sink, and years later he came back on a visit and told my mother of his time there.

Phantom said he had landed in London, England, and because he did not want to run into anyone in the Jamaican community who might have known him, he took a train to Wolverhampton, where he had no friends or relatives, and so had no one to show him the ropes. The only thing that he knew about that town was the name of the football team, the Wolverhampton Wanderers, because he bet on them when he used to buy the football pools. Nobody would rent him a room except for an old woman named Miss Dicey O'Riley, who drank glasses of jet-dark porter all the time and kept walking through the house in various stages of undress, crooning "The Rose of Tralee," thus forcing Phantom to come in late every night and leave early in the morning every cold and lonely day of the year. He got a job in a factory where the first thing that happened to him was an English boy started asking him about his Three Castle shoes. How come a Jamaican like him owned such a good pair of shoes? When the boy found out how much the shoes cost (seven pounds) and knew he couldn't afford to buy a pair, he threw one of Phantom's shoes in the lye pit, out of bad mind and spite.

Phantom had been writing to his woman and sending money home, but had received no reply. No "Dear Phantom . . . I hope these few lines find you in the best of health, enjoying the maximum capacity of relaxation." So after a while he took himself to the London dockyard, having calculated when the *Ascania* would be in port. There he looked for the cockney sailor he had befriended on the voyage coming over. He begged him to go to his yard in Jamaica and to inquire of his woman who was no longer called his queen why she did not write to him. Using Nyabinghi patience, he waited the forty-two days until the ship went to Jamaica and returned to London. The sailor said that Phantom's woman had said that she had never received a letter, much less a pound note from him since he left for England and she was just getting ready to forget him with another man.

Phantom told the sailor that every month he had put a letter with money in it in the big blue postbox. "No mate," the sailor said, "that big blue box is the garbage tip." And Phantom took that as a sign that he should return to the fold of Selassie I, for under Babylon system he was spending his labour for nought and nothing, selling his birthright for a mess of garbage.

From that day, Phantom sight up Rastafari once again. When he came back to visit he had regrown his locks and every Christmas for years he would send my mother a Christmas card, sometimes with a white Santa on it; and when we laughed at that, my mother said, "Leave him, it's the thought that counts."

After her last daughter, Ann, married and left Harvey River to go and live in Montego Bay, Margaret found herself alone in the house for the first time in her life. On this day, she got up from the rocking chair by the window and checked in every room to see that the lamps were out and the windows closed. Just to make sure, she called out to the helper Mina, knowing full well that Mina had gone about her business after she'd been paid that afternoon. Mina had gone down to the river to bathe the minute she finished serving Margaret her lunch of Saturday beef soup, then she had come back and dressed herself in the good white jersey dress that Rose and Albertha had sent from Canada in a barrel of clothes for the people of Harvey River.

"This dress must be worn to church" is what Margaret had told the girl when she had given it to her. And here it was, midday on a Saturday, and Mina had hauled on the good good white dress, pushed her feet into the nice black patent leather shoes that had also come in the barrel from Canada, and dressed to the dickens, had almost run through the gate, shouting behind her that she was going up to Dinalvah to see her mother. Margaret called out to her that she had "better not fly past her nest and come back to work late next morning." But she knew that Mina was not really going to see her mother; Mina was going to see her boyfriend, who lived in the barracks occupied by workers on the San Flebyn sugar estate.

Mina's mother's name was Delmina. The Harveys always told how all the women in that particular family were called Mina or Delmina or Elmina because Mina's great-grandmother had been shipped as a slave from the port of Al Mina on the Cape Coast of Ghana. When he was alive, David used to say, "Mina's people are determined to remember that they were stolen from Africa." Margaret herself did not see the point in remembering those things. She knew that there were people right there in Hanover who were still fully into their African ways. Right there in the neighbouring parish of Westmoreland, there was even a rocky place named Abeokuta that they said was just like a place named Abeokuta in Nigeria. People from Abeokuta called themselves "nago" people. They talked their Yoruba talk, ate pounded yam, cassava, or breadfruit, which they called "tum tum" or "fu fu," and they danced their "ettu" dance in a slow shuffling circle to the beat of goatskin drums.

When her daughter Ann was still living at home, Margaret used to overhear her and Mina giggling away together, and Ann would say to Mina, "All right now, Mina, talk some African talk for me." And the girl would talk her strange talk for Ann, who would then imitate what Mina had just said. But if they saw Margaret coming, they would stop immediately. Truth be told, Margaret just did not understand her last daughter. What could she possibly find so interesting in Mina's African business? But that was Ann all over, just so free and easy, taking serious things for a joke.

Imagine, thought Margaret, after that blessed Baptist minister Thomas Burchell rode up and down all over Hanover, all over Jamaica, preaching to help abolish slavery and to turn these people from their dark ways, you still could not take the tum tum and fu fu business out of them. They said that Thomas Burchell was so zealous in his preaching and abolitionist work that he kept five or six horses which were worn down to shadows from his constant riding across the island, preaching Christianity to people like Mina and her relatives who were still sharing out God's power. Some of these people still believed in different gods, one god for this, one god for that, one for healing and another one for war. Assistant gods did not appeal to Margaret. What would happen if one day your mouth were to miss, your tongue slip, and you summoned the god of old iron and war instead of the god of softness and peace that you badly needed? The idea of one All-Powerful God who was in charge of everyone and everything appealed more to her nature.

Now these days with her husband buried out in the front yard and with all her children grown up and gone from the house, Margaret feels the need to call upon that one All-Powerful God more than ever. She feels her own great strength waning, she is exhausted all the time; even the act of pulling off her dress exhausts her. She has to pause with her long pink flannel nightgown bunched halfway across her chest in order to catch her breath.

I imagine that Margaret never told a soul this, but it is certain that she talked about their children to her dead husband, David. After he had died, she had had to wear red and black underwear for the first time in her life because people said that if a widow did not do this, her husband's ghost would come back and try to make love to her. But red or black underwear or not, sometimes she senses his presence very strongly in the house; and every night since his death, she's certain that he gets up from under that white stone slab outside in the yard and comes into their bedroom just to look in on her, and when she feels him about, she talks to him.

"Your daughter Cleodine is doing well, she and the husband send clear to England to buy an organ for her to play her music at Rose Cottage. Oh and I hear from Doris and Marcus, the big girl Barbara is doing wonders. She get a grade one, one you know, in her Cambridge Senior certificate, and she going to work at the Gleaner Company because she want to be a reporter. I'm so glad that they will have a child working now to help them . . . I don't hear a word from Edmund this last few months . . . I hope everything is all right. Miss Jo and her Barbadian husband seem to be getting on fine but she write to say she is not feeling so well these days. Mmmm. If you ever see the sweet photograph of herself that Rose send, my god D, she have on one lovely fur coat and she just stand up there smiling in the snow like a real Canadian . . . Flavy him still going from church to church, church to church, and Ann . . . Ann as I tell you gone to Montego Bay with that man she married. That man that she choose over all the other good good Hanover men who come here to court her. She find fault with everyone, that one foot too big, this one forehead too shine, she turn down all those good responsible men for this stranger man from Montego Bay. This same man who even Ann herself admits is not the most reliable of men, but then she turn round and tell me that he make her feel like the most beautiful woman in Jamaica.

"From the first time I see that big black car drive up to our gate and this tall big chest man step out, my spirit just grow cross, especially when the man step bold bold into our yard and I ask him, 'What can I do for you?' and him say, 'I have come to see your daughter, Mother Harvey,' and David, I say, 'Well, that is between you and my daughter, but don't call me

Mother Harvey, I am not your mother, I did not give birth to you.' And David, when I say that I just get up and go inside and slam the door. I hear the two of them out there talking and I pay them no mind. From that, almost every Saturday I see him drive up in the big black car, and as I see him step into the yard, I get up and come inside, and little after that you daughter dress up in a new evening gown – she sew a new one for herself every week – with just some little piece of lace or crochet throw cross her shoulder, and she and him gone in the black car. I warn her till I tired, I say, 'Now that your father gone you think that you are a big woman who can just do as she like, but this is my dead husband house and you cannot rule me in here.' You know what she tell me? She say, 'You' – that is me, her mother, you know – 'you and Mrs. Cleodine Campbell think that God give me life just so the two of you can rule over *me*; well, make tell you, you are not the boss of me!'

"And is just so it went on, David, till a few months ago, when one day I was sitting down talking to Mina in the dining room. I say to Mina: 'Today my mind give me for a piece of dry Lucea yam and I want that yam from no other ground except my dead husband ground.'

Hear Miss Mina she: 'But Mother Harvey, yam outside in the pantry.'

'Did that yam come from Mas David ground?'

'I don't tink so, ma'am.'

'Well,' I say. 'Did you not hear me just tell you that my mind don't give me for any other yam except yam from my dead husband ground?'

'I don't even know if yam is there.'

"Well, I tell you, when I hear that I nearly drop down! I stand up on my foot and I say to her, 'If no yam is there, it must be you and you damn blasted boyfriend fault, for I'm paying him to work my husband ground, and if he is not doing that, it is because you are there dividing his mind, and the two of you are there with your quakoo bush African business!' And while I'm saying this, in walks you last daughter and the man. And hear him: 'Mother Harvey, I have come to tell you that your daughter and I are getting married.'"

Margaret did not attend the wedding of her last daughter although the wedding was held in her house at Harvey River. If her husband, David, were alive, he would surely have prevailed upon her to put on a show of support for their child's wedding, for as he always said, "Things must be done decently and in good order." But according to family lore, Margaret Aberdeen Wilson Harvey arose on the day of her last daughter's wedding and proceeded to go about her business as if that day were just any other ordinary Saturday. She dressed in one of the demoted church dresses which she usually wore around the yard, she put on her husband's old work boots, and she proceeded to attend to her usual domestic chores, paying no attention to the bride or groom or the assembled guests. Then at some point in the proceedings, she took up her usual seat in her rocking chair in the living room and right in the midst of the assembled guests, she proceeded to puff upon a long chalk pipe, blowing clouds of smoke over the wedding party.

The union did not turn out to be a success. Maybe it was the sight of swatches of her long silky black hair lying like question marks on her pillow when she raised up her head each morning, and what those swatches of hair told her, that made Ann eventually decide to leave her husband, for her hair was falling out from her grieving over her bad marriage. Whoever heard of reading hair? Well, some people can read cards and some can read tea leaves and coffee grounds. But hair reading?

As far as I know, my mother's sister Ann is one of the only people who knew how to read hair. This gift came to her during the course of her short marriage to a man who claimed that he had fallen in love with her because of her great capacity for happiness, for her bubbling over source of mirth, for her wonderful openness, her clear ringing laugh that summoned everyone who heard it to start laughing too. This man who through his irresponsible ways proceeded to snuff out her joy. But Ann grows able to read the future and to heed warnings sent to her by her guardian angels, who, three years after she married this man, begin to write frantic messages to her with her hair on the white tablet of her pillow.

Go Home reads hair. *Go Home Now. Go Home before this bad marriage kills you.* And then, *Go Home, Your Mother needs you!*

Margaret is sitting in the rocking chair by the window when the truck rolls up with Ann and the children. She tells Mina to go and help her daughter to bring the children inside. When a weeping Ann tries to explain to her why she has come back home, Margaret, sounding like the daughter of George O'Brian Wilson, cuts her off by saying, "What's done is done, you have children to raise, stop the damn bawling."

After Ann helps her mother to get dressed for bed and assists her up the three steps into her big mahogany four-poster, Margaret says, "Ann Rebeker, do one last thing there for me, just rub my foot with some of that Canadian healing oil that your sister Rose send." Margaret dozes off while Ann rubs her feet. Ann gets up and makes her way to the other side of the house to her old bedroom, where her children now lie sleeping. Before she leaves she makes sure to close the door of her parents' bedroom, where her father's jacket is still hanging in the wardrobe, his felt hat still resting on the bureau.

And Margaret would have woken up in the middle of the night, feeling blessed that she was no longer alone in the house. Pleased that once again she had children around her, and most of all relieved that her last child was safely back home, away from the dangers of a bad marriage. She would have talked to her dead husband about all this and told him how God moves in a mysterious way, for their youngest daughter is now a big help to her in her old age, that the house is much brighter with children around. How Ann seems more mature and responsible now, that she is a very good mother. "She much more considerate and obedient to me. The other day she just come and say to me, 'Mummah, I want to thank you.' I say, 'For what?' She say, 'Because now I realize what you went through to bring me into this world and to raise me,' and I say, 'Now you know what it is to be a mother, Ann Rebeker. Now you know what it is to be a mother.'"

*F*or weeks my mother's mind had been running on Margaret. As she went about her wife and mother business, it was as if her own mother was beside her, reminding her how things were to be done. "Better you buy a small piece of meat without fat, and stretch it with vegetables than to get a whole heap of fatty meat." "The first thing that a good woman do as she wake up is to put on water to make tea for her family." "No child should rule a parent."

And at night in dream after dream, she kept seeing her mother with her two long grey-and-white plaits, smoking her chalk pipe. In the most recent dream, the smoke from the pipe curled into her good eye and clouded it, then David's face appeared in the pupil of the eye.

Doris woke up washed in a cold sweat and shaking. She told Marcus that they should try to go to Harvey River to visit her mother, but he said he had to wait on his leave. By evening, the news of her mother's death reached her. It was brought to her in person by her brother Flavius.

On any other occasion she would have said, "Flavius Harvey, I long to see you till I short," but when she saw her brother standing in the doorway of her sewing room that day, she knew that this was not a time for childhood jokes.

Flavius stood in the doorway, with his hat placed over his heart. "Dor, I have bad news, I come to tell you that our mother is gone," was what he said.

"Gone? Oh my Lord, oh my God. When Flavvy, when?"

"Last night. Ann say she heard her cry out during the night 'my head, my head,' and Ann run into the room just in time to see our mother fall back onto her pillow, stone dead."

Doris, seated at her sewing machine, drops her head onto her chest; Flavius steps into the sewing room and sits down heavily on the trunk. He and Doris weep like small children.

Doris and her brother sit at the dining table and talk as if they were the only two people in the world. Every time one of my mother's children passes through the room, they mutter something like, "Sorry, Mama, sorry Uncle Flavy, sorry your mother dead."

Except for the eldest siblings, Barbara and Howard, most of the children had no real memory of Margaret because their visits to Harvey River were so infrequent, but they always felt her presence, for Doris quoted her every day on all domestic matters, including the rearing of children.

Long into the night, Doris and her brother keep a wake for their mother. Flavius tells her how a few days before she died, their mother had sent to call him to tell him she had heard that he and his wife, Arabella, were quarrelling because she did not want to leave the Seventh-day Adventists and go with him to join the Jehovah's Witnesses. "'Flavius, marriage is a give-and-take business,' she told me, 'don't you expect to find God on earth and don't expect another human being to understand everything about you.' Those were the last words she ever spoke to me," said Flavius.

It was then that Flavius told her about his recurring dream; the dream in which an angel of the Lord would appear to him as he wandered in the desert, and whenever he was about to sit down at an oasis, the seraph would say, "Keep moving, Flavius, this is not where you should pitch your tent."

He told Doris how his quest for the one true church had taken over his life. How sometimes when he prayed he found himself begging God to take him home so that he could see his Maker face to face.

Flavius said that his search for the one true religion had come about because of his need to really and truly know the Almighty, and that was what was causing him to change from one church to another. Since he had begun his quest, he said, he had received many visions in which his body moved or was moved in strange ways; and he was taken up to other worlds and shown things that he, like St. Paul, dared not speak of.

Doris sat there in silence for a while and then she reached across the table, took his hand, and said, "Oh poor you, no mine, no mine, I know that one day you will find what you are seeking for. We all have to stick together now. Now that we are motherless and fatherless."

For weeks after they returned from my grandmother's funeral, my father came home early every night and paid special attention to his grieving wife. Every evening he brought her some small present like ice cream or cake, and he tried to cheer her up by bringing her stories. My mother, who loved nothing better than a good story, was sitting with her feet in his lap as he pared her nails one Saturday evening (she would never cut her nails on a Sunday as she considered it bad luck). "Dor," he says, "guess what happen to me today? I had to make one quick swerve so as not to crash the telephone van because this man in the car ahead of me suddenly let go of his steering wheel. My God, the man give up on life right before me," he said. And then he paused for a moment before he said, "But you know, Dor, I can see with him." There was a short silence, a slightly extended beat before my mother, outraged and appalled at the thought, rose up and roared like a great wounded mammal, "Never you say a thing like that again." She wrenched her foot from my father's hands and stood up over him, shouting: "Nobody should ever take their own life, nobody. That is the biggest sin. The only sin that God will not forgive. The only way to die is to go when God call you like how He call my mother, Margaret Harvey!"

*I*n the early morning hours of Monday, September 2, 1957, when the Montego Bay-into-Kingston train reared up off the tracks at Kendal and headed for grassland, my brother Howard's shoes flew off his feet. They were indigo-coloured suede and they had completed his dance outfit, a powder-blue zoot suit which perfectly suited his slim, six-foot-two frame. We, his brothers and sisters, had watched him admiring himself in the wardrobe mirror that Saturday evening, watched how he had put himself together just so. How when he finished straightening the lapels of his light blue suit, worn with a light blue shirt, and laced on his dark blue suede shoes, he had tenderly, carefully put on his midnight blue fedora, arranging it low on his forehead, slightly to the side. That Saturday evening he was bound for a dance at Forrester's Hall, 21 North Street, in Kingston. There he was to meet up with a group of sporting friends who'd convinced him to break one of my mother's commandments. There is no evidence that among his friends was a girl with red hair, but maybe he felt that the fundraising outing in Montego Bay the next day, which was organized by the nuns and priests of St. Anne's Roman Catholic Church, was sanctified and that a Papal blessing had the power to cancel out my mother's edict. Or maybe he was just feeling restless, adventurous like any young man clad in a powder-blue zoot suit, his head crowned and protected by a midnight blue fedora. Besides, he was over twenty-one, and he could hardly tell his friends that his mother insisted he stay home on a Sunday. So he boogied, yanked, and shuffled all night and half-danced down to the railway station at Pechon Street and boarded the train from Kingston to Montego Bay in the early hours of Sunday morning, where he spent the whole of Sunday partying with his friends.

On Monday morning, the telephone at our house rang at about 3 a.m. It was one of my brother's friends.

"Hello, Mama Goodie, Howie at home?"

"Why are you calling at this hour of the morning to ask me a question like that?"

"Please, Mama Goodie, just look and see if he is there."

My mother at that moment became fully awake, put the telephone down, and went to the room where her sons slept, to check if her eldest boy had come home in the early hours of Monday morning as he often did after a weekend of partying or "bleaching," as Jamaicans call staying out all night. His bed was empty.

My brother's friend blurted, "Mama Goodie, I'm sorry to tell you, but I believe Howie was in the train that crash early this morning at Kendal and kill a whole heap of people."

Calm, for some reason my mother became completely calm, her mind goes underwater, for the next few hours she will do everything as if she was swimming under the waters of the Harvey River. She woke up my father. They woke the whole house, consisting of their eight other children, who were all fast asleep. "Your brother Howard was on a train that crashed this morning." My siblings and I always felt hurt and deprived, hard done by and wronged by my mother's ban on outings on a Sunday or public holiday. When all our schoolfriends boasted of the grand time to be had at Alterry Beach, at Dunn's River Falls, or Puerto Seco Beach, all the Goodison children could do was keep quiet.

"See me tomorrow on the choo-choo train, sorry you won't be on it," said our schoolfriend Jimmy, who was to come home from the Kendal crash without a leg.

In the cold before-day morning, my parents drive down to Kendal. The whole way there my mother sings over and over in an unsteady watery vibrato the same hymn, "God Is Working His Purpose Out." They reach the site of the crash and hand in hand they make their way through the mass of maimed and dead bodies which had been flung violently down in the wet grass by the horrible capsizing of the derailed train. My father is openly weeping. My mother – who had tied a scarf over her long pepper-and-salt hair, which she had plaited as if she was going swimming – is singing softly. Over and over she rides the calming current of the hymn's words as she and my father look and look quickly away from the bodies lying in the wet grass, searching for their son.

Then my mother sees her tall first-born son walking towards her. His forehead is bloody where death clawed him, but he is walking towards them barefooted, the morning sun behind him. Flying glass had ripped open his head, but his best friend, Hoover, who was sitting beside him, received a fatal head wound. My mother would always wonder if the Angel of Death had mixed up their names, or if her brother Howard, guardian angel of the nephew named for him, had somehow intervened.

On August 6, 1962, Jamaica became an independent country. The Union Jack went down and the black, green, and gold flag of our newly independent Jamaica was hoisted. On the radio they said that the Queen had given Up Park Camp, which was where the now departing British soldiers were billeted, as a gift to the Jamaican people, who wondered how she could have taken it back to England anyway. Independence Day was not celebrated on August 1, which was the day that slavery was finally abolished in 1838, but on August 6, and our leaders said to a country in which 80 per cent of the people are black that the black in our new black, green, and gold flag, stood for "hardship." "Hardships there are, but the land is green and the sun shines." And my father, Marcus, is dying.

For a year he suffered from constant indigestion. Eventually his dinner had to be cooked differently from the rest of the family's so that he became like a child again who had to be fed baby food, soft bland foods like steamed chicken and mashed potatoes and egg custards. Sometimes in the night he vomited in the bathroom. What did Doctor Donaldson say, Marcus? "That I have a stomach ulcer. He gave me these Gelusil tablets." For months he ate small, round, chalky white antacid tablets all the time. He ate them by the dozen, hoping that their soothing, milky chalk would coat the angry inflamed sores in his stomach. But they only got worse. My mother said, "I tell you that Doctor Donaldson is a quack. He is the Company doctor. He does not care a damn about you. You better try to see a doctor at the University Hospital."

At the University Hospital the doctors cut Marcus's stomach open, then quickly sewed him up again because the sores in his stomach were cancerous and spreading rapidly. At age fifty-five he lay in the front bedroom of the house at Harbour View that he and my mother had just bought. He lay there, in a drugged sleep, his body rapidly shrinking, taking up less and less space in their double bed.

"Marcus, what do you think we should do about adding on another bedroom?"

"I don't know, Dor, can't you see that I am not dealing with worldly things now?"

And Doris, who knows this but does not want to hear it, breaks down and weeps.

"Papa, guess what, Karl take my good shoes and give them away."

My brother Karl, who was born a social worker, would make periodic raids on our possessions, taking our shoes and clothes and giving them away to the really poor children of Kingston, then lecture us, his siblings, about having more than one pair of shoes when some people have none. Normally, my father would have told him that he should at least ask us first before he helped the really poor with our things. But my father just smiles a half-smile and says:

"That's just material goods." Then he closes his eyes.

My cousin Joan sits with him sometimes, she just sits there, quietly holding his hand. I tried to but I cannot sit still and watch my father die. So I learn to cook egg custards and milky baby foods to feed to him. Sometimes he says, "Come and sit and keep my company," but I cannot sit and watch him die. On Monday, December 6, 1963, his stomach became rock hard. He was vomiting blood, and the only place for him was the hospital.

"Hello, Dr. Thompson. How is my father?"

"Marcus went about an hour ago."

My brother Nigel was outside in the street playing football. I stood on the verandah and called out to him.

"Nigel, Papa dead."

He said nothing. He just kept on playing football, kicking the ball up and down the street. He played until the street lights came on and he kept playing, kicking the ball harder and harder. He played until people began to turn off their lights to go to bed, he kept on playing football. Then he stopped and abruptly sat down on the sidewalk under a street light and dropped his head into his hands.

*C*leodine knows that ignorant, cruel people call her "Mule" because she has never birthed a child. Sometimes they even call her "Grey Mule" because she is so light-skinned, but they never call her so to her face, never. Behind your back is "dog" but to your face is "Miss Dog." No, they never call her anything to her face but "Miss Cleo, Mi Missus." Or her married name.

All she wanted was one child. One child. Not a whole brood like her sister Doris, whom she once referred to as a "baby-factory." She eventually adopted a child from a nearby village, a girl with a yellowish complexion like hers. But try as she might to make her into a young version of herself, confident, gifted, erudite, and superior, the child proved to be gifted only at mischief-making; and by the time she ran away to Kingston with a truck driver at the age of sixteen, she had managed to earn the undying dislike of every member of the Harvey family, so dedicated to creating trouble for others was she.

"Queen Cleodine," her husband used to call her. "My queen," he called her. She wouldn't have believed that he would ever have the gall to disgrace her because he used to say himself that he was so lucky to be married to somebody like her. She had eventually told him, "Since you are mixing up with these common women in the village, you are never, never again in life to touch me." She is determined as always that they will never haul her down, never. Her back becomes straighter than ever. She walks to church each Sunday, dressed perfectly. She is partial to fine linen dresses tastefully trimmed with hand-embroidery. Her pumps are leather, soft for her long feet. She fashions her hats herself, there is no chance, none, that some blasted commerown will ever wear the same clothes as she. She walks through them every Sunday, fixing her spectacles on her narrow nose bridge.

He built her coffin while she was still alive. One day her husband came up with the suggestion that since she was so particular and fussy, since she did not like for a lot of strangers to be crowding up her yard at any time, that they should make arrangements for their funerals while they were still alive. She said nothing, just allowed him to call in the carpenters and make the two coffins, then he stored them under the house. It was her brother Flavius who noticed them and Ann remarked on it too, that her coffin was stored directly under her bed-room. It was as if the man was hoping that she would fall right through the mattress and the floorboards and nestle perfectly into the cedar dress that he built for her. Her brother Flavius asked Clement why in the name of God he had put his wife's coffin right under her bed. Clement acted as if he hadn't even heard. Flavius just stood right there in the yard and began to pray the Lord's Prayer.

In her heart Cleodine was praying too, calling on David and Margaret and all the Harvey generations to protect her. In a dream her mother came to her, right there on the front veran-dah, she came and said that she was sorry, that she had been taken in by appearances; that she should have looked past this man's dashing caballero act that he had learned in Cuba and

Panama; that she should have seen that he had lived the loose life too long and that he would never truly be able to settle down. Now that had to be a dream, for Cleodine never heard her mother say she was sorry in all the time she was on earth. Cleodine got that from her. She too did not believe in saying "I'm sorry." She believed that you should try to do a thing right in the first place and then there would be no need to be sorry. After that dream Cleodine woke up in the middle of the night and played the organ until morning. She was alone in the house so she disturbed no one.

Still, when her husband suddenly fell ill, she nursed him, cooked for him herself, tried to give him all the healthy food he didn't want to eat. "Leave out the fatty pork and the beef," she would tell him, "that kind of food is not good for your heart."

They eventually hauled out his coffin from under the house and put him in it. My mother went down for the funeral with some of her children. She was a widow too now but she had nine children. If each child represented an opportunity to help a parent, my mother had nine more chances to get a drink of water than her sister. At the funeral, when Cleodine was sitting in the front pew with her eyes dry, Doris went and put herself beside her sister and took her hand and sat there with her hand in hers for the entire funeral.

⌒

The day after my mother died, I go to Papine Market to buy food for the people who would be coming to pay their respects to the family. Weighed down by loss, I walk slowly into the market and as I approach the stall where my friend Peggy sells yams, she calls out to me, "My friend, what happen to you?" I come up and stand by Peggy, who is seated before a big heap of yams, and I say, "Peggy, my mother dead." And the minute I say that, she turns to the woman to her right, then to the one to her left and the one behind her and tells them, "Her mother dead." Immediately these women leave their stalls and come and circle me and begin to sound the Jamaican Om: "nuh mine nuh mine nuh mine nuh mine." I just stand there weeping, allowing their sounds of consolation to push back my grief. And as I am standing there in their midst, my mind drifts back to the time I'd told my mother I wished that I was dead, and how she had almost killed me for saying something so horrible.

I had been about twelve years old at the time. It was a Saturday morning, and just as I was escaping deep into one of my sister Barbara's books, my mother called me into the sewing room and presented me with a two-page shopping list which she had drawn up in her beautiful, confident handwriting. "A good fist, we Harveys all have good fists," she'd always say in admiration of her own handwriting. And so, with her good fist, she had smashed my plans to spend the day reading *The Loneliness of the Long-Distance Runner*.

I didn't like going to buy trimmings. It meant taking the bus downtown to King Street and walking from store to store and trying to get the exact match to the things on the list. My mother's standards were very exacting. If the colours were a little off, or if you bought one-inch belting instead of one and a half inches, or if you bought buttons which in her opinion looked cheap because you had skimmed off some of the trim- mings money and bought an ice-cream cone from the cafeteria on the second floor of Times Store, she would become harsh, angry, and insulting about your lack of good taste. At such times she looked just like her mother, Margaret, did in a pho- tograph taken with David in the yard at Harvey River on their fortieth wedding anniversary. "Mummah look vex in this photograph because Puppah give away almost everything that they owned," my mother would say.

As I stood there, wilting under my mother's fierce gaze, I thought on the injustice of my seeming to be the only one of her children who was available to buy trimmings. And the more I thought upon this, the more I became convinced that a serious wrong was being done to me. The boys could not be sent to buy trimmings for the same reason that my mother did not let them do housework, such activities being unmanly. My sister Barbara was at work at the newspaper, and my other sister Betty was never able to go out on her own because of her epilepsy. It just did not seem fair to my teenage self. I started to cry at the misery of it all, at being the only one chosen to do this errand which, as my mother pointed out, would help to put food into our mouths. I stood there weeping as she handed me the list of zips of various lengths and beltings of different widths and buttons to be bought at Triff Hyltons and covered buckles and accordion pleating to be collected at Amy Cruz's. Through my resentful tears, I said, "I hope that a bus runs over me and kills me when I go downtown, and then you will be sorry that you forced me to go."

I would live to regret saying those words for many years to come, for my mother repeated them to everybody as proof that I was a Don't-Care girl with a divided mind who was in danger of "becoming dead to trespasses and sins." She was not intimidated by my hysterical adolescent attempt to guilt her out. She ordered me to go and buy the trimmings anyway. As I left the house in tears, I wondered what would happen if a bus did run over me. Would people say, "the poor little girl get a warning man, her mother should never force her to go downtown and buy no trimmings that day, I am telling you, the woman well hard, look how she send the poor child to her death." Fortunately for both of us, I completed my trimmings errands without being killed by a bus, and now here I was, more than thirty years later, crying in Papine Market because my mother was dead.

One by one, the women standing around me begin to testify to the goodness of one's mother. "There is nothing like a mother, no sir, there is nothing like a mother's love." "Even if your mother is the worst woman in the world, you still have to love her because she give you life." One woman tells of her mother's peaceful passing in the care of a loving daughter: "I did just bathe her and put on a new panty on her and put her to sleep on a clean sheet, and is just so she sleep off." Each of them tell me about this rite of passage when your mother becomes your child, and I stand in that loving circle of women, like Sally Water of the children's ring game, with weeping eyes as they comfort me, no mind no mind no mind.

As I stood there with Peggy and her friends in the market, I remembered how just two days ago, the day before my mother died, I had gone to look after her and I'd noticed that her face was glowing. I swear she looked like a bride. I remembered with great shame how sometimes I had been downright ungracious about going to take care of my mother in her last days because she could be very demanding. Some days the twelve-year-old girl who resented being the one who had to go and buy trimmings would rise up in me as my mother would telephone me at 6 a.m. and issue me orders to cook her Sunday dinner and bring it to her before midday, or insist that I take her to three different doctors in the span of two days because she did not like what the first two had told her, which was essentially that her mighty heart was giving out, and that there was very little that could be done for her at age eighty-five. But the day before she died, I felt blessed and privileged that I had been able to do something for her.

"Who sent you here?" she had asked after I told her I was leaving. I had no answer for that question so she answered it for me. "God sent you," she said. We both laughed. "Is there anything else that you want me to do for you today?" I'd asked her, and she had said that she could not think of anything more that I could do.

I was standing in Papine Market thinking of how I'd spoken on the telephone to Aunt Ann and her daughters Joan and Myrna in Montreal the night before, and at the end of our tear-filled conversation they had said that they wanted to send special fabric to make my mother's shroud. I remembered how my mother had shown such strength after my father died. How she had sewed appropriate dark dresses for me and my sisters and how she had walked with such dignity down the long path from the church to the burial site in the Half Way Tree cemetery. How after the funeral she had received visitors, feeding all who came and treating them like honoured guests, and how for weeks she did not break down before her children. If she cried, it would have been in the privacy of her bedroom at night, where she now slept alone after so many years of marriage. Then one Sunday morning, she got up early and went into the kitchen to make breakfast, and as she stood by the stove, peeling green bananas from their skin before she dropped them into the pot of boiling water, she broke down and began to bawl. I will never forget the sound of her crying as long as I live, for in between those wrenching sobs that were being hauled up from her belly-bottom, she was saying, "O my Marcus. My Marcus Goodison, there will never be another man like you."

"My friend, you look shaky, you better sit down," says Peggy. "Yes, yes, make her sit down," the women say as they break up the circle to lead me to an upended wooden crate next to Peggy's stool. I gratefully sit down and one of the women says, "What you want is a water coconut to wash off your heart." She goes over to her stall and selects a green coconut which she expertly cuts open with one swift sweep of a machete, then she comes back and hands it to me. "Drink this, it good for you. Just sit down there and drink the coconut till you feel better, my friend."

"Yes, thank you. Thank you very much," I say, nodding.

Then all the women return to their respective stalls, leaving me to sit on the wooden crate, drinking the water coconut, and thinking about how my mother came to know happier days, such as when she would go to visit her sisters Rose and Ann in Montreal. In the years after my father died, my mother made several visits to Canada to see her sisters, and she was finally able to see snow for herself.

"Doris, the taxi is waiting outside," Rose said. "She change her clothes ten times already," said Ann.

"The two of you just leave me, for I am not going to Expo 67 to hear Tom Jones sing in these stockings that are too light-coloured for this dress."

My mother must have found the appropriate stockings, for she and her sisters did go to see Tom Jones, and she did have wonderful times visiting with them in the city of Montreal. When she came back to Jamaica, she told us:

"Every Sunday we would go up to see Miss Jo at the Mount Royal Cemetery. She has a lovely view of the city from where she is."

In the decade after my mother lost her husband, and with some of her children still living at home, she became a caretaker again as her brothers and sisters, recognizing her strength and compassion, turned to her as their own lives became diminished by age, illness, and fears. My mother nursed both Cleodine and Edmund in their old age, and they both died in her house.

It was with great reluctance that Cleodine had made the decision to spend her last days in my mother's humble house at Harbour View. After Clement's death, she had continued to live as mistress of Rose Cottage for more than fifteen years; but by 1975 the lifestyle she had been accustomed to was becoming too difficult for her to maintain. For one thing, full-time domestic help was now hard to come by since the passing in 1974 of the minimum-wage law, which stipulated that domestic helpers should have a five-day work week and be paid double for work done on weekends. Cleodine began to find herself more and more alone in Rose Cottage as newly liberated helpers – who were no longer to be referred to as maids – refused to do her bidding. Besides, as she got older, she did not become easier to get along with. She finally consented to go and live with my mother after she suffered a mild stroke. Before she left Rose Cottage, she locked away her prized African violets in an empty room where they gave up their intense colour to the darkness and died.

Doris finally persuaded her to come to Kingston so she could take care of her. And take care of her sister she did, drawing her hot baths and cooking her healthy foods so that Cleodine was able to recover quickly from the stroke, at which point, as she had when they were children living in David and Margaret's house, she proceeded to order about her younger sister, who by then was in her sixties. This went on for three years until one Sunday morning Cleodine arose and got dressed in all her finery to go and attend services at St. Boniface Anglican Church in Harbour View. She stood before the mirror of the mahogany bureau that she had brought with her from Rose Cottage and secured her hat with a pearl-tipped pin, then turned and picked up her handbag and fell forward, managing before she landed to snap the shining clasp on her handbag shut. My brothers drove her to the hospital, where she died before evening.

In accordance with the clear and specific directions in her will, her body was returned to Kingsvale, Hanover, where she was buried in the churchyard. In his sermon, the minister said that her disciplined, industrious, and dignified life had been an example to everyone who had ever met her.

About a year after Cleodine's death, Edmund arrived. Though he had enjoyed his taxi-man cowboy life, he had grown increasingly lonely and frail, and he feared dying alone. Doris nursed him for the last years of his life until he peacefully passed away in his sleep.

The one request he had before dying was that his body should not, under any condition, be taken back to Harvey River for burial. He hinted that his duppy would make things very uncomfortable for anyone who should try to take him back there. The family granted him his request by burying him in the May Pen Cemetery in Kingston, in a spot facing Spanish Town Road. As we stood in the cemetery watching the mason sealing Uncle Edmund's grave, my mother addressed him for the last time. "Edmund," she said, "you rest in peace now, I know you don't want to go back to Harvey River, so you just lie down right here where you can see your taxi man friends driving by."

Later, when Flavius became ill, he had wanted to come and spend his last days with his sister Doris too, but by then her mighty heart had begun to give out and she herself was in need of nursing.

It had been her beloved sister Rose's death years before that had begun to weaken my mother. Accompanied by my brother Keith, she had made her own straight-backed way across the tarmac at Norman Manley Airport and boarded an airplane to Montreal for the funeral of her beautiful sister. She had come back an old woman, leaning heavily on the arm of her son.

After my mother's death, her sister Ann would swear that all the Harvey girls came regularly to visit with her in her Montreal apartment, and she often dreamt that they were all dressed up in their finery and walking into the town of Lucea. Ann died ten years after my mother, following the tragic death of her youngest child, my cousin Joan.

My mother loved her people, her "generations" as Jamaicans call their blood relations. Every one of them meant something to her. The night before she died, I dreamt that my father had driven up to my mother's house in Harbour View in a big black limousine. He had driven straight through the locked gate and up onto the verandah, and even in the dream I knew that he had come to take Doris to where her people were congregated, waiting for her to join them and to enter into her rest. The day she died, she sat up in bed and began to say her husband Marcus's name and then the names of her parents, Margaret and David. Then one by one, she called out the names of her brothers and sisters.

I was sitting on a wooden crate in Papine Market with long eyewater running down my face when I remembered my mother's last request. "When you come again," she had said, "bring me an onion." And then she said, "Don't forget me."

And so I wiped my eyes and walked over to the food stalls, where I thanked the women who had stood in a circle and comforted me. I bought onions and Lucea yams from Peggy, and from the other women, balls of hard cocoa paste to make chocolate tea as Jamaicans call hot cocoa, and cassava bammies and a dozen limes. Then I walked across the market to Fishy the fishman, who once told me how he had fasted for seven days and seven nights, until on the last day Jesus Christ himself appeared to him at the eastern gate of the market.

"Eight pounds of butterfish please, Fishy."

"What you doing with so much fish today, Miss Lorna?"

"Fishy, my mother dead."

He looked up at me as he scraped the iridescent scales off a butterfish and said, "She is resting with the angels now."

My mother's hands always smelled of onions. My mother had a bottomless cooking pot. She could sew clothes to fit any shape and the first word that all her children learned to read was SINGER. My mother was one of the fabulous Harvey girls. She was the seventh child of Margaret and David Harvey, and the wife of Vivian Marcus Goodison. Her nine children are alive today and drawing on the blessings she earned for us. She dipped her finger in sugar when I was born and rubbed it under my tongue to give me the gift of words.

Epilogue

I have no idea where I am. I have woken in pure panic in a place solid with darkness which smells like the rusting interior of a brass trunk. The bed I'm lying in is not my own, for it does not face an east window. I cannot locate the door by which I entered here and my frantic scrabbling along the walls on either side of this narrow bed does not summon up a light switch.

"Say the Lord's Prayer, say the words 'Our father' over and over, if you can't remember the whole prayer, shorten it," my mother would say. This is urgent, chant Our father, our father, our father, our mother, our mother, our father. Mother, where am I?

And so I sing slow enough to do what I need to do next, to identify myself, to myself. Here is what I say to myself in that tomb place. My name is Lorna Goodison. I was born on the first of August, which is celebrated as Emancipation Day in Jamaica. I was born at 6 a.m. on a Saturday morning after my mother took a cold shower. My father's name is Vivian Marcus

Goodison; he died when I was fifteen years old. My mother's name is Doris Louise Goodison; she was born a Harvey, of Harvey River. Harvey River is in Hanover; Hanover is the smallest of the fourteen parishes of Jamaica, which is 345 square miles. Jamaica was first named Xamayca, which we were taught means land of wood and water. The Blue Mountains rise up to seven thousand feet. The Dolphin Head Mountains contain the headwaters of the Harvey River. My son's name is Miles. I am a writer. I can turn this darkness into the river at night. My mind like the riverbed will become cool and still. I dive and under the surface of the water, I know what I'll find. The evidence of my generations. The small schools of fish will flutter by like my mother and her sisters and brothers. Cleodine, Albertha, Howard, Rose, Edmund, Flavius, Doris, and Ann on their way to school. A pair of old mullets who rule the river will come too, representing David and Margaret, my grandparents. The wild-haired water grass and tenacious weeds will wave and bow, respect due. But I'm alert too, under this dark water, watching out for the pincers of the crabs that can bite. Under this river there are shocking eels, quick and slippery, and there are secrets hidden in the holes where they coil. The don't-care girl is still dancing there under the river. There are lost pearls and hopeless cases and the bones of runaway Africans down there as well as wedges of iron-hard brown soap which the women of Harvey River used to wash acres of clothes in this same river. As long as I swim in it, I will be borne to safety. And so I swim until morning comes and reveals that I'm sleeping in a small baroque hotel room, with the heavy velvet curtains drawn, after giving a poetry reading in Hanover, Germany, and immersing myself in the waters of the river named for the Harveys calmed my night fears.

Acknowledgements

In reconstructing and re-imagining the story of my mother's family and their forebears, I have of course taken certain liberties, including, on some occasions, changing dates to suit narrative flow.

~

First, last, and always, I give thanks and praise to the Most High.

There are many people I would like to thank for their support in making this book possible: Ann Harvey Moran, who blessed and assisted this project; Jan Sharp, the presiding spirit of this book; Myrna Moran, for her gracious help; Barbara and Ancile Gloudon, with love and thanks; Howard Goodison, who is a wise man; Paulette Goodison, my niece and my friend; Keith and Jennifer Goodison, with much thanks; Betty, Bunny, Kingsley, Karl, and Nigel Goodison, with much love; Joyce King, my cousin; Ali Darwish, sincere thanks; Reverend Michael Granzen; Jennifer Glossop, who pointed the way; Janet Irving, Sylvie Rabineau, Leigh Feldman, and Janet Silver — thank you for keeping this project alive; Roy DaSouza and Neville James, for the information about automobiles; Dr. Freddie Hickling, for information about Bellevue; Rex Nettleford and Philip Sherlock, two elders who taught us to honour our ancestors; Helen McLean; Patrick Waldemar; Petrona Morrison; Errol Moo Young; Tony Robinson; Vivian Crawford and everyone at the Institute of Jamaica; Jean Smith; Barry Chevannes; Louise Bennett, "Miss Lou," for the story of "Nayga Bun"; Maxine Brown Lawrence, who typed a very early draft of this book; Ben, Vangie, and David Clare, for their Hanover hospitality; Liz and Bob Food, with much love; the handsome Avie Bennett, with Respect Due; Ambassador John Robinson; Reverend Carol Finlay; Brian Corman; Isabel Bassett; Lincoln Faller; Sid Smith; Neville Dawes; Eddie Baugh, John La Rose, Sarah White, Michael Cooke, Larry Lieberman, Jahan Ramazani, and Michael Schmidt, for encouraging my poetry, which has fed this book.

Thanks also to the incomparable Ellen Seligman, who said "I want to bring this book home," and for doing just that with grace and authority; the amazing Anita Chong — Cleodine and I thank you, Anita; Marilyn Biderman; Elaine Melbourne, my good friend and mentor, who helped me stay the course for the twelve years it took to complete this book; my beloved son, Miles, who made me many cups of tea when I first began to write this book at the Ponds of Georgetown in Ann Arbor, Michigan. And finally to my best friend, tender companion, and unfailing encourager, John Edward, for never doubting that this book would become a book. Thanks, Sweetie.

Denis Valentine

Lorna Goodison's *From Harvey River: A Memoir of My Mother and Her People* was a finalist for the Charles Taylor Prize for Literary Non-fiction and the Trillium Book Award, and won the prestigious B.C. Award for Canadian Non-fiction. Goodison is also the author of two collections of short stories and eight books of poetry. She has received much international recognition, including the Musgrave Gold Medal. Born in Jamaica, Goodison has taught at the University of Toronto and now teaches at the University of Michigan. She divides her time between Ann Arbor, Toronto, and Halfmoon Bay.